RESIDENTIAL DUCT SYSTEMS

MANUAL D

Air Conditioning Contractors of America

Systems and Applications

Blowers and Air-side Devices

Sizing Calculations

Efficiency, Leakage and Noise

Air Conditioning Contractors of America
2800 Shirlington Road, Suite 300
Arlington, VA 22206
(703) 575-4477 • (703) 575-4449 FAX
www.acca.org

ANSI Recognition

As a result of **American National Standards Institute (ANSI)** recognition, and adoption of this ACCA manual by international code authorities, the scope of Manual D expands beyond its original objective of serving as a contractor and training/education tool for proper residential duct design. Manual D also serves to indicate industry practices in a prescriptive manner.

To accommodate the standardization of Manual D, the text passages of the manual may need to be interpreted in a specific manner. Where definitive procedures must be followed for residential duct design, mandatory language becomes necessary and the following substitutions, definitions and rules can be applied to conform to definitive procedures with mandatory language:

■ The words "may, should, could and can" are very permissive in nature. In code environments where definitive procedures must be followed, the mandatory words of "must, shall and will" should be interpreted/substituted for those permissive words found in the manual as follows:

permissive words		mandatory words
may	➠	must
should	➠	shall
could	➠	will

■ The use of "and" in a conjunctive provision means that "all" elements in the provision be compiled with, or must exist to make the provision applicable.

■ Where compliance with one or more elements suffices, or where existence of one or more elements makes the provision applicable, "or" (rather than "and/or") applies.

Approved American National Standard

Man "D"/ACCA1
ANSI/ACCA1–2002

Acknowledgments

Manual D is a comprehensive guide for designing residential air distribution systems.

The development and publication of this manual was commissioned by the **Air Conditioning Contractors of America (ACCA).** Much of the information in this manual was secured from, or based on, information published in the **American Society of Heating, Refrigerating and Air-Conditioning Engineers (ASHRAE)** handbooks, the **Sheet Metal and Air Conditioning Contractors National Association (SMACNA)** manuals and from various design manuals and engineering data sheets published by equipment manufacturers.

Grateful acknowledgment is made to those members of the **Manual D** task committee who contributed to the preparation of this manual.

This manual was written by **Hank Rutkowski,** P.E., ACCA technical director.

A special note of appreciation is extended to **James H. (Bud) Healy;** Director of Education, NHRAW and to **James M. Herritage;** certified energy manager, Energy Auditors, Inc. These two gentlemen reviewed every page of the draft version of this document and made many suggestions that improved the final product. A special thank you also is extended to **Marion Wright** for producing camera-ready versions of the tables and drawings that were required for this manual.

ACCA Manual D Task Committee:

Glenn Friedman
Engineered Air Systems
720 12th St.
Richmond, CA 94801

Pat Jopek
Merit Mechanical Systems, Inc.
810 Columbia Lane
Darien, IL 60559

Dick Pasterkamp
Pasterkamp Htg. & A/C Co.
1930 S. Cherokee
Denver, CO 80223

Elliot Sokolow
Florida Htg. & A/C Inc.
PO Box 5820
Pompano Beach, FL 33064

Frank Menditch
General Htg. Eng. Co. Inc.
9070 Euclid Ave.
Manassas, VA 22110

Fred Piff
A-C Contracting Co. Inc.
PO Box 8219
Mobile, AL 36689

Bud Healy
NHRAW
1389 Dublin Rd.
PO Box 16790
Columbus, OH 43216

Michael A. Armstrong
Pennsylvania Power & Light Co.
1801 Brookwood St.
PO Box 1461
Harrisburg, PA 17105

Bill Bean
SEI
c/o Good Sense
64 Perimeter Center East
Atlanta, GA 30346

Bert Magnuson
J.W. Brower Htg. & A/C
3424 S. Tacoma Way
Tacoma, WA 98409

Henry Armistadi
RR 2 Box 2191C
Brunswick, ME 04011

Bill Wright
Wright Associates
Ste. 12 Harrington Park
394 Lowell St.
Lexington, MA 02173

Reader Response

ACCA is dedicated to providing its members and users of all ACCA manuals with accurate, up-to-date and useful information. If you believe that any of the information contained in this manual is incomplete or inaccurate, if you have suggestions for improving the manual, or if you have general comments, we'd like to hear from you. Please write your comments below and return this form to:

Air Conditioning Contractors of America
2800 Shirlington Road, Suite 300
Arlington, VA 22206
(703) 575-4477 • (703) 575-4449 FAX
www.acca.org

Comments on ACCA's **Manual D:**

_____

_____

_____

_____

_____

_____

Name: _____

Company: _____

Address: _____

_____

Phone: _____

Introduction

Residential duct systems have a direct and significant effect on equipment size, equipment efficiency, equipment malfunctions, envelope infiltration, operating cost, utility demand loads, vent performance, exhaust system performance, indoor air quality, ambient noise, occupant comfort and owner satisfaction. Therefore, the duct system must be carefully designed and properly installed or the potential benefits that are associated with building an efficient structure and using high-efficiency equipment will not materialize.

This manual presents the methods and procedures that should be used to design residential duct systems. The subject material includes information about system selection (constant volume or variable volume), system performance characteristics, duct materials, blower performance, air-side devices and duct sizing procedures. This manual also includes information about duct system efficiency and the synergistic interactions between the duct system, the envelope, the HVAC equipment, the vents and the household appliances. Indoor air quality, noise control, testing and balancing also are discussed. Other ACCA manuals that pertain to residential HVAC system design include **Manuals J** (loads), **S** (equipment selection), **T** (basic air distribution) and **H** (heat pumps).

It is important to emphasize that the procedures documented in this manual should not be used to design commercial duct systems. This limitation is necessary because the design objectives are completely reversed. (In the residential problem, the blower data establishes the duct design criterion. In the commercial problem, the duct performance parameters define the blower selection criterion.) There also are incompatibilities associated with the maximum allowable air flow velocities. This difference invalidates the "equivalent length" approach to quantifying duct fitting losses. (In the residential problem, the velocities are limited to 900 FPM; in the commercial problem they can be much larger.)

This manual does not have to be read from cover to cover, but there is material that should not be ignored. Sections 1 and 2 are recommended reading because they provide information about systems, equipment and zoning. Sections 3 through 6 are required reading because they discuss the issues that affect the performance of residential air distribution systems. (Section 3 is especially important because it summarizes the principles that form the basis for the **Manual D** duct sizing procedure.) Sections 7 and 8 provide a step-by-step summary of the duct sizing procedure and introduce the forms that are used for making the sizing calculations. Sections 9, 10 and 11 provide a number of examples that can be studied on an ad hoc basis. These examples range from simple single-zone, extended plenum systems to complex, multi-trunk variable volume systems. Section 12 pertains to duct-related equipment loads and duct system efficiency. Section 13 discusses the synergistic effects of duct leakage. Section 14 discusses the relationship between duct leakage and indoor air quality. Section 15 covers design details, as they pertain to generated noise. And, Section 16 provides an overview of the work that is associated with testing and balancing the system.

Table of Contents

Section 1

Residential Air Distribution

Section 2

Equipment and Air-side Devices

Section 3

Basic Principles — Residential Duct Sizing Calculations

Section 4

System Operating Point

Section 5

Blowers

Section 6

Air-side Pressure Losses

Section 7

Air Distribution System Design — Prerequisites

Section 8

Duct Sizing Calculations

Section 8 (Continued)

Duct Sizing Calculations

Section 9

Constant Volume Rigid Duct Systems

Section 10

Flexible Duct Systems

Section 11

Variable Volume Systems

Section 12

Duct System Efficiency

Section 13

Duct Leakage and System Interactions

Section 14

Air Quality Issues

Section 15

Noise

Section 16

Testing and Balancing

Section 16 (Continued)

Testing and Balancing

Appendix 1

Charts, Tables and Equations

Appendix 2

Friction Charts, Duct Slide Rules and Equivalency Tables

Appendix 3

Fitting Equivalent Lengths

Appendix 4

Installation Guidelines

Section 1
Residential Air Distribution Systems

An air distribution system must be selected for each house on the basis of its performance characteristics, the local climate, the structural features of the house and the characteristics of the heating and cooling loads that are associated with the various rooms of the house. There is no single type of air distribution system that is ideal for every house. Sometimes two or more types of air distribution systems are required for a single structure.

1-1 Single Zone and Multizone Systems

In order to provide a uniform sensation of comfort throughout the entire house, there should not be more than a 2 °F temperature difference between any two rooms. However, as explained below, it is difficult, if not impossible, to satisfy this requirement with a single zone air distribution system for some homes. (As per **Manual B**, 2°F is ideal, but the maximum allowable difference is equal to 4 °F).

Rambling Floor Plan
Some floor plans spread out in all directions. The greater the sprawl, the greater the chance that the sun, wind and other weather variables will cause overheating and/or undercooling in a number of rooms. Furthermore, the room-to-room load ratios will vary throughout the day and night, and from summer to winter. These types of homes cannot be properly conditioned with a single zone system because as far as the room load patterns are concerned, the house is equivalent to two, three, or even four separate houses.

Multilevel Construction
When two or more levels are connected by an open stairwell or a balcony, the tendency is for the upper level to be too warm and the lower level to be too cold. This problem is created because warm air, which is more buoyant than cool air, floats to the upper level while cool air sinks toward the lower level. The extent of this exchange will depend on how well the room temperatures are balanced with each other. If the room air temperature is nearly the same on every level, the buoyancy forces — and consequently the floor-to-floor air exchange rate — will be small.

In theory, uniform room temperatures could be provided by careful adjustment of the branch duct balancing dampers and continuous blower operation. This way, each room would receive the correct amount of heat (or cooling) when the central heating (or cooling) unit is operating; and when the unit is off, the air in the various rooms will be continually mixed by the action of the fan. But, this strategy may not provide the desired result.

- A **fixed** branch damper setting will not balance the heating (or cooling) capacity of the supply air with the room load because the room load continually changes as the outdoor temperature, solar gains and internal loads vary.

- The off-cycle blending action that is provided by continual fan operation will not be effective unless the performance of the air distribution system is flawless. This means that an ample amount of air must be continually extracted from every room and replaced with an equivalent amount of recirculated air. Furthermore, the recirculated air has to be thoroughly mixed (by the action of the supply outlets) with the room air.

Any deficiency in the air distribution system (fan, duct runs, supply outlets and returns) will exacerbate the stratification problems that are associated with multilevel houses. This means that the fan-duct system must be designed to deliver the correct amount of air to each supply outlet; that each supply outlet must be carefully sized and located; and that the return air system must be designed to ensure that there is a low resistance return air path between every room and the return side of the air handler. (At least one return air opening is required for every level and one return air opening or transfer grille is required for every room that can be isolated by a door.)

Most designers appreciate the significance of the supply and return air paths, but some underestimate the importance of the supply air outlets. For example, if the supply outlets are too large, the supply air will not be projected out into the room and will not mix with the room air. During the cooling season, the air will just drop to the floor. At the upper level of the house, the air that falls out of the ceiling outlets will accumulate on the floor and flow down the stairwell or fall off the balcony. As this cascade of cool air reaches the lower floor, it will merge with the puddle of cold air that is being created by the (oversized) first floor outlets. When this happens, the room air, which is still relatively warm, will drift up to the upper level and stratify near the ceiling. The net effect will be that the upper level will get too warm and the lower level will be too cold. Furthermore, the same problem will be experienced during the heating season. In this case, the inadequate mixing that is associated with the oversized supply air outlets will still cause the warm supply air to stratify at the upper level.

Rooms with Incompatible Construction Features

Some homes do not require zoning. In particular, compact houses that have consistent construction features and open floor plans (unimpeded air circulation between the rooms) tend to have uniform room-to-room temperatures when comfort conditioning is provided by a single zone system.

The situation is completely different when a house contains isolated rooms that are not compatible with each other. Examples include a home that features a finished basement, a family room that is built on a slab, an attic room, a room that is built above the garage or a room that is built over a patio. Zoning is appropriate for these types of rooms because these distinctively different living areas have incompatible comfort conditioning requirements.

* Basement areas that are finished out and used as living space have unique heating and cooling requirements because the room air temperature is marginally affected by daily weather changes; but it is influenced by the ground temperature, which changes more slowly than the air temperature. For example, on a pleasant spring day the above-grade rooms may not require heat; but the basement could require a substantial amount of heat to offset the losses that are associated with the cold basement walls. And, during a warm summer day, the basement may not require cooling even though there is a substantial cooling load associated with the above-grade rooms.

* A room that is built on a slab may not be compatible with rooms that are located above a heated basement. On a cold, sunny, winter day, the room with the slab floor might require heat, but heat may not be required for a room that has a warm basement below the floor.

* Attic rooms, rooms that are built above garages and rooms that are built above open patios have a large amount of exposed surface area, which makes them relatively sensitive to changes in the outdoor conditions. Therefore these types of rooms are not compatible with the rooms that have a limited amount of exposed wall area.

Rooms with Incompatible Glass Areas

Most homes have a room with a picture window, some homes have a room that has a sliding glass door that opens to a deck or patio and some homes have rooms that feature an unusually large amount of window area. These types of rooms can be incompatible with each other if they experience substantial solar gains at different times of the day. These rooms also tend to be incompatible with the rooms that have a small amount of glass area. For example, east-facing glass is not compatible with west-facing glass.

Rooms with large glass areas also cause problems during the winter when solar gains add a substantial amount of heat to some rooms. If the thermostat is located in one of these rooms, this heat can affect the temperature in the entire house, be-

cause as far as the thermostat is concerned, the house is warm. And, during cold nights or cold cloudy weather, this condition is completely reversed because the large glass areas cause some rooms to lose large quantities of heat. If the thermostat is in one of these rooms, it will react as if the entire house is too cold.

Summer-Winter Changeover Problems

Rooms that have relatively large heat gains in the summer may have relatively small heat losses in the winter and vice-versa. With a single zone heating and cooling system, the branch runout dampers may require seasonal adjustments because the **Manual J** room-to-house heat loss ratios are not equal to the **Manual J** room-to-house heat gain ratios. (Some rooms may need more supply air during the winter than during the summer and others may need more supply air during the summer than during the winter.)

Occupancy Considerations

Normally, homeowners expect the same level of comfort in any room, but some homeowners want the ability to control the temperature on a zone-by-zone basis. For example, a homeowner may want to have the ability to increase the cooling capacity in the areas that are used to entertain a large number of people, or to control the temperature in the bedrooms in accordance with the desires of the occupants.

Apartments and Townhouses

The obvious problems that are associated with a central, multi-apartment air distribution system are related to providing temperature control and utility bills on an apartment-by-apartment basis. And, other problems are associated with controlling odor migration between apartments and the noise that can be transmitted through a centralized duct system. (The cross contamination problem is especially troublesome when an apartment only has one or two exposed walls because there is a reduced supply of fresh air via infiltration.) These problems can be resolved by providing a separate HVAC system for each apartment. (One problem associated with multiple systems is there may be some objectionable noise if the equipment is located within the apartment.)

Townhouses are similar to apartments, but they typically include rooms that are on two or more levels. Usually, the top floor of a townhouse has a higher heat loss and heat gain than the other levels because of the roof load. There also may be a relatively large heat loss associated with the lower level if the floor and door traffic loads are relatively large. A separate HVAC system is required for each townhouse, and if level-by-level zoning is required, multiple systems or a multizone system may be necessary.

1-2 Central and Distributed Air Handling Systems

Traditionally, homes are equipped with air distribution systems that feature a single, centrally located air handler. In most cases there is only one system, but some homes are equipped with two or more systems. (Multiple single-zone systems are used to solve the zoning problems that are associated with houses that have two or more levels, or the zoning and installation problems that are associated with conditioning a very large house.) Regardless of how many central systems are used, each air handler is connected to a duct system that delivers air to a number of rooms. Figure 1-1 summarizes the performance characteristics that are associated with central single zone systems.

Central Multizone System (Variable Air Volume)
- Air flow is controlled on a zone-by-zone basis (control dampers are installed in the branch ducts and controlled by room or zone thermostats.)
- The central equipment is controlled by a microprocessor that monitors the zone thermostats.
- The blower CFM could be constant, but a bypass damper will be required to maintain the air flow through the equipment.
- The blower CFM could vary if the fan and compressor RPM can be continually adjusted.

Single Zone Central System

- No control over air flow as room loads vary.
- Central equipment is controlled by a single thermostat.
- The fan CFM could be constant.
- The fan CFM could vary (multi- or variable-speed fan.)

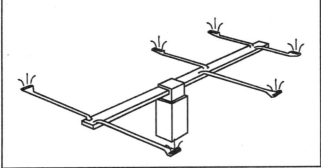

Figure 1-1

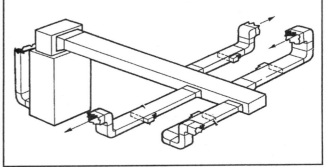

Figure 1-2

- Each air handler is equipped with its own duct system; there are no large trunk sections and the duct runs are short.

- The heating and cooling loads are small (efficient construction techniques) so duct sizes are small (6 inches or less.)

A centralized air handling system can provide zone control if it is equipped with VAV dampers, special controls and certain mechanical features. Most homes require only one of these systems, but two or more systems might be appropriate if the home is exceptionally large or architecturally complicated. The performance characteristics that are associated with central multizone systems are summarized by Figure 1-2.

One of the problems associated with central air handling systems is that the trunk ducts take up a lot of space that might otherwise be used as living space. In order to solve this problem some builders and equipment manufacturers are experimenting with integrated structural-system air-system designs that feature thermally efficient envelopes, open truss construction and distributed air-handling equipment. Figure 1-3 provides an example of a house that is equipped with a distributed air handling system. This system has the following characteristics:

- The floor plan is divided into zones and one air handler is provided for each zone. These air handlers are very small — only a few hundred CFM flows through each unit. Because they are small, the air handlers can be located near the rooms that they serve.

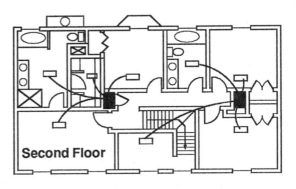

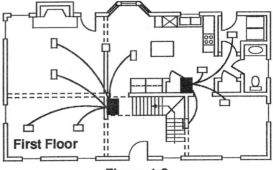

Figure 1-3

- When there is more than one level, the ducts can be routed through the floor joists providing that open trusses are used above the first floor ceiling.

- Constant-volume or variable-volume air handlers.

- Each air handler is equipped with a water coil (or coils).

- Remote fuel conversion equipment, which might be an ordinary water heater and a simple water cooler, provides a source of hot and cold water for the water coils.

1-3 Classification of Supply Duct Systems

Supply duct systems are characterized by the duct geometry, the location of the supply outlets and the duct material. Information about each of these characteristics is required to completely describe a supply duct system.

Supply Duct Geometry

Supply air duct runs can be arranged in three basic configurations — a trunk and branch configuration, a radial configuration or a perimeter loop configuration. Each of these configurations have different spatial requirements, performance characteristics and installation cost. Figure 1-4 shows the geometry of the basic configurations. More information about the advantages and disadvantages that are associated with a specific configuration is provided in Sections 1-6, 1-7 and 1-8.

Supply Air Outlet Location

Depending on the location of the supply outlets, an air distribution system could be described as a perimeter system, a ceiling supply system or an inside wall supply system. Some general comments about the strengths and weakness of these systems are made below. Refer to ACCA **Manual T** for detailed information about the performance characteristics of supply air outlets.

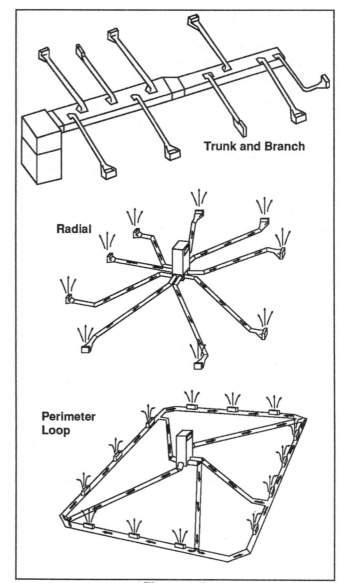

Trunk and Branch

Radial

Perimeter Loop

Figure 1-4

Perimeter Systems
Perimeter systems blanket portions of the exterior walls with supply air. This is accomplished by using floor, baseboard or low sidewall outlets that are designed to discharge the supply air straight up the wall. If the outlets are sized correctly the discharge pattern will extend up to the ceiling. (Never use outlets that blow air into the interior of the room.) It also is possible to use ceiling outlets that discharge air straight down the wall, but this arrangement is more suited for heating rooms that cannot be served by a below-the-floor duct system. (Discharging cold air straight down a wall will cause the air to stratify along the floor. A horizontal, parallel to the ceiling, discharge is preferred for cooling.)

Traditionally, perimeter systems have been recommended for homes that are located in cold climates because they provide more comfort at the floor level than the two other types of systems. However, ceiling or inside wall systems can be used in a cold climate if the home has a thermally efficient envelope and a heated basement. But, when slab construction or exposed floors are involved, perimeter systems are still preferred, even if the envelope is well insulated.

Ceiling Supply Systems
Ceiling supply outlets should discharge air parallel to the ceiling. If ceiling outlets are sized correctly the discharge pattern will extend to the walls. (Never use outlets that blow air down into the interior of the room.) Ceiling systems provide optimum performance during the cooling mode, so they are commonly used in homes that are located in warm climates. (Cold floor problems could be experienced during the heating season when ceiling outlets are installed in a room that has a slab floor or an exposed floor.)

High Inside Wall Supply Systems

High sidewall supply outlets should discharge air parallel to the ceiling toward the outside wall. If the outlets are sized correctly, the discharge pattern will extend to the opposite wall and high velocity air will not drop into the occupied zone. (An excessive drop during the cooling season is a common problem that is associated with sidewall outlets.) Sidewall outlets perform best during the cooling mode, so they are more suitable for homes that are located in warm climates. (Cold floor problems could be experienced during the heating season when high sidewall outlets are installed in a room that has a slab floor or an exposed floor.)

Duct Material

Ducts can be fabricated from different types of materials. Each type has advantages and disadvantages. Selection of the duct material will normally depend upon the location of ductwork and, in some instances, it may be governed by local building codes.

Systems placed in attics, basements, or crawl spaces offer the most options regarding materials. On the other hand, when ducts are installed underground or encased in concrete, the designer is obligated to use materials that are certified for these applications. A discussion of the common types of duct materials as it pertains to their range of application is provided below.

Stainless Steel

Stainless steel is used for ducts that will be subjected to moisture. Applications include hot tub, pool and shower exhaust ducts or ducts that are exposed to the weather. This material is not combustible or subject to corrosion. Stainless steel ducts are slightly smoother than galvanized steel ducts. The pressure drop across a section of stainless steel duct will be marginally less than the pressure drop across a similar section of galvanized steel duct.

Galvanized Steel

Galvanized steel is widely used for supply, return and exhaust ducts. This material is not combustible. Galvanized steel is subject to corrosion by concrete, so if it is embedded in concrete, it must be protected by a suitable coating such as (but not limited to) asphalt or bituminous mastic. Galvanized steel duct sections will float when the concrete is being poured. Painting is recommended when galvanized steel ducts are installed outdoors.

Plastic-coated Steel

Plastic-coated steel ducts can be used for below-grade duct systems and for applications that involve moisture. This material is not combustible or subject to corrosion by concrete, but the duct sections will float when covered by concrete. Plastic-coated ducts are smoother than galvanized steel ducts. The pressure drop across a section of plastic-coated duct will be a little less than the pressure drop across a similar section of galvanized steel duct. Plastic-coated steel ducts should not be used when temperatures exceed 200 °F.

Aluminum

Aluminum can be used for ducts that are subject to moisture or exposed to the weather. This material is not combustible. Bare aluminum ducts are not suited for exposure to chlorine or lime. Since aluminum is subject to corrosion by concrete, it should not be embedded in concrete unless it is protected by a suitable coating such as (but not limited to) asphalt or bituminous mastic. Aluminum duct sections will float when the concrete is being poured. Aluminum ducts are smoother than galvanized steel ducts. The pressure drop across a section of aluminum duct will be slightly less than the pressure drop across a similar section of galvanized duct.

Plastic Polyvinyl Chloride (PVC)

Plastic polyvinyl chloride (PVC) can be used for ducts that are subject to moisture. Applications include hot tub, pool and shower exhaust ducts and ducts that are exposed to the weather. Plastic PVC ducts are not subject to rust and corrosion, so they can be embedded in a concrete slab or used for below-grade duct systems. Plastic duct sections will float when the concrete is being poured. Plastic ducts are smoother than galvanized steel ducts. The pressure drop across a section of plastic duct will be slightly less than the pressure drop across a similar section of galvanized steel duct.

Fiberglass Reinforced Plastic

Fiberglass reinforced plastic duct can be used for air conveying ducts that are subject to moisture. Applications include hot tub, pool and shower exhaust ducts, or ducts that are exposed to the weather. This material also can be used for below-grade duct systems. Fiberglass reinforced plastic duct sections will float when the concrete is being poured. They are rougher than galvanized steel ducts. The pressure drop across a section of fiberglass reinforced plastic duct will be larger than the pressure drop across a similar section of galvanized steel duct.

Rigid Fibrous Glass

Rigid fibrous glass (duct board) can be used for HVAC duct systems that will not be subjected to physical abuse or moisture. Rigid fibrous glass should not be embedded in concrete or buried in the ground. Such ducts offer the advantages of sound attenuation and insulation and are rougher than galvanized steel ducts. The pressure drop across a section of fibrous glass duct will be greater than the pressure drop across a similar section of galvanized steel duct. Rectangular shapes are normally fabricated from duct board. Prefabricated rigid round shapes also are available. Fibrous glass ducts are not recommended for use with kitchen hoods and should not be used when temperatures exceed 250 °F.

Fibrous Glass Duct Liner

Fibrous glass duct liner offers the advantages of sound attenuation and insulation. Lined ducts are rougher than galvanized steel ducts. The pressure drop across a section of lined duct will be larger than the pressure drop across a similar section of galvanized steel duct. Lined ducts should not be used when temperatures exceed 250 °F.

Flexible Wire Helix Ducts
Flexible wire helix ducts can be used for ducts that will not be subjected to physical abuse, weather or moisture. Flexible wire helix ducts should not be embedded in concrete or buried in the ground. Such duct systems offer the advantages of sound attenuation and ease of installation. These ducts also offer the advantage of built-in insulation when they are wrapped with an insulating jacket. Flexible wire helix ducts are rougher than galvanized steel ducts. The pressure drop across a section of flexible duct will be considerably larger than the pressure drop across a similar section of galvanized steel duct. (These ducts also are rougher than fibrous glass ducts.) Flexible helix ducts should not be used when temperatures exceed 250 °F.

Flexible Metal Ducts
Flexible metal ducts can be used for residential systems, but wire helix ducts are more common. Flexible metal ducts are commonly fabricated from aluminum or stainless steel and they can be purchased with an insulating jacket. This material is not combustible. Flexible metal ducts are rougher than galvanized steel ducts. The pressure drop across a section of flexible metal duct will be larger than the pressure drop across a similar section of galvanized steel duct.

Concrete
Concrete ducts are used for underground duct systems. This material is not combustible and does not float. Concrete ducts are rougher than galvanized steel ducts. The pressure drop across a section of concrete duct will be greater than the pressure drop across a similar section of galvanized steel duct.

Asbestos Cement
Asbestos cement material has been used for below-grade duct systems. However, the use of this material was discontinued because asbestos is considered to be a health hazard.

Materials and Installation Standards
Material and installation requirements may be defined by local codes and regulations; also refer to the standards that are published by the National Fire Protection Association (NFPA); the American Society of Heating, Refrigeration and Air Conditioning Engineers (ASHRAE); the Sheet Metal and Air Conditioning Contractors National Association (SMACNA); the North American Insulation Manufacturers Association (NAIMA); the Council of American Building Officials (CABO); the U.S. Department of Housing and Urban Development (HUD); and the Federal Housing Administration (FHA).

1-4 Classification of Return Duct Systems

Return duct systems are commonly characterized by the number of the return openings. Return inlet location, duct run geometry and duct material are secondary features that can be used to describe a return duct system.

Number of Return Openings
Return duct systems can be classified as a single, central return system, a multiple return system or as a system that has a return in every room. Regardless of which type of return duct system is used, there must be a low-resistance return air path between every room and the air handler. A system that features a return in every room automatically satisfies this requirement. If a single return system or a multiple return system is used, there must be a low resistance path between every isolated room and the closest return air opening. This path can be established by using transfer grilles, door grilles or by undercutting doors. Refer to ACCA **Manual T**, Section 11, for more information about how two or more isolated rooms can be connected to a common return air opening.

Return Inlet Location
Return air duct systems can be characterized by the location of the return air openings. If all of the return openings are installed in the ceilings or located high on the walls, the system is called a "high return system." If all of the return openings are installed in the floor or in a low sidewall position, the system is called a "low return system."

Since the return inlet location (high or low) has a negligible effect on the air motion within the room (refer to ACCA **Manual T**, Section 7), the return openings should be placed at positions that are compatible with the location of the equipment and the duct runs. High return systems are typically used for rooms that have air handling equipment that is located above the ceiling and low returns are the logical choice for rooms that have air handling equipment installed below the floor.

> The air motion within the occupied zone depends on the performance of the supply air terminal. If the air terminal is sized correctly, the jet of discharge air will entrain a large amount of room air as it develops into a secondary air pattern. (The amount of air that is associated with the secondary air pattern is about 10 to 20 times more than the supply air CFM — refer to **Manual T**, Section 2-4.) Even more mixing will take place as the secondary air exchanges its momentum with the room air. (This mixing action must take place outside of the occupied zone, which means it has to occur near the wall or ceiling.) Ultimately, all of the air in the occupied zone will be induced into motion and there will be no drafts or stratified air in the occupied zone. (Stratification does not cause discomfort if it occurs outside of the occupied zone — near the ceiling, for example.)

Return Duct Geometry
A return duct system could have a trunk and branch configuration, a radial configuration or even a perimeter loop config-

uration. The return duct system geometry will be dictated by the number and location of the return inlets and the spatial requirements of the supply air duct system.

Trunk and branch return systems are very common because they provide an effective way to connect the air handler with multiple returns that are located near the core of the floor plan. Radial duct systems also could be used if there are no interference problems with the supply duct system. Returns are not usually located around the perimeter of the floor plan, but if they were, a radial system or a loop system could be used to connect the returns to the air handler.

Sometimes the return duct system consists of a simple stub duct or elbow and in some cases, there is no return duct. In these designs, the air handler (and its return air opening) is either installed close to a central return grille or is located within the living space — perhaps in a utility closet.

• If a central return is used, there must be a low resistance path between every room and the central return.

• Equipment noise can be a problem when the equipment is located within or close to the living space.

Return Duct Material
Return ducts can be made out of any of the materials that are used for supply ducts. Information about these materials is provided above in Section 1-3.

1-5 System Selection

The four traditional factors that affect the air distribution system selection process are zoning requirements, envelope construction details, climate and installation cost. Other factors include duct losses, building codes, energy codes and noise levels. There is no particular type of system that is ideally suited for every house because the relative importance of these factors varies in each case. Therefore, at the beginning of a project, the designer should rank these factors in order of importance and select a system that is compatible with this ranking.

Zoning Requirements
Some types of homes must have zone control and there are many homes that would benefit from zone control. (As explained in Section 1-1, the zoning requirements depend on the floor plan, the construction details and on preferences expressed by the owner or builder.) If zoning is required, it can be provided by installing one or more of the following types of ducted air distribution systems:

• Multiple, single zone or constant volume systems

• A central variable volume system

• Distributed air-handling units equipped with water coils

Envelope Construction Features
Envelope construction features affect the zoning requirements and they influence decisions that are associated with the supply air outlet positions, return air inlet locations, equipment placement and duct run locations. As far as air distribution and duct placement are concerned, the most important construction features are associated with the type of foundation, the type of roof and the number of floors or levels.

Slab Construction
When the structure is built on a ground slab, the blower equipment can be located within the house, in the attic or outside of the structure. If the blower is located in the house, it can either feed air down to ducts that are embedded in the slab or up to ducts that are located in the attic or above a drop ceiling. A perimeter supply air system is compatible with ducts that are embedded in the slab. Ceiling outlets are preferred if the ducts are installed in the attic, and high inside wall outlets can be used if the ducts run through a drop ceiling. (If attic ducts are used to feed high sidewall outlets, the ducts will have to penetrate the plates at the top of the partition walls.) If the blower equipment is located in the house, air can be returned through a free return that is located at or near the unit (providing that transfer grilles are used to establish a return path from every isolated room); or air can be returned through multiple returns that are located in the ceiling (providing that a return duct system can be routed back to the unit). If the blower equipment is located in the attic, multiple ceiling returns can be used to route the air back to the unit.

Crawl Space Construction
When the structure is built above a crawl space, the blower equipment can be located within the house, in the crawl space, in the attic or outside of the structure. If the blower is located in the house, it can either feed air down to ducts that are installed below the floor, or up to ducts that are located in the attic or above a drop ceiling. A perimeter supply air system is compatible with ducts that are installed below the floor, ceiling outlets are preferred if the ducts are installed in the attic, and high inside wall outlets can be used if the duct runs are in a drop ceiling. (If attic ducts are used to feed high sidewall outlets, ducts will have to penetrate the plates at the top of the partition walls.) If the blower equipment is located in the house, air can be returned through a free return that is located at or near the unit (providing that transfer grilles are used to establish a return path from every isolated room); or a return air duct system can be installed below the floor. If the blower equipment is located in the crawl space, low returns can be used to route the air back to the unit. If the blower equipment is located in the attic, ceiling returns can be used to route the air back to the unit.

Basement Construction
When the structure has a basement, the blower equipment and duct runs are usually located in the basement; and a perimeter

supply air system is normally used to deliver air to the first floor rooms. One or more sidewall outlets can be used to deliver air to the basement, providing that the basement is not used as a living space. If the basement is used as a living space, air can be supplied through ceiling outlets, high sidewall outlets or through low outlets that are positioned around the perimeter of the basement. If low perimeter outlets are used in the basement, they can be supplied by duct runs that drop down from the basement ceiling or by a duct system that is embedded in the basement floor. (Low outlets are preferred in the basement because they provide the most comfort.) Low returns can be used to route the first floor air back to the unit and high returns can be used to route the basement air back to the unit.

Multistory and Split Level Homes
Multiple systems are used to solve zoning problems, but they also are used when it is too difficult to route risers and drops from one level to another. If multiple systems are used, a multistory or split level house can be treated as a combination of the types of construction that are listed above. For example, if the house has two levels on framing, a level on a slab and a basement, one system could be installed in the basement and a second system could be installed in the attic. The basement system could serve the first level, the slab level and the basement, and the attic system could serve the second floor — or, it might be possible to use the attic system to supply air to the second level and the slab level.

Climate
The local climate must be considered when making decisions regarding the location of the supply air outlets. Perimeter supply air systems furnish superior heating performance and ceiling supply air systems provide optimum cooling performance. It follows that a perimeter system would be preferred in a cold climate and a ceiling system would be preferred in a hot climate. In some climates, heating and cooling are equally important. In this case, a perimeter system is preferred for some types of homes because the cooling performance of a perimeter system is better than the heating performance of the ceiling system.

> Even though the perimeter system offers the best heating performance, it is not absolutely necessary to install a perimeter system in a house that is located in a cold climate. Ceiling or high sidewall systems can provide acceptable comfort if the house is tight and well insulated, if it does not have unusually large glass areas, and if it has a heated basement. However, a perimeter system is recommended for rooms that have a slab floor or for rooms that are located above an unheated crawl space.

The local climate also dictates the envelope insulation requirements, which are important because the insulation details can have an effect on the performance of the air

Envelope Insulation and Supply Air Outlet Location						
Construction	HDD Exceeding 3500		3500 HDD to 2000 HDD		HDD Below 2000	
	Insulation	Supply Air	Insulation	Supply Air	Insulation	Supply Air
Slab	Slab Edge R10 (HDD>7000) R8 (HDD>5000) R6 (HDD>3500)	Perimeter	Slab Edge R8 Slab Edge R4	R8 ... Ceiling or HSW R4 ... Perimeter	Slab Edge R0 to R4	Ceiling or HSW
Open or Vented Crawl Space	Below Floor (3) R20 (HDD>6000) R14 (HDD>3500)	Perimeter	Below Floor R20 Below Floor R14	R20 ... Ceiling or HSW R14 ... Perimeter	Below Floor R4 to R14	Perimeter Ceiling or HSW
Enclosed Crawl Space	Crawl Space Walls (4) R16 (HDD>6000) R10 (HDD>3500)	Perimeter (recommended) Ceiling or HSW (acceptable)	Crawl Space Walls (4) R8	Perimeter Ceiling or HSW	Crawl Space Walls (4) R0 to R8	Perimeter Ceiling or HSW
Basement	Basement Walls R16 (HDD>6000) R10 (HDD>3500)	Perimeter (recommended) Ceiling or HSW (acceptable)	Basement Walls R8	Perimeter Ceiling or HSW	Basement Walls R0 to R8	Perimeter Ceiling or HSW

(1) HDD — Heating degree days — refer to ACCA **Manual J**, Table 1
(2) Insulation levels are for comfort, but they are compatible with ASHRAE 90.2P Energy Standard
(3) Vapor retarder below framed floor
(4) Vapor retarder on crawl space walls; limestone over vapor retarder (or concrete) on crawl space floor

Table 1-1

distribution system. When the home is properly insulated, the air distribution system performance and the comfort of the occupant is enhanced; but when the insulation is inadequate, performance and comfort will be degraded. On the previous page, Table 1-1 provides some recommendations regarding the insulation levels and supply air outlet locations for various types of construction and climates.

Installation Costs

Installation costs can be minimized by keeping the duct runs as short and simple as possible, by using as few fittings as possible, by using as few returns as feasible and by using materials that are inexpensive and easy to install. In this regard, the locations of the supply air outlets and the positions of the return air inlets have a significant effect on the installed cost of the duct system. For example, the installation costs would be relatively low if flexible duct runs, arranged in a radial configuration, connect ceiling outlets with an air handler that is located above a central ceiling return.

Duct Losses

Duct losses affect comfort and operating costs. Ideally, the ducts should be installed inside the conditioned space. When ducts are installed outside of the conditioned space, they must be sealed and insulated and, in some cases, a vapor retarder may be required. Some comments about duct losses, as they pertain to the location of the duct run, are provided below. More information about insulating and sealing exposed ducts is provided in Appendix 4.

Slab Construction

Radial and perimeter-loop duct systems that are embedded in a concrete slab lose heat through the edge of the slab. However, there is less heat loss associated with a radial system than there is with a perimeter loop system. Moisture is another problem when ducts are installed below-grade. Moisture must not accumulate inside of the duct system because it will affect the humidity level and the quality of the indoor air. And, moisture should not be allowed to saturate the material that surrounds the duct runs because it will increase the heat transfer through the duct walls.

Open Crawl Space

Ducts that are installed in an open crawl space are subject to outdoor conditions (temperature and humidity). These ducts must be tightly sealed and insulated. The duct insulation also should include a vapor retarding jacket if the temperature of the duct wall is expected to be lower than the dew point temperature of the outdoor air. (A vapor retarder is recommended for climates that routinely have outdoor dew point temperatures that exceed 60 °F during the cooling season.)

Enclosed Crawl Space

Ducts that are installed in an enclosed crawl space are subject to conditions (temperature and humidity) that fall somewhere between the outdoor conditions and the indoor conditions. If the crawl space walls are tight and well insulated, the crawl space temperature might be close to the room temperature —

probably within 20 °F or less. Therefore, the amount of duct insulation that is required for an enclosed crawl space will be less than the amount of duct insulation that is required for an open crawl space, but the duct runs still should be tightly sealed. (A vapor retarder is recommended for climates that routinely have outdoor dew point temperatures in excess of 60 °F during the cooling season.)

Basements

Basements should be tight and well insulated. If the basement is used as a living space, it will be maintained at the desired indoor design conditions during the heating and cooling seasons. Duct insulation is not required in this case, but the duct runs should be reasonably tight. If the basement is not used as a living space it will probably be heated, but not cooled. In this case, duct insulation is recommended because it will reduce the duct losses during the cooling season.

Attics

Ducts that are located in attics are subject to conditions that are equal to or more severe (during the summer) than the outdoor conditions. In this case, the duct runs must be sealed and insulated. The duct insulation also should include a vapor retarding jacket if the temperature of the duct wall is expected to be less than the dew point temperature of the outdoor air. (A vapor retarder is recommended for climates that routinely have outdoor dew point temperatures in excess of 60 °F during the cooling season.)

Drop Ceilings

Ducts that are installed in a drop ceiling are subject to conditions (temperature and humidity) that fall somewhere between the outdoor and indoor conditions. If the ceiling cavity is tight, well insulated and protected by a vapor retarder, the conditions in the ceiling cavity will be similar to the indoor design conditions. In this case, duct insulation is not required, but the duct runs should be sealed. If the conditions in the ceiling cavity are expected to be substantially different than the conditions in the occupied space, the duct runs must be insulated, tightly sealed and wrapped with a vapor retardant jacket if the ceiling cavity is not protected by a vapor retarder.

Risers in Outside Wall Stud Spaces

Ducts that are installed in an outside wall stud space are subject to conditions (temperature and humidity) that fall somewhere between the outdoor conditions and the indoor conditions. These ducts must be tightly sealed and insulated. The duct insulation also should include a vapor retarding jacket if the temperature of the duct wall is expected to be less than the dew point temperature of the outdoor air. (A vapor retarder is recommended for climates that routinely have outdoor dew point temperatures in excess of 60 °F during the cooling season.)

Noise

Excessive fan noise, noise that is generated in the duct system and noise that is generated by dampers or supply air outlets is not acceptable. Preferably, the equipment should be located outside of the conditioned space, and there should be no noise problems associated with the duct runs that are in or adjacent to the occupied space.

Codes

Building codes, energy codes, fire codes, insurance regulations and utility regulations may require or disallow certain envelope construction features, and they might mandate or prohibit certain air system installation procedures and practices. Duct placement, duct materials, duct insulation, duct sealing and vapor barriers are some of the things that might be codified. Make sure that the installation is in compliance with all of the codes and regulations that apply at the site.

1-6 Trunk and Branch Systems

There are various types of trunk and branch systems, some of which are identified by more common names — the "extended plenum" system or the "reducing plenum" system, for example. The flexible duct system also is classified as a trunk and branch system. Information about the various types of trunk and branch systems is provided below.

Extended Plenum System

The extended plenum system is the most common type of residential duct system. This system consists of a relatively large trunk duct that serves as an elongated plenum and a number of small branch ducts that are used to deliver the supply air to each room. A drawing of an extended plenum system is provided by Figure 1-5.

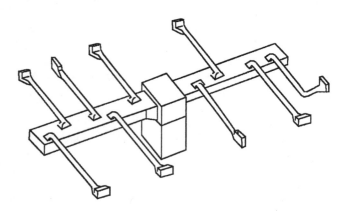

Figure 1-5

An extended plenum system is easy to fabricate and inexpensive to install. The trunk run is just a straight section of rectangular or round duct and simple fittings and boots are used to connect the branch ducts and the supply air outlets.

Ideally, the blower equipment should be centrally located with respect to the floor plan of the house. In this case, two plenums would extend across the length of the house, as indicated by Figure 1-5. This configuration is preferred because it produces a reasonably balanced system — as far as air flow is concerned. (There are no large differences between the lengths of the various duct runs.)

Quite often, for one reason or another, the blower equipment cannot be centrally located with respect to the floor plan of the house. In this case, one long plenum must extend cross the length of the house, as illustrated by Figure 1-6. This geometry produces large differences in the lengths of the various duct runs and these differences make it difficult to turn the air into the branch ducts that are near the blower.

A long plenum degrades the air flow through the branches that are close to the blower

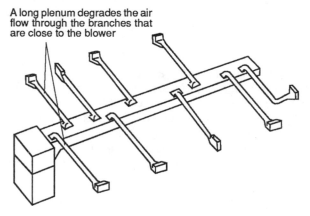

Figure 1-6

Reducing Plenum System

A reducing plenum design, which is illustrated by Figure 1-7, improves the performance of a long extended plenum because the trunk reduction tends to equalize the branch duct takeoff fitting losses, which helps turn the air into the branches that are closest to the blower.

A trunk reducer improves the air flow through branch ducts that are closest to the blower

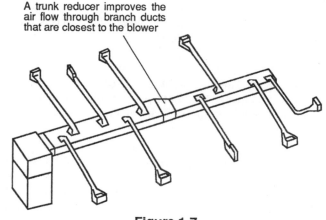

Figure 1-7

Historically, duct design manuals (including previous editions of **Manual D**) have recommended that the plenum reduction be located at a point that is about 24 feet downstream from the blower. However, this recommendation is arbitrary because it is based on the assumption that a substantial number of branch ducts will be installed in the first 24 feet of the trunk run and that a comparable number of branch ducts will be installed downstream from the reduction. Since this may not always be true, it is better to use the velocity of the air in the plenum as the criterion for establishing the location of the trunk duct reducer. If the velocity of the air in the plenum gets too low — to about 50 percent of the velocity that is associated with the first section of the plenum — the size of the trunk should be reduced. Figure 1-8 shows how to apply this rule. In this case, a reduction after the fifth branch duct takeoff fitting would be appropriate because the velocity in the trunk duct has dropped from 900 FPM to 450 FPM.

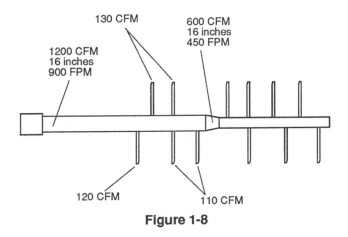

Figure 1-8

The velocity of the air that is moving through a section of duct depends on the CFM that is flowing through the duct and on the cross-sectional area of the duct. This velocity can be found by using the ACCA duct sizing calculator or by dividing the CFM value by the sectional area (in SQ.FT.)

Reducing Trunk Systems

A reducing trunk duct is similar to an extended plenum duct except that the cross-sectional area of the reducing trunk is decreased after every branch take-off. This type of trunk duct geometry is created when the equal friction method (which is commonly used to size duct runs for commercial duct systems) is used to size the duct runs. Less sheet metal is required to fabricate a reducing trunk duct, but there is more work associated with building the duct because each section is a different size. For small systems, it is usually less expensive to use the extended plenum geometry or the reducing plenum geometry. Figure 1-9 provides an illustration of a reducing trunk system.

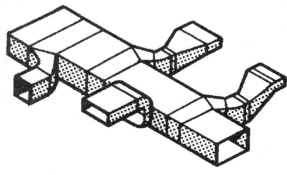

Figure 1-9

Primary-Secondary Trunk Systems

Some trunk and branch systems have a primary trunk and two or more secondary trunks, as illustrated by Figure 1-10. This type of system could be used in a home that spreads out in two or more directions. Note that with this type of system, the diverting "Tee" at the end of the main trunk run performs the same function as the reducer fitting that is used in the reducing plenum system. (The secondary trunk ducts have a smaller cross-sectional area than the main trunk duct.)

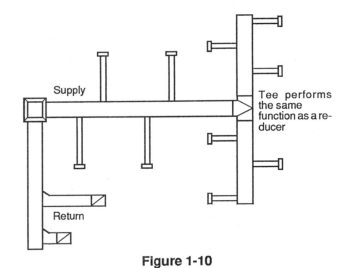

Figure 1-10

Flexible Duct Systems

Flexible duct systems are easy to fabricate and inexpensive to install. These systems consist of large diameter flexible trunk ducts, triangular or rectangular junction boxes (which are normally fabricated from duct board) and smaller diameter flexible branch ducts. This type of system is normally used for attic installations, but basement and crawl space installations are possible. Regardless of where the duct system is located, the flexible duct runs should be installed as straight as possible and they should be cut to length. (Kinked turns, coils and loops will create unnecessary pressure losses and reduced air flow.) Figure 1-11 provides an example of a flexible duct system.

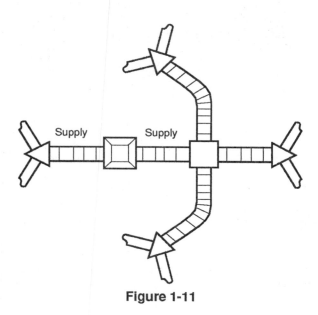

Figure 1-11

Application — Trunk and Branch Systems

Trunk and branch systems are versatile because they can be installed in a basement, a crawl space, an attic or above a drop ceiling. Because of this versatility, the extended plenum system is commonly found in single story, two story and split level homes. Table 1-2 on the next page provides some information about how trunk and branch duct systems can be installed in various types of homes.

1-7 Radial Systems

Radial duct systems consist of supply plenum that feeds branch ducts that are arranged in a radial pattern. These systems are easy and inexpensive to install because there is no trunk duct. The radial geometry is often used for duct systems that are embedded in a concrete slab because a low perimeter supply system provides superior comfort during the heating season. These types of systems also are installed in attics and they can be installed in a crawl space or basement. Traditionally, the radial geometry has been associated with applications that have blower equipment that is centrally located with respect to the supply air outlets, but symmetry is not mandatory (if the duct runs are sized correctly, any amount of off-set is acceptable). Figure 1-12 provides an example of a radial duct system that has rigid (metal or plastic) branch ducts. Rigid materials should be used if the duct runs are embedded in a slab, but they also could be used for crawl space and attic installations. Flexible duct materials are com-

monly used when a radial system is installed in an attic because the flexible material is easier to work with and less expensive to install.

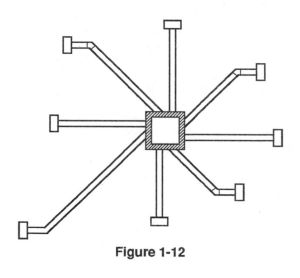

Figure 1-12

A radial duct system also can be installed above a drop ceiling. Figure 1-13 provides an example of how radial duct runs can be used to feed air to high sidewall outlets that are located on the inside walls of the structure.

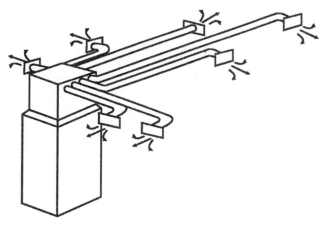

Figure 1-13

Application

Radial systems can be installed in a basement, a crawl space, an attic or above a drop ceiling. They are not normally used in basements but they could be if the basement has enough head room. Usually, a radial system is designed to serve one level; if multiple levels are involved, two or more radial systems can be used. (Most of the information that is provided by Table 1-2 on the next page about trunk and duct systems also applies to radial systems.)

Preferred Construction — Trunk and Branch Duct Systems						
Situation	**Distribution**	**Supply Runs**	**Return Runs**	**Duct Shape**	**Duct Materials**	**Insulation**
Equipment in basement — air delivery to the first floor and to the basement	*First Floor* Low perimeter supplies and low return(s) *Basement* Ceiling, high or low perimeter supplies	Trunk ducts below first floor framing; runouts below or between floor joists — no panned airways	Duct runs below first floor framing and/or between floor joists — no panned airways	Rectangular trunks provide more headroom — round or rectangular branch duct runouts	Metal or duct board trunks (consider potential for physical abuse) — metal, rigid Fiberglass or flex-duct runouts	Duct insulation is required if basement is not fully conditioned
Equipment in crawl space — air delivery to the first floor	Low perimeter supplies and low return(s)	Trunk ducts below floor framing; runouts below or between floor joists — no panned airways	Duct runs below floor framing and/or between floor joists — no panned airways	Rectangular or round trunks — round or rectangular branch duct runouts	Metal for open crawl space (animals-rodents); metal, rigid Fiberglass or flex-duct for closed crawl space	Duct insulation is required if crawl space is open or if it is enclosed with poorly insulated walls
Equipment in basement or crawl space — air delivery to the second floor	Low perimeter supplies and low return(s); — or ceiling supplies and high return(s)	Risers in interior partition walls, chases or closets; perimeter runouts between floor joists — or horizontal runs in the attic — no panned airways	Drops located in interior partition walls, chases or closets; horizontal runs between joists — or horizontal runs in the attic — no panned airways	Rectangular or oval risers and drops — round or rectangular perimeter runouts — round or rectangular trunks and runouts in attic	Metal or duct board risers — metal, rigid Fiberglass or flex-duct for perimeter runouts — metal, rigid Fiberglass or flex-duct for the attic	Insulation not required for duct in interior wall — duct must be inside of the wall insulation if it is in an exterior wall — insulate attic duct runs
Equipment installed on the first floor — air delivery to the first floor (slab or crawl space construction)	Low perimeter supplies — or ceiling supplies — or high sidewall supplies — single central return; or multiple returns (located low or high, depending on the installation cost)	Perimeter outlets supplied by ducts buried in slab or installed in crawl space — ceiling outlets supplied by duct system in attic — sidewall outlets supplied by duct system in drop ceiling	Central return at unit (with return path from every room) — or return duct system below crawl space floor — or return duct system in attic with drop to unit	Round duct embedded in slab — rectangular or round duct in crawl space — rectangular or round duct in attic — rectangular duct in ceiling cavity	Plastic or plastic covered metal in slab — metal in open crawl space (animals-rodents) — metal, rigid Fiberglass or flex for enclosed crawl space or attic — metal or rigid Fiberglass in ceiling cavity	Slab edge insulation for ducts embedded in slab — duct insulation is required in an attic, in an open crawl space; or if an enclosed crawl space is poorly insulated
Equipment installed on the first floor — air delivery to the first floor and second floor	Perimeter ceiling outlets for first floor; perimeter floor outlets for second floor; return(s) for each level	Supply trunk located in drop ceiling, runouts between ceiling joists to first and second floor outlets	Returns on both levels; drops located in interior partition walls, chases or closets	Rectangular trunks provide more headroom — round or rectangular branch duct runouts	Metal or rigid Fiberglass in ceiling cavity; metal, rigid Fiberglass or flex-duct for perimeter runouts	Insulation not required for duct in interior ceiling cavity
Split level home no basement	Central equipment in crawl space or on slab level. Low perimeter supplies for all levels. Ducts in crawl space, embedded in slab and in ceiling cavity below upper level. Refer to situations described above for details.					
Split level home with basement	Central equipment in basement. Low perimeter supplies for all levels. Ducts in basement, embedded in slab or in crawl space, risers in partitions to second floor outlets. Refer to situations described above for details.					
Note: Duct runs located outdoors, in unconditioned spaces or within the framing spaces must be tightly sealed.						

Table 1-2

1-8 Perimeter Loop Systems

Figure 1-14 provides an example of a perimeter loop duct system. This type of duct system would normally be used in a cold climate when the structure is built on a ground slab because it is particularly effective at maintaining comfort at the floor level during the heating season. (In this respect, the loop system is somewhat better than the radial system, but this advantage is offset because the loop system is more difficult to design and more expensive to install.)

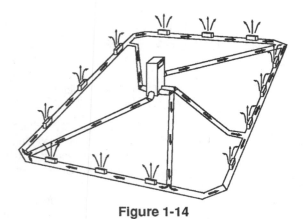

Figure 1-14

1-9 Return Air Paths

The return air system must establish a low resistance return air path between every room and the return side of the blower cabinet. If these paths are not established, the air flow through some or all of the supply air outlets will be affected. For example, if a closed door and a thick carpet isolates one or more rooms from a central return air opening, the isolated rooms will be pressurized and the flow of supply air into these rooms will be inadequate. In this case, the doors perform the same function as balancing dampers, shutting off the flow of air to the isolated rooms. Furthermore, the reduction of air flow to the isolated rooms causes an increase in the air flow to the remaining rooms. The net result is that the system is thrown out of balance — some rooms get too little air and other rooms get too much air. (Note that under these circumstances, the infiltration that is associated with the building envelope could increase because some rooms will be pressurized and some rooms will be subject to a negative pressure.)

Return in Every Room
The ultimate return air system would consist of a ducted return for every room that could be isolated from the rest of the house. This would guarantee adequate air flow — even if the interior doors are closed. This strategy also provides more privacy because there is no need to install transfer grilles or to undercut the doors. Another advantage is that this type of return air system is quiet because the return air openings are small and because they are acoustically isolated (by distance and multiple turns) from the blower equipment. There also is

an advantage associated with aesthetics because the individual return grilles are much smaller than a central return grille. However, this type of return system is geometrically complex, requires more space, increases the equivalent length of the return path, increases the number of potential leakage points and is relatively expensive.

Central Return
A single central return is the least expensive system to install. (In multilevel homes, a central return should be installed on each level.) Usually, the return duct is short; consequently, the return-side pressure drop is small. This type of return air system occupies a minimal amount of space, is easy to install and is inexpensive. The disadvantages of this system are that each isolated room must be equipped with an air transfer opening (grille or door undercut), equipment noise may not be effectively isolated from the living space and a large return air grille may be unattractive.

Multiple Returns
A return air system that has multiple return air openings provides a compromise between the performance benefits that are associated with individual returns and space-cost benefits that are associated with a single central return. With this system, a return air opening is provided for every major room and transfer grilles are used for the secondary rooms. (At least one return should be provided for each level of a multilevel or multistory house.)

1-10 Plenum Systems

It is possible to use a crawl space or a hall ceiling cavity as a supply air plenum or as a return air plenum. In either case, the primary motivation for using a crawl space or ceiling cavity as a plenum is rooted in a desire to reduce the installed cost of the duct system. ACCA does not recommend this practice, but plenum systems can provide acceptable performance and comfort if certain installation requirements are satisfied. These requirements are discussed below.

Crawl Space Supply Plenum
As shown on the next page by Fig 1-15, a crawl space supply plenum is used in conjunction with a perimeter air distribution system. However, this system differs substantially from other types of perimeter systems because there are no duct connections between the supply air opening in the HVAC equipment cabinet and the supply air terminals.

In order for this type of system to work, the plenum pressure should be maintained at 0.15 to 0.20 inches water gauge. This is the amount of pressure that is required to move the air through the abbreviated duct runs that feed air to the supply air diffusers. (The abbreviated duct runs are required for balancing, to ensure that the air will have a uniform approach to the outlet and to ensure that the air will leave the outlet with enough velocity to throw the air up to the ceiling.)

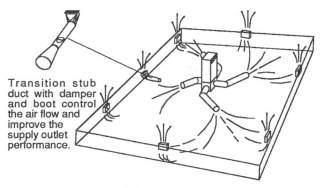

Transition stub duct with damper and boot control the air flow and improve the supply outlet performance.

Figure 1-15

The problems that are associated with this design are plenum leakage, plenum heat losses, moisture control, acceptable air outlet performance and odor control. This system should not be used if one or more of these problems cannot be satisfactorily resolved.

- The entire crawl space must be tightly sealed so that it can be pressurized. Air leakage to the outdoors, to unconditioned spaces and to conditioned spaces is unacceptable.

- The plenum walls must be well insulated. During the winter, the crawl space temperature will be about 30 degrees higher than the temperature of a crawl space that contains a ducted supply air system.

- The crawl space floor and walls should be covered with a vapor retarder to ensure that the supply air does not absorb moisture that evaporates out of the soil or moisture that leaks or migrates through the walls.

- Each supply outlet should be equipped with a short "feeder duct," which consists of a converging transition, a stub duct that is equipped with a hand damper and an aerodynamic boot fitting. (The purpose of the feeder duct system is to control the acceleration of the air so that it obtains a uniform velocity before it enters the air terminal. The purpose of the hand damper is to balance the air flow.)

- The supply air must be isolated from the soil by an impermeable retarder because odors, mildew and other air quality problems are associated with soil.

- If a furnace is used, it must be located outside of the crawl space because the burner performance could be adversely affected by the positive pressure in the crawl space.

Ceiling Cavity Supply Plenum

A ceiling cavity supply plenum system could be used in conjunction with a high inside wall air distribution system. (It also is possible to run one or more ducts from the plenum to one or more ceiling outlets.)

In order for this system to work, the plenum pressure should be maintained at about 0.15 inches water gauge. This is the amount of pressure that is required to move the air through the stub duct runs that feed air to the supply air diffusers. (The stub duct runs are required for balancing and to ensure that the air will have a uniform approach to the outlet.)

The problems with this design are associated with plenum leakage, plenum heat losses and acceptable air outlet performance. This system should not be used if one or more of these problems cannot be satisfactorily resolved.

- The ceiling cavity must be tightly sealed so that it can be pressurized. Air leakage to the attic, to unconditioned spaces and to conditioned spaces is unacceptable.

- The top of the ceiling cavity must be well insulated. During the winter, the temperature in the cavity will be 15 to 30 degrees warmer than the room temperature.

- Each supply outlet should be equipped with a short stub duct that is equipped with a hand damper. (The purpose of the stub duct is to control the acceleration of the air so that it enters the air terminal with a uniform velocity. The purpose of the hand damper is to balance the air flow.)

Return Plenums

A tightly constructed crawl space or ceiling space could be used as a return plenum. In this case the return air flows through return air openings, circulates through the plenum space and is drawn into the return side of the equipment. The problems with this design are plenum leakage, plenum heat losses, moisture control and air quality.

- The entire return plenum must be tightly sealed. Infiltration from the outdoors, from unconditioned spaces and from conditioned space is not acceptable.

- The exposed surfaces must be well insulated.

- If the crawl space is used as a plenum, the floor and walls should be covered with a vapor retarder to ensure that the supply air does not absorb moisture that evaporates out of the soil or moisture that leaks or migrates through the walls.

- If the crawl space is used as a plenum, the return air must be isolated from the soil by an impermeable retarder because odors, mildew and other air quality problems are associated with the soil.

- If a furnace is used, it must be located outside of the plenum space because the burner performance could be adversely affected by the negative pressure in the plenum.

SECTION 2
Equipment and Air-side Devices

This section provides information about conventional types of residential HVAC equipment and devices. This presentation emphasizes the attributes and characteristics that are associated with air-side performance.

2-1 Air Distribution System Components

A complete air distribution system, whether intended for winter, summer or year-round use, consists of primary equipment, secondary equipment, air-side devices and duct runs. Primary equipment contains components that are installed in the air stream and components that have nothing to do with the air side of the system. Secondary equipment and air-side devices are always installed in the air stream.

Primary Equipment
The primary equipment provides the basic functions that are associated with comfort conditioning (heat, sensible cooling, latent cooling and air filtration) and an air moving device (the blower). The primary conditioning equipment could be a furnace, a cooling-only unit or a heat pump. This unitized equipment contains air-side components that are an integral part of the assembly (a fan, cooling coil or heat exchanger) and accessory components that can easily be added to, or removed from, the basic assembly (a filter or a supplemental electric resistance heater). Some equipment packages place all of the components in one cabinet (single package unit) and other designs place the air-side components (fan, coil and filter) in a separate cabinet (split system).

Secondary Equipment
Secondary equipment consists of the optional components that are normally supplied with the primary conditioning equipment and devices that are used to supplement the performance of the primary conditioning equipment. Examples of this type of equipment include electric duct-mounted heating coils, DX cooling coils, heat-reclaim water coils, media filters, electronic filters and humidifiers.

Air-side Devices
Air-side devices are used to control air flow. Supply outlets introduce the supply air into the room, grilles capture the return air, dampers and junction boxes control the air flow in the duct system.

2-2 Primary Heating and Cooling Equipment

Forced air heating, cooling or year-round conditioning equipment includes an energy conversion device, which may be fuel-fired or electrically powered. A fuel-fired conversion device usually consists of a burner (gas or oil) and a combustion chamber (heat exchanger). An electrically powered conversion device could be a simple electric resistance heating element or an assembly of refrigeration cycle machinery and hardware (air conditioner or heat pump). Regardless of whether the equipment is fossil-fueled or electrically powered, it will include a blower. Therefore, as far as the duct system is concerned, the performance of the heating and cooling equipment is defined by the performance and the arrangement of the blower section.

Furnaces
Furnaces, which are the primary component of many forced air heating systems, can be supplemented with a DX coil when cooling is required. Furnace manufacturers provide a number of configuration options that are designed to accommodate the "available space" situations that are associated with installing equipment in a basement, crawl space or attic. The configuration also must be compatible with the location of the trunk ducts.

Low-boy Arrangement
A low-boy unit features a blower compartment that is located at floor level and to the side or rear of the heat exchanger. This design minimizes the amount of head room that is required to install the equipment. Because they have a low profile and a vertical discharge, these units are usually installed in basements. In this case, the vertical discharge is compatible with an air distribution system that is located above the equipment. Figure 2-1 provides examples of gas-fired and oil-fired low-boy furnaces.

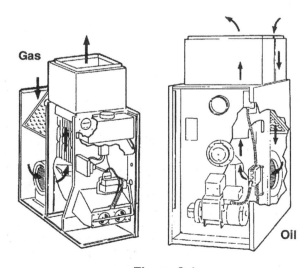

Figure 2-1

Up-flow Arrangement
An up-flow (hi-boy) unit features a blower compartment that is located directly below the heat exchanger. This type of furnace is generally installed in closets, small utility rooms or in basements (where ceiling heights permit). Because this unit has a vertical discharge, it is compatible with trunk ducts that are located above the equipment. Figure 2-2 provides examples of gas-fired and oil-fired up-flow furnaces.

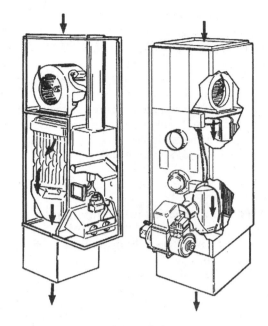

Figure 2-3

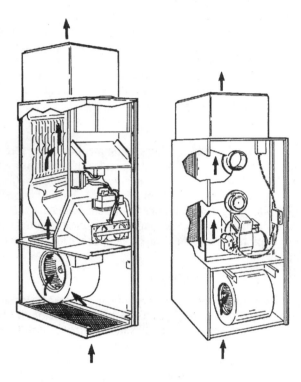

Figure 2-2

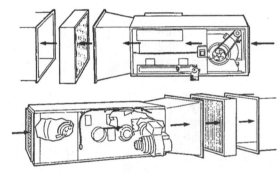

Figure 2-4

Down-flow Arrangement
The down-flow arrangement places the blower compartment above the heat exchanger. This configuration is compatible with a duct system that is located below the equipment. Down-flow units are usually installed in homes that have slab floor or crawl space construction and are normally located in a closet or small utility room. Figure 2-3 provides examples of gas-fired and oil-fired down-flow furnaces.

Horizontal Arrangement
Horizontal furnaces require a minimum amount of vertical clearance. This is accomplished by placing the blower compartment and the heat exchanger on the same level. This type of equipment is commonly installed in an attic or crawl space, but it could be hung below a basement ceiling or a utility room ceiling. Since the unit features a horizontal discharge, it can be connected to a duct system that is located above, below or at the same level as the furnace. Figure 2-4 provides examples of horizontal gas-fired and oil-fired furnaces.

Multi-position Furnaces
Most manufacturers offer a multi-position furnace. This equipment is compatible with up-flow, down-flow and horizontal arrangements.

Blower Performance
Some furnaces are designed for heating-only applications and others are compatible with heating-cooling applications. The difference is that the heating-cooling units are equipped with a more powerful blower. This extra blower power is required to overcome the pressure drop that is created when a DX coil is added to the furnace. In any case, blower performance data is usually included with the technical information that is published by the furnace manufacturer. This blower data is required in order to design the duct system. (Blower performance data is generated by testing a furnace that has a specific set of air-side components. This test may not account for all of the air-side components that might be added to the basic package (refer to Sections 6-3 and 6-5).

Air Conditioners and Heat Pumps

Air conditioners and heat pumps (air source and water source) may be manufactured as a split system or as a single-packaged unit. Split systems, which are the most common, consist of an outdoor unit (condensing unit) and an indoor unit (air handler or blower coil). Single-package units, which are installed outdoors (typically on a rooftop or on a ground pad), are used when the space inside the home is limited.

Split Systems — Cooling-only and Heat Pump
Split, cooling-only systems and split heat pump systems feature blower coil units (or air handlers), which normally consist of a cabinet, a DX coil, a blower and a filter. (Electric resistance heaters are commonly included with heat pump equipment.) These air-moving modules are available in up-flow, down-flow or horizontal configurations. These configuration options allow the designer to specify an arrangement that is compatible with the location of the equipment (attic, basement, crawl space or utility closet) and the location of the duct system (above, below or at the same level as the unit). It also is important to make sure that the cabinet dimensions are compatible with the space that is available for the unit. Figure 2-5 provides an example of split system equipment.

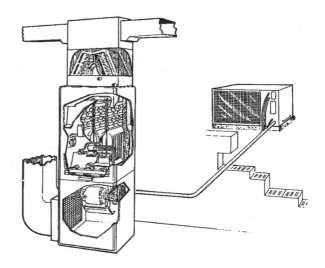

Figure 2-6

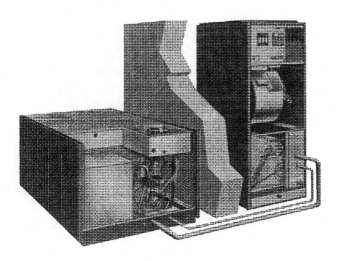

Figure 2-5

Cooling Added to a Furnace
Split system air conditioning equipment is often used with forced air furnaces (fossil fuel or electric). In this application, the indoor air conditioning equipment simply consists of a DX coil, which is added to the discharge side of the furnace (the blower and the filter are included with the furnace package.) Coils, coil cabinets and coil casings are generally available for up-flow, down-flow and horizontal applications. Figure 2-6 shows an up-flow furnace that is equipped with a DX cooling coil.

Heat Pump Added to a Furnace
Split system heat pump equipment can be used with fossil fuel furnaces. In this application, the indoor heat pump equipment simply consists of a DX coil, which is added to the discharge side of the furnace. (The blower and the filter are included with the furnace package.)

Single Package Systems — Cooling-only and Heat Pump
Self-contained cooling units and heat pumps contain all the necessary air-side components (blower, coil and filter). Heat pump units also include an electric heating coil (for supplemental heat). Because these units are installed outdoors, the supply and return duct systems have to penetrate a wall or roof.

Blower Performance
Information about the blower performance is required in order to design the duct system. This information is usually included in the performance data that is published by the equipment manufacturer. (The blower performance data is generated by testing a unit that has a specific set of air-side components. This test may not account for all of the air-side components that can be installed in the equipment package. Refer to Section 5-7 for more information about using blower performance data.)

2-3 Secondary Equipment

Secondary equipment includes filters, supplemental heating coils and humidifiers. A DX coil that is added to a furnace also can be classified as secondary equipment.

Usually, there is an increase in the resistance to the air flow when secondary equipment is added to the air distribution system. This additional resistance is equal to the pressure drop across the device. The value for this pressure drop is provided in the manufacturer's performance data. Compensation for this pressure drop is achieved by subtracting the pressure drop value from the available static pressure that is produced by the blower. (Refer to Section 5-7 for more information about adjusting blower performance data.)

Filters

Filters are used to remove particles (dust and pollen, for example) and mists that are entrained in the air flow. However, most filters will not remove the small particles, gases and odors that are associated with tobacco smoke. (High efficiency filters can be used to trap small particles; absorption equipment and air-washer equipment can be used to remove odors and gases.)

Media filters and electronic filters are normally used for residential applications. Media filters provide two types of cleaning action. First, they strain particles from the air, but this action only removes the particles that are larger than the openings in the filter media. Second, they use a viscous coating or an electrostatic charge to snare small particles that come in contact with the fibers of the filter. Various types of filters are described in the following paragraphs. In some situations it may be necessary to pass air through two filters in order to obtain the desired result.

Viscous Media Filters

Viscous media filters are normally furnished with residential equipment. These filters feature a media (mat of coarse material such as glass fiber, expanded metal, animal hair, nylon thread, or some combination of these materials) that is coated with a viscous or sticky substance. This media strains the air, but it also acts like low-velocity centrifuge. When air passes through the mat, it changes direction suddenly and often. This churning action causes the particles — which are unable to change direction as quickly as the air — to strike and stick to the media. The ASHRAE dust spot efficiency of this type of filter varies from less than 10 percent to about 30 percent, depending on the product. This means that it will protect the HVAC equipment from lint, fibers and large particles, but it will not be able to remove most of the particles that affect the indoor air quality. The pressure drop across a simple viscous media filter (when it is clean) is about 0.10 inches water column (IWC), but a more precise value should be obtained from the manufacturer's performance data. Figure 2-7 provides an example of a viscous media filter.

Electronic Air Cleaners

Electronic air cleaners ionize the particles that are in the air stream. After they are ionized, the particles are attracted to a charged plate. Once in contact with the plate, the particles lose their charge and are held on the plate by natural adhesion or by a viscous film. The ASHRAE dust spot efficiency of an electronic filter varies from less than 30 percent to about 70 percent, depending on the product. If the filter efficiency exceeds 60 percent it will effectively eliminate particles that cause allergic reactions, smudges and stains; it will be par-

Figure 2-7

tially effective at removing the particles that are associated with tobacco smoke. (If it is not included with the unit, a prefilter should be installed upstream from the electronic filter.) The pressure drop across an electronic air cleaner is about 0.10 IWC, but a precise value should be obtained from the manufacturer's performance data. Figure 2-8 provides an example of an electronic air cleaner.

Figure 2-8

Charged-media Filters

Charged-media air cleaners also make use of an electrostatic field, but in this case a voltage is applied to the filter media. When the particles pass through the filter, they are attracted to the media by electrostatic action. However, this type of filter is not nearly as effective as an electronic air cleaner because the particles have a limited ability to be polarized by the field. The ASHRAE dust spot efficiency of this type of filter is only slightly better than the dust spot efficiency of a conventional viscous media filter. Refer to the manufacturer's performance data for information about the pressure drop across this type of filter.

Plastic Static-charge Filters
Some filters are made of a material that, when air passes through at a relatively high velocity, generates its own charge of static electricity. However, the ionizing effect on dirt particles is less than the effect that is produced by a charged-media filter and the effect diminishes as the relative humidity rises. The ASHRAE dust spot efficiency of this type of filter is similar to the dust spot efficiency of a conventional viscous media filter. Refer to the manufacturer's performance data for information about the pressure drop across this type of filter.

Plastic Foam Filters
Open-pore plastic foam filters depend upon a straining action to remove large particles, and upon a clinging action to capture the small particles that are entrained in the air stream. The ASHRAE dust spot efficiency of this type of filter is similar to the dust spot efficiency of a conventional viscous media filter. Refer to the manufacturer's performance data for information about the pressure drop across this type of filter.

Dry Extended Surface Filters
Dry extended surface filters are made of materials that have very fine pores. Normally these filters employ a pleated (extended surface) geometry to compensate for the air flow resistance that is created by the media. The ASHRAE dust spot efficiency of this type of filter varies from less than 30 percent to more than 90 percent, depending on the product. If the filter efficiency exceeds 60 percent it will effectively eliminate particles that cause allergic reactions, smudges and stains; and it will be partially effective at removing the particles that are associated with tobacco smoke. Note that the pressure drop across an extended surface filter could be considerably more than the 0.10 IWC value that is associated with the filters that are normally installed in residential HVAC systems. Refer to the manufacturer's performance data for information about the pressure drop across this type of filter.

The velocity of the air passing through the filter and the amount of dirt on it affect the pressure drop across the filter. Many furnaces and air handlers are tested and rated with clean filters installed. In this case, the rated air handling characteristics of the blower accounts for the pressure loss that is associated with a clean filter. If, however, the blower is rated without a filter installed, the blower performance data must be adjusted to account for the pressure drop across the filter. This adjustment also will be necessary if a second filter is added to the system, if another type of filter is substituted for the one that came with the unit or if the filter is too dirty.

Supplemental Heaters
The electric heating coils that are added to heat pump air handling equipment are the most common type of supplemental heat. Since these coils are installed in the air handler, they are controlled by the central thermostat and they add heat to every room that is served by the system. Smaller coils, which are designed to fit into a duct or into a special boot fitting, can provide supplemental heat on a localized basis. These types of heaters are controlled by a low-limit thermostat that operates independently of the central thermostat. The pressure drop across a supplemental electric heater can vary from less than 0.10 IWC to more than 0.20 IWC, depending on the product and the rate of air flow. Refer to the manufacturer's performance data for this important pressure drop information. Figure 2-9 shows an example of a duct heater.

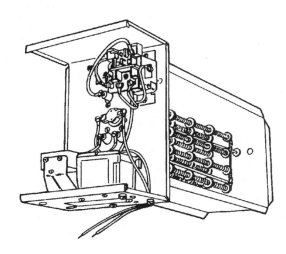

Figure 2-9

Humidifiers
Add-on humidifiers, which are used to increase the indoor humidity during the heating season, can be classified as adiabatic (no heat added by the humidification device) or isothermal (no air temperature rise associated with the humidification process). Adiabatic equipment is also referred to as evaporative equipment. This type of humidifying equipment could be an atomizing device, a wetted element device or an evaporative pan humidifier. Adiabatic devices are not equipped with a source of heat; all the heat that is required to evaporate the water comes from the supply air. Therefore, humidification with this type of equipment produces a drop in the temperature of the supply air. However, there is no temperature change associated with isothermal humidification equipment. In this case, the heat that is required for the evaporation process is provided by an integral heater or by an external heat source. Heated pan humidifiers are an example of isothermal humidification equipment.

The source of heat that drives the evaporation process is important because humidification equipment can affect the performance of heating equipment. Units that have their own heat source are not a problem because they do not depress the temperature of the supply air; therefore, they can be installed on any type of forced air heating system. Humidifiers that extract heat from the supply air are questionable candidates for heat pump systems (or furnace systems that do not have a large temperature rise) because they lower the temperature of the supply air.

Air quality is another important issue that is associated with the use of humidification equipment. Humidifiers must not produce biological contaminants, such as bacteria, algae, mold or fungus. (Most of these biological agents do not cause serious health problems, but they can cause allergic reactions and odor problems. However, there is one important exception: the bacteria that is associated with Legionnaires disease, which is deadly.) Reservoirs, drain pans, dripping or spitting nozzles and condensation on duct materials or building components are all potential sources of biological contamination. The likelihood of the occurrence of an air quality problem depends on the type of humidification device. In general, sterile feed water, a high operating temperature, proper sizing and installation, proper water treatment, scheduled inspection and proper maintenance will keep biological growth under control.

Most of the humidification devices that are added to residential HVAC systems are installed in a duct or plenum, but there are some devices that can be installed within a room. Both types of devices must be mounted so that clearances are maintained and condensation is prevented. Information about some of the most common types of residential humidification equipment is provided below.

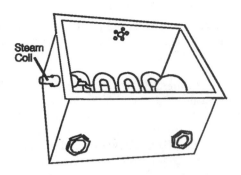

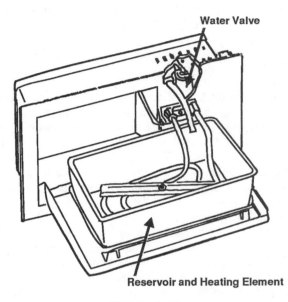

Water Valve

Reservoir and Heating Element

Figure 2-10

Pan Humidifiers

Pan humidifiers are simple devices that are designed to evaporate water from the surface of a heated reservoir. (If the reservoir is not heated, the device is not very effective.) Heat is supplied by an electric coil. These devices will not cause a significant change in the temperature of the humidified air because the heat of evaporation is supplied by an external source. Pan humidifiers are suitable for small loads and they can either be installed in a supply air duct or in the room. Regular blowdown and weekly or monthly maintenance is required to keep the pan and the heating coils free of biological, chemical or mineral deposits. If they are properly installed, there should be no water droplet, wetting, or duct corrosion problems. These humidifiers are on-off devices and, because of the dynamics of the evaporation process, they have a sluggish response to a call for humidity and they are slow to shut down. If the parts of the humidifier project into the air stream, they will produce a resistance to the air flow, but this pressure drop information may not be documented in the manufacturer's performance data. (The pressure drop penalty will probably be less than 0.10 IWC.) Figure 2-10 shows a pan humidifier.

Wetted Media Humidifiers

Wetted media humidifiers are designed to evaporate water from the surface of a wet pad. The media can either be wetted by a nozzle or by immersion in a sump. (Nozzle units use considerably more water, but they provide continual blowdown.) Usually, the heat of evaporation is supplied by the air that is flowing through the media. This psychrometric process causes a drop in the temperature of the humidified air. (In some cases, performance may be enhanced by a supplemental heater that adds heat to the water or the air.) Wetted media humidifiers are suitable for small loads and there are many different types of duct-mounted and self-contained room units to choose from. Wetted media humidifiers require regular maintenance to clear the sump or reservoir of any biological, chemical or mineral deposits. If they are properly installed, there should be no water droplet, wetting or duct corrosion problems. Mineral fallout (dusting) is not a problem with this type of equipment. Wetted media humidifiers are on-off devices. Depending on the design, they have a slow to good response to a call for humidity and a reasonably quick response to a shut-down signal.

Figure 2-11 shows a wetted media unit that protrudes into the duct system. This device will produce a resistance to the air flow, but this pressure drop information may not be documented in the manufacturer's performance data. (The pressure drop penalty will probably be less than 0.10 IWC.)

2-11

Figure 2-12 shows a duct-mounted bypass unit. In this case the air flow through the media is induced by the pressure difference across the blower equipment. This design does not produce much resistance to the air flow in the supply duct, but the air that is continuously diverted through the bypass may cause an undesirable reduction in the supply CFM.

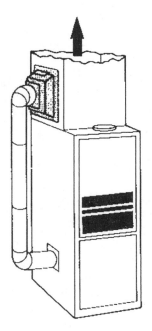

Figure 2-12

Figure 2-13 shows a fan powered bypass unit. In this case an integral fan causes the air to flow from the duct, through the media and back to the duct. This equipment does not produce much resistance to the air flow in the supply duct and it does not cause a reduction in the supply CFM.

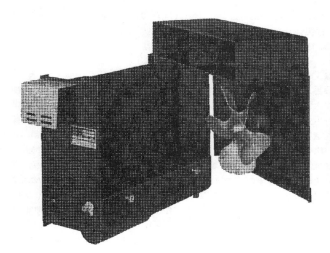

Figure 2-13

Figure 2-14

Atomizing Humidifiers
Atomizing humidifiers are designed to spray a fine mist of water droplets into the air. This means that the air must supply the heat that is required to complete the evaporation process. This psychrometric process causes a drop in the temperature of the humidified air. Spinning disk and diffusing screen units are designed for very small loads. Small nozzle spray units also are available. Normally these units are installed in a duct. Note that there is always the possibility that any type of

atomizing equipment could wet nearby surfaces. However, this should not be a problem providing that the equipment is properly sized, controlled and installed. Regular maintenance is required to keep biological and mineral deposits under control. Small atomizing humidifiers are usually on-off devices and they have a good response to a call for humidity and to a shut-down signal. Units that do not protrude into the air stream will have a negligible effect on the air flow in the supply duct. Figure 2-14 on the previous page shows an example of an atomizing humidifier.

DX Coils and Water Coils

DX coils that are added to furnaces can be part of a cooling-only system or part of an add-on heat pump system. Water coils that are added to an air distribution system can be part of a hot water heating system or a thermal storage system. In either case, the coil will add a considerable amount of resistance (pressure drop) to the supply side of the air distribution system. It is very important for the system designer to verify that the furnace blower has enough power to overcome this additional resistance. Information about the pressure drop that is associated with a DX coil or a water coil can be found in the coil manufacturer's performance data. (The pressure drop across a wet DX coil will be greater than the pressure drop across a dry DX coil. Normally the wet-coil value is required, but the dry-coil value can be used when the climate is so dry that there will never be a need for latent cooling.) Figure 2-6 shows a furnace that is equipped with a DX coil.

2-4 Air-Side Devices

Air-side devices include supply air outlets, return inlets, balancing dampers, variable volume control dampers (VAV dampers) and flex-duct junction boxes. There always is an increase in the resistance to the air flow when these devices are added to the air distribution system. This additional resistance is equal to the pressure drop across the device. The value for this pressure drop is usually provided in the manufacturer's performance data. Compensation for this pressure drop is achieved by subtracting the pressure drop value from the available static pressure that is produced by the blower. (Refer to Section 5-7 for more information about adjusting blower performance data.)

Supply Outlets and Return Inlets

Supply outlets are diffusers, registers or grilles that are designed to mix the supply air with the room air. Return inlets are usually grilles, but they could be registers. Usually the pressure drop that is associated with theses types of devices is less than 0.030 IWC. (Refer to ACCA **Manual T** for information about selecting, sizing and positioning this type of hardware.)

Dampers

Volume dampers and VAV dampers are normally located in the branch supply ducts. Volume dampers, which are used for balancing the system, are manually set to insure that the desired flow of air is delivered to the room. VAV dampers, which are controlled by a room thermostat, are used to maintain room temperature. The pressure drop across a simple balancing damper, when it is in the full open position, is about 0.03 IWC; but the pressure drop that is associated with an open VAV damper may be larger. Refer to the manufacturer's performance data for this information.

Flex-duct Junction Boxes

A pressure loss occurs when air enters a flex-duct junction box and a second pressure loss occurs when air leaves a flexible duct junction box. These pressure losses depend on the geometry of the junction box, on the upstream velocity of the air and on the downstream velocity of the air. When these velocities are in the neighborhood of 600 FPM, the total pressure drop that is associated with a junction box is about 0.05 IWC.

Section 3
Basic Principles — Residential Duct Sizing Calculations

Air-side design is critical. Poor air-side design can result in inadequate heating and/or cooling in some or all rooms. It is not uncommon for poor heating and cooling performance to be attributed to insufficient equipment size when the actual problem was caused by a restrictive duct system. This section introduces the basic principles that are associated with sizing duct runs. These principles are the foundation of the **Manual D** duct sizing procedures.

3-1 Pressure Units

The pressures that are associated with air distribution systems are quite small — typically less than 0.025 pounds per square inch (positive or negative) for residential systems. Because the operating pressures are so small, it is convenient to use inches of water column (IWC) when pressure is discussed. (For reference, a pressure of 27.7 inches water column is equal to 1.0 pound per square inch.)

3-2 Blower Performance

Blowers are required to move air through the duct system. **The amount of air flow (CFM) that is delivered by a blower depends on the resistance (pressure) that the blower has to work against.** This behavior is summarized by blower data, which can take the form of a table (blower table) or a

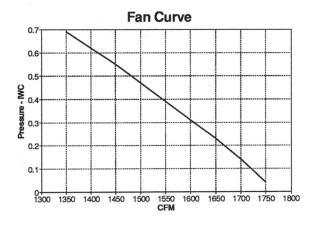

Figure 3-2

graph (blower curve). Figure 3-1 provides an example of tabular performance data and Figure 3-2 provides an example of a graph of the same data. Notice that the air flow decreases as the resistance increases.

3-3 Duct Performance

A resistance is created when air is forced through a duct. This resistance is caused by friction. Figure 3-3 provides an example of duct performance. Notice that the resistance increases rapidly as more and more air is forced through the duct.

Blower Data	
CFM	**Resistance (IWC)**
1300	—
1350	0.69
1400	0.62
1450	0.55
1500	0.47
1550	0.39
1600	0.31
1650	0.23
1700	0.14
1750	0.04
1800	—

Figure 3-1

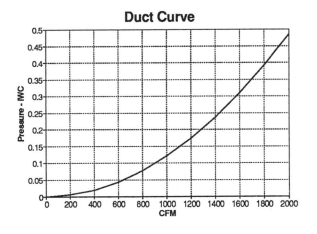

Figure 3-3

3-4 System Operating Point

If a fan (Figure 3-2, for example) is connected to a duct (Figure 3-3, for example) there is only one possible operating point. Since this point must be compatible with the fan performance, the operating point must fall on the fan curve. And since this point must be compatible with the duct performance, the operating point must fall on the duct curve. This can happen only at the point where the two performance curves intersect, as demonstrated by Figure 3-4.

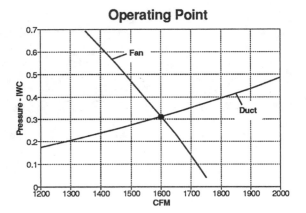

Figure 3-4

In this case the system will deliver 1600 CFM to the space. If the designer is not satisfied with the 1600 CFM value, the fan performance must be modified or the duct performance must be altered. Since the fan performance curve (Figure 3-2) depends on the fan geometry, which is fixed by the manufacturer's design and the fan speed, the only way to change the fan performance characteristic is to change the fan speed. Likewise, since the duct performance (Figure 3-3) depends on the duct geometry and the duct material, the only way to change the duct performance is to alter the duct geometry or to change the duct material.

3-5 Objective of the Residential Sizing Procedure

Residential equipment manufacturers provide a blower with the equipment package (furnace or air handler). The basic objective of the **Manual D** procedure is to size the duct system so that it will work with the blower that is supplied with the HVAC equipment. **To meet this objective, the duct system must be designed so that the air flow resistance — in terms of static pressure drop — matches the external static pressure that is produced by the blower when the blower delivers the desired CFM.**

This concept is demonstrated by Figure 3-5. In this case the fan can deliver 1,000 CFM when it works against a resistance of 0.20 IWC. Therefore, the only acceptable duct size will be the size that produces a resistance of 0.20 IWC when the flow is equal to 1,000 CFM. Ultimately, this size will be determined by using a friction chart or a duct slide rule, but first it is necessary to make a distinction between the pressure drop that is associated with the duct and the friction rate that is associated with the duct.

3-6 Pressure Drop and Friction Rate

A pressure drop is equal to the total pressure loss that occurs between any two points in a duct system. For example, in Figure 3-5, the pressure drop that is associated with 300 feet of duct is equal to 0.20 IWC. (Note that IWC units are used to identify pressure drop data.)

A friction rate is equal to the pressure loss that occurs between two points in a duct system that are separated by a specific distance. Friction charts and duct slide rules use 100 feet for the reference distance (refer to Appendix 2). Therefore, in order to use the duct slide rule to size a duct run, the pressure drop data must be converted to the friction rate that is associated with 100 feet of duct. (Friction rate units are expressed as inches water column per 100 feet of duct, or for convenience, IWC/100.)

The following equation can be used to convert the pressure drop (PD) that is associated with a duct run to a friction rate (FR). In this equation, TEL represents the total effective length of the duct run. (More information about total effective length is provided in the following sections.)

$$FR = \frac{PD \times 100}{TEL}$$

For example, in Figure 3-5, the friction rate that is associated with the duct run is equal to 0.067 IWC/100. This value was determined as follows:

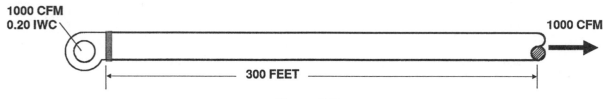

Figure 3-5

$$FR = \frac{0.20 \times 100}{300} = 0.067 \quad IWC/100$$

Now that the friction rate is known, the duct size can be determined by using a friction chart or a duct slide rule. Figure 3-6 shows that a 15-inch diameter sheet metal duct will be required if the design flow rate is equal to 1,000 CFM and the design value for the friction rate is equal to 0.067 IWC/100. (Refer to Appendix 2 for more information about using friction charts and duct slide rules.)

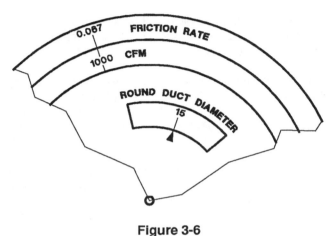

Figure 3-6

3-7 Effective Length
Duct runs consist of straight sections and fittings; a pressure loss is associated with both types of components. Therefore, the total pressure drop that is associated with a duct run is equal to the pressure losses that are associated with the straight sections plus the pressure losses that are associated with each and every fitting that is found in the run.

It is not unusual for the pressure loss that is associated with a fitting to be equal to or greater than the pressure loss that is associated with a fairly long section of straight duct. For example, a fitting could produce the same flow resistance as

a 60-foot section of straight duct. In this case the fitting is said to have an equivalent length of 60 feet.

Fitting equivalent lengths are a convenient way to describe fitting pressure losses because these values are easily added to the straight run lengths. The resulting "total effective length" (TEL) represents the total flow resistance of the duct run by virtue of the relationship between the pressure drop (PD), friction rate (F/100) and duct length. The equation that was introduced in Section 3-6 summarizes this relationship.

For example, if a few jogs are added to the duct system that is described by Figure 3-5, they could increase the effective length of the run by 80 feet (see Figure 3-7). In this case the fan performance is the same and the CFM is the same, but the duct length is 80 feet longer (TEL = 380 feet). Since the duct is longer, there is more resistance — so a larger duct will be required. (As explained in Section 3-5, the only acceptable duct size is equal to the size that it produces a resistance of 0.20 IWC when the flow rate is equal to 1,000 CFM.)

In this example the friction rate that is associated with the duct run is equal to 0.053 IWC/100. This value was determined as follows:

$$FR = \frac{0.20 \times 100}{380} = 0.053 \quad IWC/100$$

Now that the friction rate is known, the duct size can be determined by using a friction chart or a duct slide rule, which indicates that a 16-inch diameter sheet metal duct will be required if the design flow rate is equal to 1,000 CFM and the design value for the friction rate is equal to 0.053 IWC/100.

3-8 Ducted Return

In the two previous examples there was no return duct, so all of the fan pressure was used to move the air through the supply duct. If a ducted return is added to the system (see Figure 3-8 on the next page), some of the fan pressure will be used to move the air through the return duct, so there will be less pressure available for the supply-side of the system.

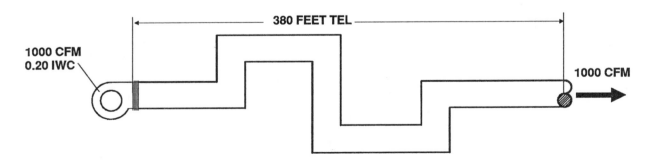

Figure 3-7

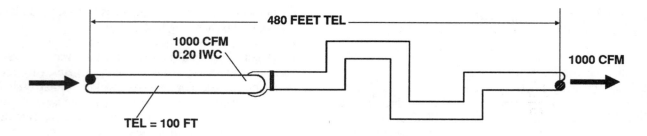

Figure 3-8

Actually, this system is not any different from the systems that were analyzed in the previous two examples, except for the fact that the return duct adds 100 feet of effective length to the system. The fan performance is still the same, the CFM is still the same, but now the duct length is equal to 480 feet. Since the total effective length is longer, there is more resistance, so a larger duct diameter will be required.

When the sizing calculations are based on 480 feet, the design friction rate is equal to 0.042 IWC/100. This value was determined as follows:

$$FR = \frac{0.20 \times 100}{480} = 0.042 \quad IWC/100$$

Now that the friction rate is known, it can be applied to both sides of the system. In this case the duct slide rule indicates that 17-inch diameter (rounded up from 16.6 inches), sheet metal duct will be required if the design flow rate is equal to 1,000 CFM and the design value for the friction rate is equal to 0.042 IWC/100.

3-9 Branch Ducts

Supply air systems normally have more than one outlet and many return air systems have more than one inlet. For exam-

ple, Figure 3-9 shows a system that has three outlets and two inlets. In this case there are a number of effective lengths associated with the system.

Basically, the approach to designing this system is not any different from the method that was used for the previous system. In this case, an acceptable design can be obtained by working with the largest effective length value, which is equal to 380 feet for the supply side plus 100 feet for the return side. (If the fan can deliver the required amount of air to the most remote outlet and capture the required amount of air at the most remote inlet, it will certainly meet the requirements of the other supply and return openings.) As demonstrated above, when the sizing calculations are based on a 480-foot length, the design friction rate is equal to 0.042 IWC/100. This friction rate can be used to size the trunk ducts and the branch runouts. Using this value, the duct slide rule provides the duct sizes that are summarized on the next page by Figure 3-10.

Note that the duct sizes that are provided by Figure 3-10 will not produce a perfectly balanced system. When all the duct sizes are based on the "worst case" friction rate, the sizes that are associated with the longest runs will be correct, but the sizes that are associated with the other runs will be larger than necessary. As a result of this oversizing, there will be some extra air flowing through the shorter runs. To correct this situation, balancing dampers should be installed in the branch runout ducts. Once the balancing dampers are adjusted, the

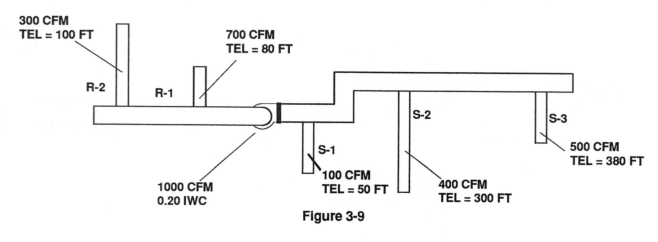

Figure 3-9

total effective length of all the runs will be approximately equal and each run will deliver the desired CFM.

Trunks	CFM	F/100	Diameter
Fan to S-1	1000	0.042	17"
S-1 to S-2	900	0.042	16"
S-2 to S-3	500	0.042	13"
Fan to R-1	1000	0.042	17"
R-1 to R-2	300	0.042	11"

Runouts	CFM	F/100	Diameter
S-1	100	0.042	7"
S-2	400	0.042	12"
S-3	500	0.042	13"
R-1	700	0.042	15"
R-2	300	0.042	11"

Figure 3-10

through the duct runs. **This means that the duct sizes are not based on the amount of pressure that the fan produces, but on the net pressure that is available to move the air through the straight runs and the fittings.** Therefore, for a given amount of available fan pressure, the ducts will have to be larger in order to compensate for the pressure that is dissipated by a device that is inserted into the system.

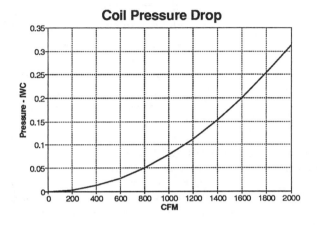

Figure 3-11

3-10 Pressure Losses Associated with Devices

A resistance is created when air is forced through a device that is installed in the air stream — a filter, coil, damper, supply outlet or return grille, for example. This resistance appears as a pressure drop across the device. The size of this pressure drop depends on the flow rate (CFM) through the device. Figure 3-11 provides an example of the air-side performance of an electric heating coil. Notice that the pressure drop increases rapidly as more and more air is forced through the coil. The pressure losses that are associated with devices are very important because the pressure that is dissipated by a device must be subtracted from the pressure that is available to move the air

This concept is demonstrated by Figure 3-12. In this case the fan can deliver 1,000 CFM when it works against a resistance of 0.20 IWC, but 0.08 IWC of pressure is dissipated by the coil. Therefore, the only acceptable duct size will be the size that produces a resistance of 0.12 IWC when the flow is equal to 1,000 CFM. Based on this value (0.12 IWC), the friction rate will be equal to 0.025 IWC/100 and the duct size will be equal to 18.6 inches. Notice that if no coil was installed, the duct size would have been based on 0.20 IWC of pressure, which would have resulted in a 0.42 IWC/100 friction rate and a duct size of 16.6 inches (see Section 3-8).

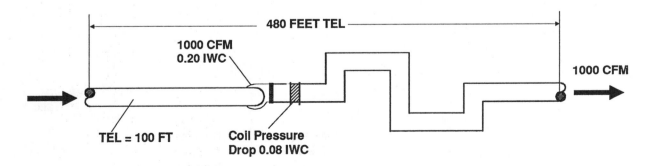

Figure 3-12

Recommended Velocity (FPM)								
	Supply Side				Return Side			
	Recommended		Maximum		Recommended		Maximum	
	Rigid	Flex	Rigid	Flex	Rigid	Flex	Rigid	Flex
Trunk Ducts	700	600	900	700	600	600	700	700
Branch Ducts	600	600	900	700	400	400	700	700
Supply Outlet Face Velocity	Size for Throw		700		—		—	
Return Grille Face Velocity	—		—		—		500	
Filter Grille Face Velocity	—		—		—		300	

Table 3-1

3-11 Velocity Limits

The procedure that has been described above will always produce a design that provides the correct air flow (CFM) to each outlet — and from each return. Therefore, if adequate air flow was the only design criterion, the velocity of the air that flows through the duct runs could be ignored. However, this is not the case, because if the velocity of the flow gets too high, the turbulence that is generated produces an objectionable amount of noise. Therefore, in some cases, the duct size that satisfies the friction rate requirement will have to be increased so that the velocity of the air flow does not exceed the limit that is specified by Table 3-1.

Once the design value for the velocity is established, a friction chart or a duct sizing slide rule can be used to determine the duct size that is compatible with the desired value. For example, Figure 3-13 shows that a 14.5 inch size is required if the flow rate is equal to 1,000 CFM and the maximum allowable velocity is equal to 900 FPM.

Figure 3-14 provides an example that shows how velocity limits affect the final duct size. In this case a sheet metal duct

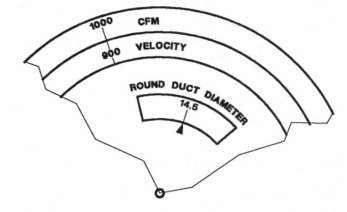

Figure 3-13

system is equipped with a fan that produces a relatively large amount of pressure when it moves 1,000 CFM through the system. The figure shows that the available pressure is equal to 0.60 IWC and the total effective length is equal to 480

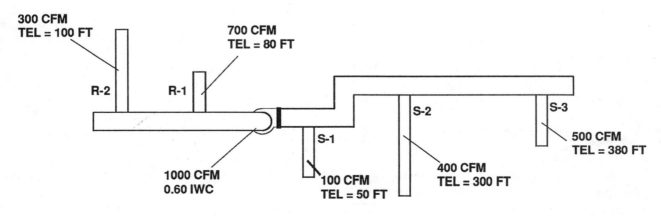

Figure 3-14

Trunk Section	CFM	F/100	Diameter for Air Flow	Velocity (FPM)	Design Velocity (FPM)	Diameter for Velocity	Design Diameter
Fan to S-1	1000	0.125	13.5"	1050	900	14.5"	15"
S-1 to S-2	900	0.125	13.0"	1000	900	13.8"	14"
S-2 to S-3	500	0.125	10.3"	890	900	10.2"	11"
Fan to R-1	1000	0.125	13.5"	1050	700	16.5"	17"
R-1 to R-2	300	0.125	8.5"	780	700	9.0"	9"

Runouts	CFM	F/100	Diameter for Air Flow	Velocity (FPM)	Design Velocity (FPM	Diameter for Velocity	Design Diameter
S-1	100	0.125	5.5"	600	900	4.5"	6"
S-2	400	0.125	9.5"	840	900	9.1"	10"
S-3	500	0.125	10.3"	880	900	10.2"	11"
R-1	700	0.125	11.7"	960	600	14.8"	15"
R-2	300	0.125	8.5"	780	600	9.6"	10"

Sheet metal duct diameters rounded up to eliminate fractional dimensions.

Figure 3-15

feet, so the design friction rate is equal to 0.125 IWC/100. The ducts can be sized for this friction rate, provided that the air flow velocities do not exceed the values that are recommended by Table 3-1.

Figure 3-15 summarizes the design calculations that are required for the system that is described above. In this example, most of the duct sizes that satisfy the air flow requirement are too small to satisfy the Table 3-1 velocity limit. When this is the case, the final duct size is based on the size that is compatible with the velocity limit.

So, there are two sizes associated with every duct section — the size that satisfies the air flow requirement and the size that satisfies the velocity limit. The final design is always based on the larger of these two sizes. (Note that if the larger size is dictated by a velocity limit, the duct run will produce less resistance than a smaller size that only satisfies the air flow requirement. And, because there is less resistance, the air flow that is associated with this duct run will exceed the desired value. Therefore, balancing dampers must be installed and adjusted in order to obtain the desired air flow rates.)

3-12 Air Flow Rates (CFM)

The air flow (CFM) that is required for the entire house either depends on the sensible cooling load or the heating load, and on the temperature difference (TD) between the supply air and the room air. This relationship is summarized by the sensible heat equation, which is provided below.

$$CFM = \frac{Load}{1.1 \times TD}$$

For example, 1,435 CFM is required if the **Manual J** load calculation indicates that the sensible cooling load is equal to 30,000 BTUH and the equipment manufacturer's performance data indicates that the difference between the room temperature and the supply air temperature is equal to 19 °F. (When cooling and heating are desired, the cooling CFM is usually larger than the heating CFM.)

$$CFM = \frac{30000}{1.1 \times 19} = 1435$$

This design value for the blower CFM must be available before the **Manual D** duct sizing calculations can begin. Note that this piece of information is normally determined when the equipment is selected in accordance with the procedures that are documented in **Manual S** (which in turn, depends on the results of the **Manual J** load estimate).

Once the design value for the blower CFM is known, the air flow (CFM) that is required for each room can be estimated by multiplying the blower CFM by the room load and then dividing the result by the **Manual J** design load that was used to select the equipment. The following equation shows the mathematics of this relationship.

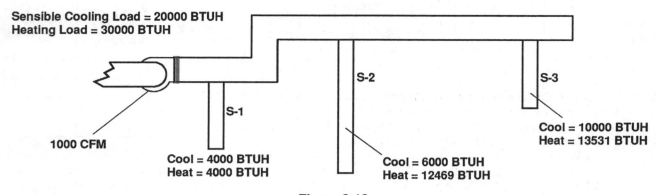

Figure 3-16

$$Room\ CFM = \frac{Blower\ CFM \times Room\ Load}{Manual\ J\ Design\ Load}$$

Actually two calculations will be required for each room. One calculation is based on the sensible cooling load and the other is based on the heating load. In order to expedite these calculations, it is convenient to create a heating factor (HF) and a cooling factor (CF). These factors are defined by the following equations.

$$HF = \frac{Blower\ CFM}{Design\ Heating\ Load}$$

$$CF = \frac{Blower\ CFM}{Design\ Sensible\ Cooling\ Load}$$

Once the heating and cooling factors are calculated, the CFM that is required for heating and the CFM that is required for cooling can be estimated by multiplying the room load by the corresponding factor. However, only the larger of these two values will be used to size the duct run.

For example, Figure 3-16 shows a system that provides cooling and heat for three large rooms. In this case, the **Manual J** and the **Manual S** design procedures would have been used to generate the load data and to obtain the blower CFM value, as noted on the diagram. This is all of the information that is required to determine the design CFM for each room.

Figure 3-17 summarizes the room CFM calculations that are associated with the system that is described above. Note that the larger of the two room CFM values (the cooling CFM or the heating CFM) is selected as the design value.

Room	Cooling			Heating			Design CFM
	Load	CF	CFM	Load	HF	CFM	
S-1	4000	0.050	200	4000	0.033	133	200
S-2	6000	0.050	300	12469	0.033	415	415
S-3	10000	0.050	500	13531	0.033	450	500
	CF = 1000/20000 = 0.050			HF = 1000/30000 = 0.033			

Figure 3-17

Section 4
System Operating Point

The concept of the air distribution system operating point was introduced in Section 3-4. This section shows how fan adjustments and duct resistance changes affect the operating point. This section also shows how to determine the operating point, how to adjust the operating point and how to use this information during field tests.

4-1 System Operating Point

Fan performance is defined by a pressure versus flow relationship and duct system performance is characterized by a resistance versus flow relationship. These relationships can be presented in tabular form or can be graphed. One advantage that is associated with using a graph is that the operating point is obvious, as illustrated by Figure 4-1.

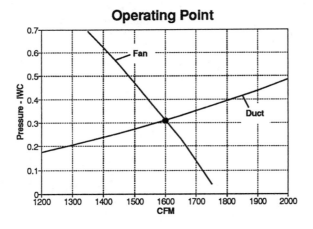

Figure 4-1

The significance of the operating point is that it represents the only possible operating condition that can be obtained by mating a particular fan (or fan setup) with a particular duct system. Therefore, it is the designer's responsibility to make sure that the CFM value that is associated with this operating point matches the design air flow value. (The design air flow is determined when the **Manual J** loads are used to select the HVAC equipment.) Since the fan is normally an integral part of the HVAC equipment, this means that the designer must create an air distribution system that has a characteristic curve that intersects the fan curve at the design CFM value.

4-2 Changing the Fan Speed

If the duct curve does not intersect the fan curve at the desired point, the operating point can be adjusted by changing the fan speed. Figure 4-2 shows the operating points that are associated with a three-speed fan. (The operating points occur at the intersection of the duct curve and the fan curves that correspond to the three fan speeds.)

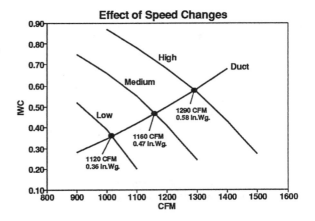

Figure 4-2

Note that when the fan speed is adjusted, it is not possible to predict how the adjustment will affect the system CFM by just looking at the blower table data. The only thing that can be said is that an increase in fan speed will result in more air flow and a decrease in fan speed will result in less air flow. Blower data, by itself, cannot be used to evaluate the effect of a fan speed change because the blower performance depends on the flow resistance that is created by the air distribution system. A duct-fan balance point diagram, such as Figure 4-2, is required in order to predict the consequences of a fan speed change.

4-3 Changing the System Resistance

If the duct curve does not intersect the fan curve at the desired point, the operating point can be adjusted by changing the resistance of the air distribution system. Changes in the system resistance may be intentional or unintentional. Intentional system resistance adjustments are normally made by opening or closing balancing dampers. In this case, the damper position decreases or increases the duct resistance and the new operating point occurs at the intersection of the fan curve and the new duct resistance curve. The system resistance also will change if a component—an electronic filter, for example—is added to or removed from the system. Or, the system resistance can be modified by replacing inefficient fittings with more efficient fittings, or vice versa. Also note that the resistance that is associated with any device or fitting is unintentionally modified when the component is fouled by dirt, debris or biological growth. Figure 4-3 illustrates how a change in the system resistance affects the operating point. Note that when the system resistance is changed, the new operating point occurs at the intersection of the fan curve and the new duct curve.

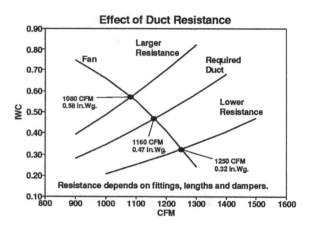

Figure 4-3

Duct resistance curves alone cannot be used to evaluate the effect of a system modification because the flow (CFM) depends on the fan performance. The only thing that can be said is that an increase in resistance will result in less air flow and a decrease will result in more air flow. Therefore, a duct-fan balance point diagram (Figure 4-3, for example) is required in order to predict the consequences of a system resistance change.

4-4 Operating Range

Hand dampers and fan speed adjustments can be used to produce a wide range of operating points. The fan speed should be adjusted first. Ideally, the fan CFM should slightly exceed the design CFM when all of the registers, balancing dampers and control dampers are in the wide open position. After the fan speed is set, the branch runout dampers should be adjusted so that each outlet receives the correct air flow. Figure 4-4 provides an example of the operating range that is associated with fan speed changes and damper adjustments.

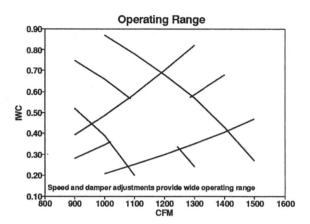

Figure 4-4

4-5 Drawing the Duct Curve

The duct performance curve can be drawn if one point (P_1, CFM_1) on the duct curve is known. This point might be the desired operating point or it could be a point that was determined during a system balancing test. The following equation can be used to associate duct resistance (P_x) with air flow (CFM_x) for any point on the duct curve. Figure 4-5 shows how to use this equation (P_1 = 0.216 IWC and CFM_1 = 1,200.)

$$Resistance_x = P_1 \left(\frac{CFM_x}{CFM_1} \right)^2$$

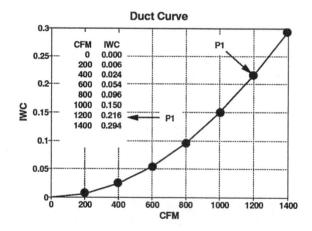

Figure 4-5

Note that the duct sizing slide rule CFM and friction rate scales can be used to find the data points that are required to draw the duct curve. Simply align the CFM that is associated with the reference point (CFM_1) with the corresponding resistance value (P_1) that is associated with this reference point and read any other data point (P_x) off of the same set of scales. Figure 4-6 shows how the duct slide rule can be used to find a few of the data points that are associated with the duct curve that is illustrated by Figure 4-5.

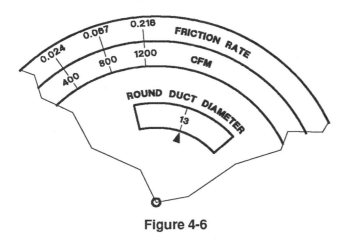

Figure 4-6

4-6 Drawing the Fan Curve

Some manufacturers present the fan performance data in graph form, which means that the fan curve is immediately available. Figure 4-7 provides an example of this type of presentation.

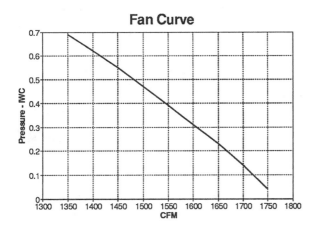

Figure 4-7

If the blower performance is not presented in graph form, it will be summarized by a data table that correlates flow (CFM) and pressure (IWC). In this case, the fan curve can be sketched by using the information that is provided by the manufacturer's blower data table. Figure 4-8 shows the blower table that was used to generate the fan curve that appears in Figure 4-7.

Blower Data	
CFM	IWC
1300	—
1350	0.69
1400	0.62
1450	0.55
1500	0.47 .
1550	0.39
1600	0.31
1650	0.23
1700	0.14
1750	0.04
1800	—

Figure 4-8

4-7 Establishing the Operating Point

The operating point can be determined by drawing the fan curve and the duct curve on the same piece of graph paper. This work produces a balance point diagram and the operating point is defined by the intersection of the two curves, as shown by Figure 4-9.

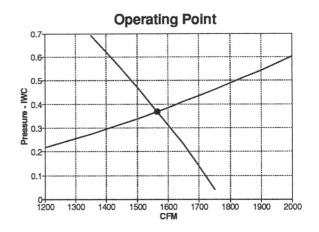

Figure 4-9

Note that it is not necessary to draw a balance point diagram in order to design a residential duct system. In practice, the CFM value that is associated with the operating point is established by the load calculation and equipment selection procedures. (Refer to **Manual S** for a comprehensive discussion of the procedures that are used to select residential HVAC equipment.) Therefore, the pressure value that corresponds to the design CFM value can be read directly from the equipment manufacturer's blower data table.

- The operating point CFM will be equal to the design CFM, as determined when the equipment was selected.

- The operating point pressure is equal to the blower pressure that corresponds to the desired CFM.

For example, suppose that the equipment selection procedure indicates that 1,350 CFM is required and that the blower performance is summarized by Figure 4-10. In this case, there are two possible operating points. The external static pressure value has to be equal to 0.25 IWC if the fan is operated at medium speed or 0.69 IWC if the fan is operated at high speed. (The fan cannot deliver 1,350 CFM at low speed.)

Once the pressure value is known, it is the designer's job to size the duct runs so that the resistance of the air distribution system — in terms of static pressure loss — equals the external static pressure produced by the blower. In other words, if the system resistance curve was graphed, it would intersect the fan curve at the desired operating point.

External Static (IWC)			
CFM	High	Med	Low
1150			0.45
1200			0.30
1250		0.49	0.05
1300		0.37	
1350	0.69	0.25	
1400	0.62	0.14	
1450	0.55	0.04	
1500	0.47		
1550	0.39		
1600	0.31		
1650	0.23		

Figure 4-10

4-8 Fan Speed Design Value

Normally, the equipment is selected at a mid-range (medium) fan speed because this practice provides the most flexibility for field adjustments. However, there are instances in which the equipment may be selected at a high or low fan speed. In any case, the air distribution system operating point should be compatible with the CFM value that was established during the equipment selection procedure.

For example, suppose that the equipment selection procedure was based on a medium fan speed and that 1,350 CFM is required. Figure 4-10 shows that one operating point is compatible with 0.25 IWC of resistance and the other is compatible with 0.69 IWC of resistance. In this case, the medium

speed setting is desired. This speed will be appropriate if the maximum resistance of any flow path (supply side plus return side) can be held to the 0.25 IWC value. However, the high speed setting will be preferred if the definitive flow path produces a larger resistance. In this case, the definitive flow path will have to be held to the 0.69 IWC value. (Balancing dampers can be used to dissipate excess pressure if the resistance of the flow path is less than the available pressure.)

4-9 Balance Point Diagram — Application

After the air distribution system has been designed and installed, the air flow rates should be verified by field tests. One of the primary tasks that is associated with this work involves a test that measures the total air flow (CFM) that is delivered by the fan when all of the dampers and registers are in the wide open position. A fan speed adjustment will be required if this test indicates that the total air flow is too large or too small. However, the consequences of a fan speed change cannot be predicted by simply inspecting the blower table.

For example, suppose that Figure 4-10 summarizes the blower performance, that the design has been based on the medium speed setting and that 1,600 CFM is the desired air flow rate. But field measurements, which are made at medium speed, indicate that the blower delivers 1,330 CFM against a measured resistance of 0.29 IWC. Since the air flow is less than desired, it will be necessary to investigate the performance that is associated with the high speed setting.

Figure 4-10 indicates that the blower has more air moving capability at the high speed setting, but a balance point diagram is required to determine the consequences of this speed change. (The new operating point must fall on the duct curve and the fan curve.) Figure 4-11 shows that the flow rate will be equal to 1,550 CFM at the high speed setting, which is just a little low. (If a larger flow rate is required, the resistance of the definitive flow path must be reduced.)

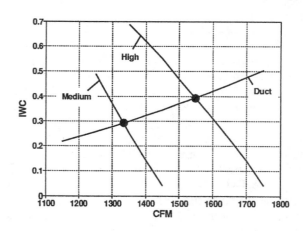

Figure 4-11

Section 5
Blowers

A centrifugal fan, which is commonly referred to as a blower, is designed to move air against the resistance that is imposed by the air distribution system (return air intake, return ductwork, filter(s), casing, heat exchanger devices, supply ductwork, balancing dampers and supply air outlets). This section provides more information about the types of blowers that are associated with residential HVAC equipment.

5-1 Blower Selection

Normally, the system designer does not have the opportunity to select the blower as a separate item because it is (typically) an integral component of the package that is supplied by the HVAC equipment manufacturer. Instead, the designer must verify that the air handling capability of the equipment package is *generally compatible* with the anticipated flow and resistance requirements of the air distribution system. After verifying this capability, the duct system must be designed so that the air flow resistance matches the external static pressure that is produced by the blower when the blower delivers the desired CFM, as explained in Section 3.

5-2 Blower Performance

The performance of a blower is normally specified in the manufacturer's literature by a table or graph that correlates the air flow (CFM) that can be delivered by the blower with the resistance that the blower works against. For example, Figure 5-1 shows the tabular data that is associated with a three-speed fan. Note that for each fan speed, data points are only listed for a few CFM values. These data points define the operating range that is associated with a particular speed. This range defines the upper and lower limits of the blower's air delivery capability. The upper limit corresponds to the flow (CFM) that can be delivered against a small amount of system resistance and the lower limit is established by the aerodynamic stability of the fan blades. If the flow is too low, the fan blades will stall and the fan performance will become very erratic. Therefore, at any particular fan speed, the resistance of the air distribution system must never exceed the value that will cause the fan to stall. For example, Figure 5-1 shows that the maximum resistance that can be accommodated without causing stall is equal to 0.69 IWC at high speed, 0.49 IWC at medium speed or 0.45 IWC at low speed.

Multispeed Drives
Multispeed blowers may be driven directly by a multispeed motor or indirectly by a belt drive. The performance characteristics of these configurations are summarized by tables that

External Static (IWC)			
CFM	High	Med	Low
1150			0.45
1200			0.30
1250		0.49	0.05
1300		0.37	
1350	0.69	0.25	
1400	0.62	0.14	
1450	0.55	0.04	
1500	0.47		
1550	0.39		
1600	0.31		
1650	0.23		

Figure 5-1

are similar to Figure 5-1 or performance curves that are similar to Figure 5-2. Note that one performance curve is required for each distinct speed. Also note that as the CFM increases, there is a rapid decrease in the amount of resistance that the blower can work against. Therefore, in order to obtain the desired flow, the resistance that is associated with the air distribution system must be carefully matched to the (available) pressure, as indicated by the fan curve. For example, if the blower is operated at medium speed and if the desired flow rate is equal to 1,300 CFM, Figures 5-1 and 5-2 indicate that the air distribution system must be designed and balanced so that the system resistance is equal to 0.37 IWC.

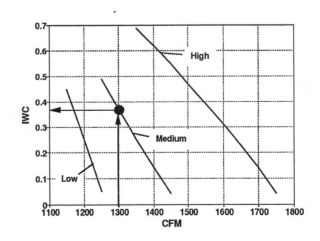

Figure 5-2

Variable Speed Drives

The blower speed may be continually adjusted if it is driven by a variable speed motor. In this case, an unlimited number of fan curves are required to describe the blower performance. Figure 5-3 shows just a few of the fan curves that are associated with a variable speed blower that operates between 300 and 1,400 RPM. Obviously, this blower is very versatile because it will accommodate any combination of flow and resistance values that fall within the envelope that is defined by the collection of fan curves.

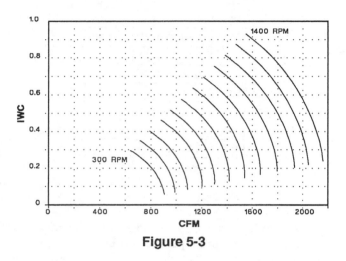

Figure 5-3

Figure 5-3 is not the only way to summarize the performance of a variable speed blower. In fact, manufacturers usually present the performance data in tabular form, but there is no standard format for arranging the information.

An example of tabular variable speed blower data is provided by Figure 5-4. In this case, the table correlates a blower speed setting with a CFM value and a range of external static pressure (resistance) values. For example, if setting SR-5 is

selected, the blower will be able to deliver a steady flow of air (1,600 CFM) when it operates against a wide range of resistance values (0.15 IWC to 0.80 IWC). In this case, the blower speed can range between 300 RPM and 1,300 RPM.

Figure 5-5 shows the relationship between the tabular data (Figure 5-4) and the graphical data (Figure 5-3). In this diagram, the tabular data corresponds to a set of vertical lines. Each of these lines correlate a range of static pressure values and RPM values with a particular CFM value. Note that there are an unlimited number of these lines (one for each CFM value), but only a few are required to define the operating envelope.

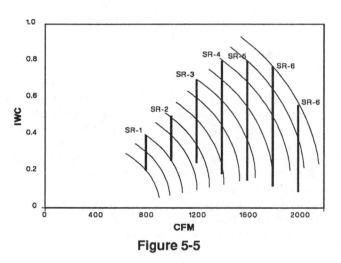

Figure 5-5

Figure 5-6 shows how a variable speed blower interacts with an air distribution system. Consider the SR-4 speed setting, which corresponds to 1,400 CFM. The diagram shows that as the system resistance varies (curves A, B and C), the CFM will hold steady as the fan speed modulates between 600 and 1,200 RPM.

Variable-speed Blower Performance			
Setting	Max. RPM	CFM	ESP (IWC)
SR-1	500	800	0.22 — 0.40
SR-2	700	1000	0.24 — 0.50
SR-3	1000	1200	0.23 — 0.70
SR-4	1200	1400	0.19 — 0.80
SR-5	1300	1600	0.15 — 0.80
SR-6	1400	1800	0.11 — 0.75
SR-7	1400	2000	0.08 — 0.50
Fan speed range = 300 to 1400 RPM			

Figure 5-4

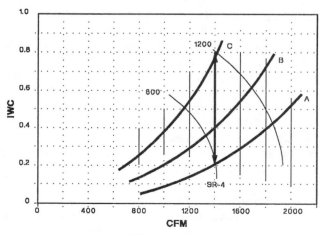

Figure 5-6

Figure 5-6 shows that variable speed blowers are more accommodating than conventional blowers because when this type of equipment is used, the resistance that is associated with the air distribution system does not have to be carefully matched to a specific external static pressure value — it just has to fall within a range of resistance values. For example, if the desired flow rate is equal to 1,600 CFM and if the blower motor is operated on the SR-5 speed setting, the resistance that is associated with the air distribution system can vary between 0.15 and 0.80 IWC.

Another example of variable speed performance data is provided by Figure 5-7. In this case, the performance is tabulated for 10 wiring arrangements (speed taps) that correspond to 10 distinct motor speeds. For example, speed tap 1 corresponds to the lowest speed (400 RPM), speed taps 2 through 9 correspond to seven intermediate speeds and speed tap 10 corresponds to the highest speed (1,400 RPM).

Normally, the speed range that is required for a particular application is smaller than the range that is associated with the minimum and maximum fan speed values (taps 1 and 10). In this case, the blower speed operating range can be adjusted to match the performance requirements of the mechanical equipment and the air distribution system by using jumper wires to select the speed taps that correspond to the lowest desired speed and the highest desired speed. For example, consider a VAV system. If 800 CFM is equal to the minimum air flow value, tap 4 could be used to establish the minimum blower speed; and if the air side design condition is equal to 1,200 CFM at 0.45 IWC, tap 8 could be used to establish the maximum RPM value. In this case the fan speed would be allowed to vary between 700 RPM and 1,200 RPM.

Note that when variable-speed blowers are used, the blower speed range must be compatible with the operating character-istics of the energy conversion equipment. For example, the minimum and maximum CFM that is associated with a furnace blower must be compatible with the heat exchanger temperature rise limits, and the minimum and maximum CFM that is associated with a cooling unit must be compatible with the DX coil air flow requirements. Some manufacturers use a microprocessor-based control system to deal with this issue and others rely on manual speed tap settings.

5-3 Altitude and Temperature Corrections

Unless stated otherwise, the data that is presented in a blower table corresponds to the performance that would be expected when "standard air" is flowing through the blower. Standard air has a specific weight of 0.075 pounds per cubic foot, which corresponds to the density that is associated with 70 °F air at sea level. Other temperatures and altitudes are classified as nonstandard conditions.

The influence, with regard to the performance of the blower and the air distribution system, of nonstandard air can be ignored if the elevation is less than 1,500 feet and the air temperature is between 40°F and 110°F. Therefore, a temperature correction is not usually required for residential applications because the temperature of the air that flows through the blower is normally within this range. However, the effect of altitude should be evaluated when the elevation exceeds 1,500 feet.

On the next page, Figure 5-8 shows how altitude affects the performance of the blower, the resistance of the air distribution system and the system operating point. The diagram shows that there is no change in the CFM that is delivered by the fan — the CFM at altitude is the same as the CFM at sea level. But, the mass flow (pounds of air per minute) is smaller

Air-side Performance (CFM versus Resistance)										
Speed Tap	RPM	Resistance — IWC								
		.10	.20	.30	.40	.50	.60	.70	.80	.90
1	400	407	387	363	352	—	—	—	—	—
2	500	530	503	489	475	—	—	—	—	—
3	600	673	669	650	631	610	584	556	524	500
4	700	809	800	795	796	801	811	810	800	793
5	800	930	931	924	908	884	852	811	761	703
6	900	1045	1040	1035	1027	1019	1009	998	985	972
7	1000	1167	1161	1156	1144	1132	1126	1117	1107	1097
8	1200	1257	1254	1253	1234	1213	1205	1189	1165	1142
9	1300	1347	1342	1332	1315	1293	1263	1227	1185	1136
10	1400	1394	1375	1349	1319	1283	1251	1209	1171	1126

Figure 5-7

at altitude because the air is less dense. The diagram also shows that there is less system resistance and fan pressure at altitude, and that both of these values are reduced by the same amount. Therefore, at altitude, the operating point is defined by the sea level CFM value and a pressure value that is smaller than the sea level value. Also note that less fan power is required at altitude because the mass flow rate is reduced and because the system resistance is smaller.

Operating Point

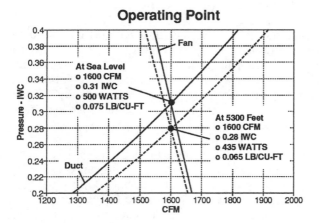

Figure 5-8

Since altitude does not affect the air flow that is delivered by the blower, standard (sea level) blower data and standard (sea level) duct sizing slide rules (or friction charts) can be used to size the duct runs. No altitude corrections are required. In other words, there will be no difference in performance — as far as air flow is concerned — if the effect of altitude is ignored. However, when the system is installed and tested, the pressures that are associated with various parts of it will be smaller and the fan power requirement will be reduced.

> Published HVAC equipment performance (heating and cooling capacity) is based on sea-level conditions. At altitude, the heating and cooling capacity of any particular piece of HVAC equipment will be reduced. Therefore, a slightly larger piece of equipment and slightly larger design CFM values will be required to compensate for this loss of capacity. But, once the adjusted design CFM values have been established (when the equipment is selected), the duct sizing procedure is identical to the procedure that is used for sea-level applications.

5-4 Inlet and Discharge Conditions

Normally, residential air moving equipment consists of a blower that is enclosed in the same cabinet that houses the

heating or cooling device — a furnace or an air handler, for example. When this equipment is tested, straight, full-size duct sections are fitted to the inlet and discharge openings. These straight sections ensure that the approaching and leaving flow paths are characterized by uniform (non-turbulent), velocity profiles. Any deviation from these ideal conditions will degrade the performance of the air moving equipment.

When the equipment is installed, the conditions at the inlet and discharge openings seldom duplicate the test stand conditions. Occasionally, elbows and tees are placed close to — or may even be attached to — the cabinet. This practice can degrade the performance of the blower. This loss of performance can be accounted for when the total equivalent length of the duct system is calculated. Refer to Appendix 3 for estimates of the equivalent lengths that are associated with the fittings that are associated with the air handling equipment.

5-5 Blower Noise

A blower must be capable of moving the required quantity of air against the resistance that is imposed by the duct system. When possible, a medium blower speed should be used as the basis for the duct sizing calculations because high speed operation generates more noise. But, if the maximum amount of blower pressure is required, it is acceptable to base the design calculations on the high speed setting. In any case, it is preferable to locate the air moving equipment in a room that is physically and acoustically isolated from the occupied areas. If it is necessary to locate the blower in or near an occupied area, special measures should be taken to reduce the amount of noise that can be detected by the occupants. Refer to Section 13 for more information about noise control.

5-6 Operating Speed

Normally, a constant blower speed is associated with single zone applications, but in some cases, two-speed operation may be required. Variable speed blowers are desirable when zoning capabilities are provided by a variable air volume (VAV) system. Variable speed blowers also can be used for single zone applications. Certain benefits and disadvantages are associated with each type of blower speed control strategy.

Single Speed Operation
Many single zone systems (a furnace, with or without a cooling coil, a cooling-only unit or heat pump) can be set up for constant speed operation without degrading the year-round performance. But if a single speed is used, the blower speed setting must ensure that an adequate flow of air passes through the heat exchange device (furnace heat exchanger, cooling coil or indoor heat pump coil) during any operating condition. (The minimum and maximum air flow requirements are specified by the equipment manufacturer.) The blower speed setting also must be compatible with the sensible and latent cooling loads because the air flow across a DX cooling coil has a

substantial effect on how the total capacity of the coil is split between sensible capacity and latent capacity. As far as air distribution is concerned, single-speed operation is very desirable because the supply air grilles and registers are (typically) constant volume devices.

Two-speed Operation

In some cases, single-zone equipment must accommodate a mismatch between the size of the design cooling load and the size of the design heating load, particularly when a DX coil is added to a furnace. For example, a relatively large flow of air might be ideal for cooling, but incompatible with the minimum temperature rise requirement that is associated with heating. In this case a high blower speed is appropriate for cooling, but a lower blower speed should be used for heating.

However, two-speed blower operation also can be used to extend the comfort capability of single-zone equipment, providing that the capacity of the heating and cooling equipment can be staged. For example, heat pumps that have two stages of compressor capacity can take advantage of two fan speeds. In this case, comfort is enhanced because there is a better match between the load, the equipment capacity and the air flow during any particular operating condition.

Two-speed operation might cause air distribution problems. If the supply outlet sizes are based on the maximum air flow requirements, they may not perform properly when the fan speed is reduced, or vice versa. If the spread between the maximum and the minimum CFM values is not too large, this problem can be minimized by using average CFM values to size the supply outlets.

Variable-speed Blowers

Variable-speed blowers are well suited for VAV systems, particularly if the capacity of the heating and cooling machinery can be modulated. This way, the system air flow rate can be continuously monitored and adjusted as the VAV dampers regulate the heating or cooling capacity that is delivered to each zone.

A minimum flow of air through heat exchangers and DX coils must be maintained during any operating condition. (The minimum flow that is associated with variable capacity equipment is typically less than the minimum flow that is associated with constant speed equipment.) A bypass duct will be required if there is any chance that the fully modulated flow rate will be less than the minimum CFM that is required for the heat exchange device.

A variable-speed blower also can be used to accommodate a mismatch between the size of the design cooling load and the size of the design heating load. For example, if the design CFM that is associated with a cooling coil is substantially larger than the CFM that is required for a furnace heat exchanger,

a variable speed blower can improve the comfort index of single-zone equipment, providing that the capacity of the heating and cooling equipment can be staged or modulated. Therefore, a variable-speed fan would enhance the performance of a furnace that is equipped with a two-stage burner.

Variable-speed operation does have the potential to cause air distribution problems. Ideally, variable volume diffusers should be used in conjunction with variable-speed fans. If constant volume outlets are used, they may not be able to accommodate the range of air flow rates that are associated with the maximum and minimum blower speeds. But, if the spread between the maximum and the minimum CFM is not too large, this problem may not be too severe.

5-7 External Static Pressure

Blower table information is based on laboratory tests that document the performance of a specific equipment configuration. This performance data does not apply to any other configuration. For example, if a furnace is tested with a filter in place, the blower table would apply to any heating-only application that uses a similar filter; but it would not apply to a design that incorporates a DX cooling coil. In this case, it is necessary to subtract the pressure drop that is associated with the DX coil from the external static pressure that is listed in the blower table.

Always read the footnotes that accompany the blower table. These notes list the devices that were not included when the laboratory test was conducted. For example, the footnotes that are associated with Figure 5-9 indicate that the pressure drops that are associated with a wet DX coil and a standard filter are accounted for, but the pressure loss that is associated with an electric resistance heater is not included. In this case, the pressure drop that is associated with the electric resistance coil must be subtracted from the external static pressure that is listed in the blower table.

External Static (IWC)			
CFM	High	Med	Low
1200			0.45
1250		0.49	0.30
1300		0.37	0.08
1350		0.25	
1400	0.62	0.14	
1450	0.55	0.04	
1500	0.47		
1550	0.39		
1600	0.31		
Tested with wet coil and filter in place. Subtract pressure drop associated with resistance heating coil.			

Figure 5-9

Section 6
Air-side Pressure Losses

Residential duct system components fall into four categories: straight duct sections, fittings, air-side equipment and air distribution devices. This section provides information about the pressure losses that are associated with these components.

6-1 Straight-section Pressure Drop

As air flows through a straight section of duct, friction causes the static pressure in the duct to decrease in the direction of flow. Figure 6-1 illustrates this behavior and the following equation can be used to compute the total pressure loss (PD) that is associated with a section of duct. In this equation, FR represents the friction rate (IWC per 100 feet of duct) — which can be obtained from a duct slide rule or a friction chart — and L represents the length (in feet) of the straight section.

$$PD = \frac{FR \times L}{100}$$

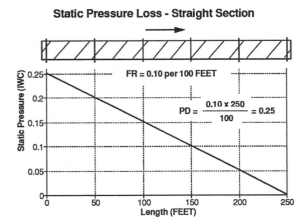

Figure 6-1

Duct Material

The friction rate that is associated with a duct section depends on the surface properties of the airway material. Smooth materials have smaller friction rates than rough materials. For example, the friction rate that is associated with an aluminum duct is noticeably smaller than the friction rate that is associated with a flexible wire helix duct. Therefore, always use a duct slide rule or friction chart that documents the performance of the material that will actually be used to fabricate the duct.

Note that the ACCA duct slide rule has friction rate scales for four common materials — sheet metal, duct board, duct liner and flexible wire helix construction. The ACCA duct slide rule also can be used for other types of materials that may have undocumented friction properties. Stainless steel, aluminum, clean carbon steel, spiral galvanized steel, smooth plastic and PVC materials have roughness indexes that are less than the roughness index that is associated with galvanized metal duct (at 40 joints per 100 feet). If the galvanized metal scale is used for these materials, the error will be small and on the safe side. Flexible metal and concrete ducts have roughness indexes that are comparable to the roughness index that is associated with flexible wire helix duct. Therefore, the flexible wire helix duct scale can be used for these materials.

Panned Joists and Stud Spaces

Panned joists and stud spaces are often used as airways — usually as part of the return air system. Since ACCA does not endorse this type of construction (refer to Appendix 3), the following comments should not be interpreted as an approval of this practice.

Friction rate information for panned airways and stud spaces is not available, but it is reasonable to assume that panned joists and stud spaces have roughness indexes that are larger than the roughness index that is associated with galvanized steel duct. And, since the surface irregularities that are associated with framing and sheathing materials are smaller than the surface irregularities that are associated with flexible wire helix duct, it is reasonable to assume that panned joists and stud spaces have roughness indexes that are smaller than the roughness index that is associated with flexible duct. Therefore, for lack of better information, assume that the friction rate information that is used for duct liner also can be used to estimate the pressure losses that are associated with panned airways and stud spaces.

6-2 Fitting Pressure Losses

Duct fittings fall into two categories — those that are characterized by an entering-leaving velocity difference and those that are characterized by a constant "flow-through" velocity. In the first case, it is not technically correct to use an equivalent length value to represent the pressure loss across the fitting; but in the second case, the static pressure loss can be accurately expressed as an equivalent length value.

Velocity Change Across the Fitting

When velocities at the entrance and exit of the fitting are not equal, some static pressure is used to increase the air velocity or some static pressure is recovered if the velocity decreases. Some examples of this type of fitting include:

- Transitions between straight sections of different sizes
- Elbows with different entrance and exit areas
- Tees with different entrance and exit velocities
- Inlets and outlets

With these fitting types, it is not appropriate to assign an equivalent length to the fitting because this approach does not account for pressure conversion that is associated with the velocity change. However, for residential designs, this technicality is commonly ignored because the design velocities, velocity changes and the associated pressure conversions are relatively small.

Constant Velocity Situations

When velocities at the entrance and exit of the fitting are equal, there are no pressure differences associated with velocity changes because the velocity is constant. Therefore, the pressure drop across the fitting is entirely caused by friction and aerodynamic turbulence. In this case, an equivalent length value will accurately account for all of the factors that are associated with the pressure drop across the fitting.

Equivalent Length Information

Traditionally, equivalent length values have been assigned to all types of residential duct fittings. This manual carries on in this tradition because it is a very convenient way to account for the pressure losses that are associated with these fittings. As explained in Section 3-7, the resistance of a duct run is directly related to the total effective length of a duct run, which is easily calculated by adding the length of the straight sections to the equivalent lengths of the fittings that are associated with the run.

Refer to Appendix 3 for a comprehensive listing of the equivalent length values that are associated with the types of fittings that are commonly used for residential duct systems. As explained by the text that is included at the beginning of that appendix, these equivalent length values are based on a particular reference velocity and on a specific friction rate. These reference values are intended to represent "worst case" scenarios (maximum velocities and a moderate friction rates). Corrections for other sets of velocities and friction rates can be made, but these corrections are not absolutely necessary because the published equivalent length values are conservative. (Overestimating the resistance of a duct run is not a problem because balancing dampers can be used to compensate for the error.)

Fitting and Duct Run Pressure Drop Calculations

Usually, there is no need to calculate the pressure drop that is associated with a single fitting. Normally, the designer is interested in the pressure drop that is associated with the entire duct run. As explained in Section 3-6, the pressure drop (PD) across a single fitting or the pressure drop that is associated with an entire duct run is directly related to the equivalent

length or total effective length (EL or TEL) and the friction rate (FR) that is associated with the duct run. The equation that describes this relationship is repeated below.

$$PD = \frac{FR \times EL}{100} \quad or \quad \frac{FR \times TEL}{100}$$

6-3 Pressure Losses Across Air-side Equipment

When a device or piece of equipment is installed in a duct system airway, it will produce a resistance to the air flow and there will be a pressure drop across the device. Examples of the various kinds of devices that are commonly installed in residential duct systems include variable air volume dampers, filters (new and dirty), DX cooling coils (dry and wet), hot water coils, electric heating coils and humidifiers. Information about the pressure drop that is associated with a particular device can be obtained from the engineering data that is published in the manufacturer's literature. Examples of the pressure drop information that is associated with a DX cooling coil, an electronic filter and an electric resistance heating coil is provided by Figure 6-2.

DX Coil Resistance (IWC)		
CFM	Dry	Wet
1000	0.11	0.18
1200	0.15	0.26
1400	0.22	0.35
1600	0.28	0.46

Electric Filter Resistance	
CFM	IWC
1000	0.06
1200	0.08
1400	0.12
1600	0.15

Heater Resistance	
CFM	IWC
1000	0.09
1200	0.13
1400	0.18
1600	0.23

Figure 6-2

As indicated on the previous page by Figure 6-2, the pressure drop across a piece of air-side equipment (DX coil, filter, electric resistance coil, etc.) grows rapidly as the flow (CFM) through the device increases. This resistance versus flow relationship is governed by the following equation (which also applies to an entire duct run — see Section 4-5.)

$$Resistance_x = P_1 \left(\frac{CFM_x}{CFM_1}\right)^2$$

This equation is useful when the performance of an air-side component is not documented by a comprehensive table (see Figure 6-2.) For example, if a field flow rate and pressure drop measurement only provides one set of resistance and flow values, this equation can be used to calculate the resistance that is associated with any other flow rate. This is demonstrated by the following calculation, which shows that if the pressure drop across a wet DX coil is equal to 0.26 IWC when 1,200 CFM flows through the coil, the pressure drop will be equal to 0.46 IWC if the air flow rate is increased to 1,600 CFM.

$$0.46 = 0.26 \; x \left(\frac{1600}{1200}\right)^2$$

6-4 Supply Outlet and Return Grille Pressure Drops

The pressure losses that are associated with supply outlet and return inlet hardware are small, typically 0.03 IWC or less. In this manual, this 0.03 IWC value will be used as a generic pressure loss value, which can be applied to any type of air distribution device. If more accurate information is desired, it can be found in the manufacturer's performance data, but the increase in accuracy will not have a noticeable effect on the final design.

Section 7
Air Distribution System Design — Prerequisites

The air distribution system design procedure is linked to tasks that must precede the work that is associated with the duct sizing calculations. Figure 7-1 summarizes the relationship between the duct design procedure and the other tasks that are associated with designing a residential HVAC system. Comentary regarding the work that is associated with this diagram is also provided.

7-1 System Selection

Decisions regarding the type of heating and cooling equipment and the type of air distribution system should precede the design calculations. Select the type of supply air system and return air system that is compatible with the heating and cooling equipment, the local climate, the architectural features of the house, the structural features of the house, the characteristics of the heating and cooling loads that are associated with the various rooms of the house and the cost

constraints that are associated with the project. Also consider the zoning requirements, the number of return air openings that are required, the location of the primary equipment, the space that is available for the duct runs, the location of the supply outlets, the location of the return openings, the advantages (and disadvantages) that are associated with the various types of duct materials and construction techniques, duct losses (conduction and leakage), noise and building codes.

The supply air system might be some type of trunk and branch system, a radial system, a perimeter loop system or a plenum system. The return air system might feature a single central return, multiple returns or a return in every room. Refer to Section 1 for a comprehensive discussion of residential air distribution systems. This material provides detailed information on zoning requirements, system classification criteria and system selection criteria. Detailed information about the various types of trunk and branch systems, radial systems, perimeter loop systems, plenum systems and return systems also is included.

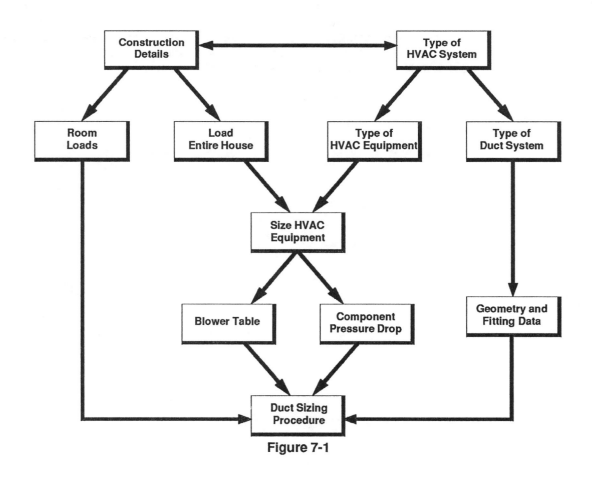

Figure 7-1

7-2 Load Calculations

The duct system design work must be based on the information that is provided by the **Manual J** load calculation procedure. Estimates of the room loads and the loads that are associated with the entire house are required. (If multiple units or zoned systems are used, estimates of the combined load that is associated with the rooms that define each zone are required.)

- The loads that are associated with each conditioned room are used to determine the air flow that is required for those rooms.

- The loads that pertain to the entire house are used to select the heating and cooling equipment.

7-3 Equipment Sizing

The work that is associated with sizing the heating and cooling equipment (as outlined in **Manual S**) must precede the duct system design work because information about the blower performance is essential. This information is provided by the manufacturer's equipment performance data, usually in the form of a blower table.

In some cases, the information that is contained in the blower table has to be adjusted for the pressure drops that are associated with components and devices that were not included when the blower was tested. This adjustment is made by subtracting the pressure drop that is associated with a device from the external static pressure that is listed in the blower table (refer to Section 5-7). The information about the pressure drop that is associated with a particular component or device (filter, DX coil, electric resistance heater, humidifier, for example) is documented in the manufacturer's performance data.

7-4 Geometry and Fittings

Information about the length of the straight duct sections and the equivalent length of the fittings is required to calculate the effective length of the duct runs. Therefore, a scale drawing or a rough sketch that includes dimensional information is required. This drawing (or sketch) should show the location of the air handling equipment, the location of the supply outlets, the loads and CFM that are associated with each supply outlet, the location of the return openings, the CFM that is associated with each return and the location of the duct runs. It also should show the distances that are associated with the straight runs, the fitting identification numbers (see Appendix 3) and the corresponding equivalent lengths.

7-5 Perform the Duct Sizing Calculations

The **Manual D** duct sizing calculations are based on the loads that are associated with each room, the blower data, the pressure drop information that is associated with the air-side devices and the effective length information. The details of the **Manual D** duct sizing procedure are presented in the next section. Sections 9, 10 and 11 provide examples that show how to apply this procedure to various types of trunk and branch systems, radial systems, flexible duct systems and variable volume systems.

Section 8
Duct Sizing Calculations

If noise was not a consideration, the size of every duct run could be based on a single friction rate value (which depends on the available static pressure and the longest total effective length that is associated with the duct system) and the CFM value that is associated with the run. (A duct run could be a branch runout, a secondary trunk, a primary trunk or a section of a trunk duct.) However, noise is an important design consideration, so these friction rate sizes are tentative.

The designer also must verify that all of the duct sizes are compatible with the velocity limits that are associated with supply side and the return side of the duct system. If a velocity limit is exceeded, the duct run that is associated with an unacceptably high velocity must be resized. In these cases, the final duct size is based on the maximum allowable velocity and the CFM that flows through the corresponding section of duct.

A set of worksheets and a reference chart have been developed to organize the details of the sizing calculations. The material in this section explains the procedures and calculations that are associated with these worksheets. (The worksheets formalize the procedure that was presented in Section 3.)

8-1 Basis for the Sizing Procedure

The duct sizing calculations must be based on the blower performance data (including the associated footnotes) and the air-side accessory device pressure drop data (when applicable) that is provided by the HVAC equipment manufacturer. This information is required to correlate the design value for the system CFM with the design value for the available static pressure. It is the designer's responsibility to ensure that the pressure drop that is associated with the longest possible circulation path (longest supply run plus the longest return run) does not exceed the available static pressure. It also is the designer's responsibility to ensure that the velocity that is associated with any section of duct system does not exceed the recommended limit.

8-2 Balancing Dampers are Required

A duct system could be self-balancing if the ducts are sized to ensure that the pressure drop that is associated with each independent circulation path is exactly equal to the available static pressure. In this case the following rules would apply:

• Trunk ducts, which are common to multiple circulation paths, must be sized to accommodate the path that has the longest effective length.

• Since the trunk sizes will be too large, as far as the shorter paths are concerned, the runout ducts must be sized to compensate for trunk sections that do not provide the required resistance.

Even though this design strategy will produce a duct system that is self-balancing, it is not practical and the system could be noisy. The following comments apply:

• The calculations would be complex and time consuming.

• Nonstandard runout sizes will be required to obtain the desired pressure drops.

• The velocities that are associated with some of the shorter circulation paths could be too high.

Obviously, these problems (complex calculation procedure, nonstandard sizes and noise) cannot be ignored. Therefore, the size of any duct section is a compromise between the standard size that provides the desired amount of resistance and the standard size that is associated with a quiet system. This means that a properly designed system will not be self-balancing. Therefore, a balancing damper must be installed in each runout duct. (In this regard, it does not make any difference if the duct system is designed by the simplified method that is presented in this edition of **Manual D** or the more elaborate method that formed the basis for the previous editions of this manual.)

8-3 Available Static Pressure

It is absolutely essential for the designer to verify how much static pressure is available to move the air through the supply and return ducts. Steps 1, 2 and 3, which are found on the "Friction Rate Worksheet" can be used to process this information. (An example of this worksheet is provided on the next page.)

Step 1
Use the manufacturer's blower data to determine how much external static pressure (ESP) is produced by the fan when it delivers the design CFM. (The value for the design CFM is discovered during the equipment selection process. As explained in **Manual S**, the HVAC equipment must be selected and sized to satisfy the **Manual J** loads.) Note that it is prudent (but not absolutely necessary) to base the design calculations on a medium fan speed. (Designing for medium speed provides the ability to adjust the fan performance after the equipment has been installed.)

Friction Rate Worksheet

Step 1) Manufacturer's Blower Data

External static pressure (ESP) = _____ IWC   CFM = _____

Step 2) Device Pressure Losses

Direct expansion refrigerant coil	_____
Electric resistance heating coil	_____
Hot water coil	_____
Heat exchanger	_____
Low efficiency filter	_____
High or mid-efficiency filter	_____
Electronic filter	_____
Humidifier	_____
Supply outlet	_____
Return grille	_____
Balancing damper	_____
Other device	_____

Total device losses (DPL) .... _____ IWC

Step 3) Available Static Pressure

ASP = (ESP - DPL) = (_____ - _____) = _____ IWC

Step 4) Total Effective Length (TEL)

Supply-side TEL + Return-side TEL = (_____ + _____) = _____ FEET

Step 5) Friction Rate Design Value (FR)

FR value from friction rate chart = _____ IWC/100

Friction Rate Chart

For example, refer to the blower data that is summarized by Figure 8-1. If 1,250 CFM is required for the application, this table indicates that, at medium speed, the fan will deliver 1,250 CFM when it operates against a resistance of 0.49 IWC.

Blower Performance			
	External Static — IWC		
CFM	High	Med	Low
1200			0.45
1250		0.49	0.30
1300		0.37	0.08
1350		0.25	
1400	0.62	0.14	
1450	0.55	0.04	
1500	0.47		
1550	0.39		
1600	0.31		

Tested with wet coil and filter in place. Subtract pressure drop associated with resistance heating coil.

Figure 8-1

Step 2

Evaluate the device pressure losses (DPL) that are associated with the air-side components that will be installed in the critical circulation path, and that are not generic to the blower performance data. This is important because the pressure that is dissipated by external air-side devices will not be available to move the air through the fittings and the straight duct runs.

Some of the pressure dissipating devices that may not be associated with the published blower data include DX coils, electric resistance heating coils, heat exchangers, filters and humidifiers. Refer to the footnotes below the manufacturer's blower table for information about the devices that are not associated with the blower data.

For example, refer to Figure 8-1. The notes at the bottom of this blower table indicate that the pressure losses that are associated with a wet DX coil and a standard low efficiency air filter are incorporated in the tabular data. These notes also indicate that the pressure loss that is associated with a supplemental electrical resistance heating coil is not generic to the blower data.

The exact values for the pressure drops that are associated with air-side devices are normally provided in the manufacturer's engineering information sheets. These pressure losses must be subtracted from the external static pressure that is generated by the blower. For example, Figure 8-2 presents the pressure loss data that is associated with a particular electric resistance heating coil. This data indicates that the pressure loss is equal to 0.14 IWC (approximate) when 1,250 CFM flows through the device.

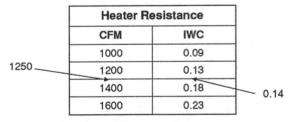

Heater Resistance	
CFM	**IWC**
1000	0.09
1200	0.13
1400	0.18
1600	0.23

1250 → 0.14

Figure 8-2

Component substitution

Sometimes an accessory component is substituted for a standard component that was tested with the blower assembly. In this case the difference between the pressure drops that are associated with the accessory component and the standard component must be subtracted from (or added to) the available static pressure. For example:

- A high efficiency media filter (a pleated filter, for example) usually will have a larger pressure drop than a standard filter.

- An electronic filter that has a prefilter assembly may have a larger pressure drop than a standard filter.

- If the standard filter is used as a prefilter for an electronic grid, the additional pressure loss is equal to the pressure drop across the electronic grid.

Air distribution and balancing devices
Air distribution devices such as air outlets, return grilles and balancing dampers dissipate pressure. The exact values for the pressure drops across these devices can be found in the manufacturer's performance data. However, it is an acceptable and conservative practice to use a generic value of 0.03 IWC for the pressure loss that is associated with these devices. (For example, the pressure loss that is associated with one supply outlet, one return inlet and a balancing damper would be equal to 0.09 IWC.)

Step 3
Determine how much pressure will be available to move the air through the fittings and the straight duct sections. To calculate this available static pressure (ASP) value, simply subtract the device pressure losses (DPL) from the external static pressure (ESP) value.

Refer to the data used in steps 1 and 2 above. In this case, the pressure losses for the auxiliary heating coil, one supply outlet, one return inlet and a balancing damper must be subtracted from the external static pressure. The following calculation shows that the available static pressure is equal to 0.26 IWC.

$$ASP = 0.49 - (0.14 + 0.03 + 0.03 + 0.03) = 0.26\ IWC$$

For most designs, the available static pressure (ASP) value should be equal to about 0.20 IWC. Values below 0.10 IWC are normally not acceptable unless the total effective length of the longest circulation path is relatively short. Values above 0.35 IWC are usually too large unless the total effective length

of the longest circulation path is very long. (More information about the relationship between the ASP value and the TEL value is provided in Section 8-5.)

8-4 Effective Length Design Value

The effective length of a particular duct run is calculated by summing the straight lengths and fitting equivalent lengths that are associated with the run. These effective length calculations can be made on the effective length work sheet (see exhibit below). The group numbers on this worksheet refer to the Appendix 3 fitting identification system, which organizes similar types of fittings into groups.

An estimate of the effective length of every duct run is not required; it is necessary only to calculate the effective length of the critical circulation path, which consists of the longest supply run and the longest return run. (If inefficient fittings are associated with the return system, it is possible for the effective length of the longest return run to be larger than the effective length of the longest supply run.)

Sometimes the longest runs can be selected by inspection, but do not jump to conclusions. Depending on the equivalent length of the fittings, the run that has the longest effective length may not be the run that has the longest measured length. If there is any doubt about which run is the longest, check the effective length of each likely candidate. (These calculations do not have to be perfect. A 10 percent error will not produce a significant change in the final duct sizes.)

Once the total effective lengths of the supply runs and return runs are determined, the "Friction Rate Worksheet" should be used to calculate the total effective length of the critical circulation path. Step 4 on this worksheet can be used for this calculation. Select the largest supply-side TEL value and the largest return-side TEL value. Enter these values in the appropriate spaces, add these values and enter the sum on the worksheet.

Effective Length Calculation Sheet									
Element	Supply Run ID Number				Element	Return Run ID Number			
	#	#	#	#		#	#	#	#
Trunk Length					Trunk Length				
Trunk Length					Trunk Length				
Trunk Length					Trunk Length				
Runout Length					Runout Length				
Group 1					Group 5				
Group 2					Group 6				
Group 3					Group 7				
Group 4					Group 8				
Group 8					Group 10				
Group 9					Group 11				
Group 11					Group 12				
Group 12					Other				
Other					Other				
Other					Other				
Other					Other				

Effective Length Worksheet

8-5 Friction Rate Design Value

The design value for the friction rate (FR) is based on the available static pressure (ASP) value and the total effective length (TEL) value. The friction rate design value can be calculated by using the following equation or it can be obtained graphically by using the chart that is located at the bottom of the "Friction Rate Worksheet." Once the design value for the friction rate is determined, enter this value on the worksheet in the space that is associated with Step 5.

$$FR = \frac{ASP \times 100}{TEL} \quad (IWC/100)$$

Friction Rate Chart

The friction rate chart consists of a set of friction rate lines that slope from the lower left corner of the chart to the upper right corner. These lines represent a graphical solution to the previous equation.

To use the friction rate chart, draw a vertical line that represents the ASP value and a horizontal line that represents the TEL value. The friction rate design value is found at the intersection of these two lines. (It will be necessary to interpolate between two friction rate values if this point does not fall on a friction rate line.) For example, Figure 8-3 shows that a friction rate of 0.07 is associated with 300 feet of effective length and 0.21 IWC of available static pressure.

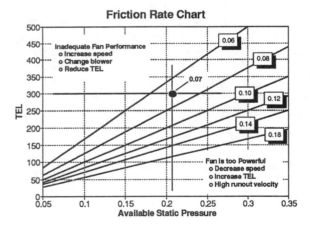

Friction Rate Chart

Figure 8-3

One advantage that is associated with the chart method is that it immediately reveals incompatibilities between the available pressure and the effective length. For example, the chart shows that more blower power is required if the point of intersection falls above the 0.06 friction rate line, and less blower power is required if the point of intersection falls below the 0.18 friction rate line.

Another feature of the chart method is that it indicates whether or not the velocities in the runout ducts are acceptable. For example, the friction chart shows that the velocity in the runout ducts will be too high (in excess of 900 FPM) if the point of intersection falls below the 0.18 friction rate line.

In other words, the blower performance will be compatible with the total effective length value if the point of intersection falls within the envelope (or wedge) that is bounded by the 0.06 friction rate line and the 0.18 friction rate line. If the point of intersection does not fall within this wedge it will be necessary to adjust the blower speed and to recalculate the available static pressure value (re-evaluate Steps 1, 2 and 3), or to change the length of the critical circulation path and adjust the total effective length value (re-evaluate Step 4).

At this point it is necessary to stop and consider the implications of the sizing guidelines that are printed on some duct sizing slide rules. The guideline in question is the one that suggests that a duct system can be designed for a specific friction rate value, typically 0.10 IWC/100.

The first objection to this sizing recommendation is related to the fact the design value for the friction *rate* is not arbitrary (the friction rate design value depends on the available static pressure and the total effective length of the longest circulation path). For example, if the length of the critical path is 200 feet, a design friction rate value of 0.10 IWC/100 would be correct only when the available static pressure is equal to 0.20 IWC.

The second objection to this sizing recommendation is related to noise. Some velocities may exceed the recommended limits if the duct sizes are based on an arbitrary friction rate. For example, the velocity in a trunk duct that carries 1,200 CFM will be equal to 1,000 FPM if the duct size is based on a 0.10 IWC/100 friction rate.

8-6 Room CFM

The air flow that must be delivered to each room is proportional to the size of the room load, in comparison to the equipment sizing load. For example, if the room load is equal to 7,000 BTUH and the equipment sizing load is equal to 35,000 BTUH, the room supply CFM would be 20 percent of the blower CFM (7,000 divided by 35,000). The following equation can be used to calculate the room CFM values.

$$Room\ CFM = \frac{Blower\ CFM \times Room\ Load}{Equipment\ Sizing\ Load}$$

While it would be perfectly correct to apply this equation to every room, the room CFM calculations can be expedited by combining the blower CFM value (which is a constant) with the equipment sizing load value (which also is a constant). As shown below, this intermediate calculation creates a "flow factor" that represents the amount of air flow that is required to offset one BTUH of load.

$$Flow\ factor\ =\ \frac{Blower\ CFM}{Equipment\ Sizing\ Load}$$

Now the room CFM calculation can be reduced to a simple multiplication. As shown below, the room air flow rate is equal to the product of the flow factor and the room load.

Room CFM = Flow Factor x Room Load

Actually, there are two room loads. One load is associated with heating and the other load is associated with cooling. It follows that there must be two flow factors, one for heating and one for cooling. As shown below, the cooling flow factor is equal to the blower CFM divided by the cooling season sizing load and the heating flow factor is equal to the blower CFM divided by the heating season sizing load. For convenience, these factors are called the cooling factor (CF) and the heating factor (HF).

$$CF =\ \frac{Blower\ CFM}{Sensible\ Cooling\ Design\ Load}$$

$$HF =\ \frac{Blower\ CFM}{Design\ Heating\ Load}$$

Since there are two flow factors, there will be two room CFM values. As shown below, these room air flow values are calculated by multiplying the room load by the corresponding flow factor.

Room Cooling CFM = CF x Sensible Cooling Load

Room Heating CFM = HF x Room Heating Load

These room CFM values represent the air flow that must be delivered to the room during each season. Usually, one value will be larger than the other, so the design value for the room CFM must be equal to the larger value.

The design value from the room CFM can be determined by using the "Duct Sizing Worksheet," which is exhibited below. At the top of this worksheet, there is a space for the CF and HF calculations and at the left side of the worksheet there are columns for recording the room heating loads (H-BTUH) and the room cooling loads (C-BTUH). The next two columns (which are labeled H-CFM and C-CFM) can be used to record the results of the heating CFM and the cooling CFM calculations and the fifth column (which is labeled Dsn CFM) can be used to record the design CFM value.

8-7 Branch Runout Air Flow Rates

A branch runout duct is required for each supply air outlet and at least one supply air outlet will be required for each room. However, some rooms may require two or more supply air

Duct Sizing Worksheet								
HF = Blower CFM / Manual J Heat Loss = ( )/( ) = _____								FR Value
CF = Blower CFM / Manual J Sensible Heat Gain = ( )/( ) = _____								
Supply Duct System								
Run - Trunk	H-BTUH	C-BTUH	H-CFM	C-CFM	Dsn CFM	Round Size	Velocity	Final Size
1 —								
2 —								
3 —								
4 —								
5 —								
6 —								
7 —								
8 —								
9 —								
10 —								
11 —								
12 —								
13 —								
14 —								
15 —								
	Trunk							
	Trunk							
	Trunk							
	Trunk							
Return Duct System								
Run - Trunk	Associated Supply Runs	H-CFM	C-CFM	Dsn CFM	Round Size	Velocity	Final Size	
1 —								

Duct Sizing Worksheet

outlets, depending on the design CFM value and the architectural details that are associated with the room.

• Rooms that require a relatively large flow of supply air will require two or more supply air registers (or grilles) because one properly sized register (or grille) might be objectionably large.

• When a room is relatively large, two or more properly sized supply air registers (or grilles) may be required to obtain adequate air motion within the occupied zone.

• In a cold climate, when a room has a relatively large amount of exposed wall and glass area, it may be desirable to use two or more properly sized supply air registers (or grilles) to assure comfort in the occupied zone.

There are no fixed rules regarding the number of supply air outlets that should be used for a room. It is the designer's responsibly to minimize complexity and installed cost without sacrificing comfort. The designer also must be sensitive to aesthetics. Refer to ACCA **Manual T** for more information about selecting and sizing air distribution devices.

If two or more runouts are associated with a given room, the duct sizing worksheet can be used to record the runout CFM values, but two or more lines will be required. In these situations, use the first line to calculate the H-CFM and C-CFM values that are associated with the room; but do not record the largest value on the form (in the Dsn CFM column) because it will be distributed by two or more branch runs. After the larger CFM value is split into runout CFM values, they can be entered on the form (using as many lines as necessary). An example of a multiple runout calculation is provided by Figure 8-4 (lines 4 and 5). In this case, two branch runout ducts deliver 200 CFM of supply air to the room.

Run	H-BTUH	C-BTUH	H-CFM	C-CFM	Dsn CFM
3 —	3040	2100	94	105	10-5
4 —	5500	4000	170	(200)	(100
5 —					100)
6 —	4500	2900	139	145	145

Figure 8-4

8-8 Supply Trunk Flow Rates

The sectional dimensions of a supply trunk may be constant along the whole length of the duct (extended plenum design), or the sectional area may be reduced one or more times at various points along the run (reducing plenum or reducing trunk design). In any case, the size of a particular duct section is based on the CFM that enters the section. This trunk sizing parameter is determined by summing the CFM values that are associated with the downstream supply air outlets.

The flow rate information that is associated with a system of trunk ducts depends on the complexity of the arrangement. Only one CFM value is required to size an extended plenum system, but two or more CFM values are required to size a reducing trunk system or a system that features primary and secondary duct runs. For example, Figure 8-5 shows how to calculate the CFM values that are associated with a system that has primary and secondary trunks and a reduction in the primary trunk.

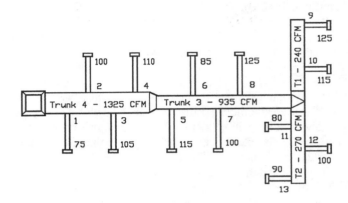

Figure 8-5

The duct sizing worksheet can be used to calculate the CFM values that are associated with each different section of trunk duct. For example, Figure 8-6 shows the flow rate calculations that are associated with the supply air system that is depicted by Figure 8-5.

Run - Trunk		H-CFM	C-CFM	Dsn-CFM
1 — T-4		65	75	
2 — T-4		115	100	
3 — T-4		95	105	
4 — T-4		95	110	
5 — T-3		100	115	
6 — T-3		85	85	
7 — T-3		90	100	
8 — T-3		110	125	
9 — T-1		115	125	
10 — T-1		110	115	
11 — T-2		95	80	
12 — T-2		85	100	
13 — T-2		80	90	
	Trunk T1	225	240	240
	Trunk T2	260	270	270
	Trunk T3	870	935	935
	Trunk T4	1250	1325	1315

Figure 8-6

8-9 Return Branch Flow Rates

The number of branch return ducts that are associated with a particular system is related to the number of return air openings. For example, if a return air grille is installed in every room, there will be as many return branches as there are rooms. Or, at the other extreme, there are no return branches associated with a system that features a central return. (Transfer grilles or door undercuts are required for isolated rooms that do not have a return.) In any case, the CFM that is associated with a particular return is equal to the total supply CFM that was delivered to the rooms or areas that are served by the return.

The "Duct Sizing Worksheet" below can be used to determine the design CFM value for a return branch. If a single room is associated with a given return, the CFM that is associated with the return run is equal to the CFM that is delivered to the room. If two or more rooms are associated with a given return, the CFM that is associated with the return run is equal to the total CFM that is delivered to the associated rooms. (Refer to the supply duct system calculations for a list of the room CFM values.)

An example of a multiple return runout system is provided by Figure 8-7. In this case, four return grilles and four branch return ducts are used to collect the air that was distributed to four different areas of the home.

The portion of the duct sizing worksheet that pertains to the return duct system can be used to calculate the CFM values that are associated with the branch return runs. For example,

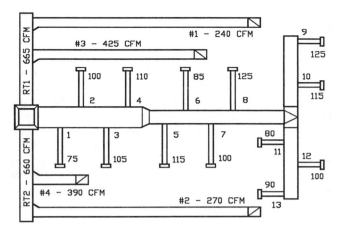

Figure 8-7

Figure 8-8 shows the calculations that are associated with the return duct system that is illustrated above. In this case return branch 1 is associated with supply runs 9 and 10; return branch 2 is associated with supply runs 11, 12 and 13; return branch

Run - Trunk	Asso. Supply Runs	H-CFM	C-CFM	D-CFM
1 — R-1	9, 10	225	240	240
2 — R-2	11, 12, 13	260	270	270
3 — R-3	5, 6, 7, 8	385	425	425
4 — R-4	1, 2, 3, 4	370	390	390

Figure 8-8

13 —								
14 —								
15 —								
		Trunk						
		Trunk						
		Trunk						
		Trunk						

			Return Duct System					
Run - Trunk	Associated Supply Runs	H-CFM	C-CFM	Dsn CFM	Round Size	Velocity	Final Size	
1 —								
2 —								
3 —								
4 —								
5 —								
6 —								
7 —								
8 —								
9 —								
10 —								
11 —								
12 —								
		Trunk						
		Trunk						
		Trunk						

1) H-BTUH and C-BTUH from the Manual J room load calculation procedure
2) H-CFM = HF x H-BTUH and C-CFM = CF x C–BTUH
3) Dsn CFM = larger of the H-CFM or C-CFM values (runout ducts) . . . or . . . total downstream CFM (trunk ducts)
4) Round size based on FR value. Final size based on FR value (if the velocity is acceptable) or the maximum allowable velocity value

Duct Sizing Worksheet

3 is associated with supply runs 5, 6, 7 and 8; and return branch 4 is associated with supply runs 1, 2, 3 and 4.

8-10 Return Trunk Flow Rates

The size of a particular return trunk section is based on the CFM that enters the trunk section. This trunk sizing parameter is determined by summing all the CFM values that are associated with the return air inlets that are located upstream of the section of interest. The "Duct Sizing Worksheet" can be used to calculate these values. For example, Figure 8-9 shows the calculations that are associated with the return trunk system that is described by Figure 8-7.

Run - Trunk	Asso. Supply Runs	H-CFM	C-CFM	D-CFM
1 — R-1	9, 10	225	240	
2 — R-2	11, 12, 13	260	270	
3 — R-3	5, 6, 7, 8	385	425	
4 — R-4	1, 2, 3, 4	370	390	
	Trunk RT-1 (R1, R3)	610	665	665
	Trunk RT-2 (R2, R4)	630	660	660

Figure 8-9

8-11 Branch Sizing (Supply or Return)

Once the design values for the friction rate and the branch CFM are known, the size of the branch duct can be determined by using a duct slide rule or a friction chart. For example, Figure 8-10 shows that if the design value for the friction rate is equal to 0.07 IWC/100 (metal duct), a 6.3 inch diameter would be associated with 100 CFM of branch flow.

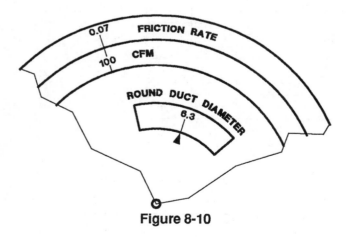

Figure 8-10

It also is necessary to verify that the velocities that are associated with the branch ducts do not exceed the recommended limit. (Maximum velocities are listed in Table 3-1, on page

3-6.) The work that is associated with this survey depends on how the design value for the friction rate was determined.

- If the design value for the friction rate was determined by using the friction rate chart (see Figure 8-3), the runout velocities will automatically be less than the recommended maximum, providing that the friction rate falls within the "wedge" that is bounded by the 0.06 and the 0.18 friction rate lines.

- If the design value for the friction rate was determined by using the friction rate equation (see page 8-4), the duct slide rule or a friction chart must be used to verify that the runout velocity is acceptable.

If a runout velocity exceeds the recommended value, the branch duct must be resized. The new size, which is based on the branch CFM and the allowable velocity, can be determined by using a duct slide rule or a friction chart. For example, Figure 8-11 shows that a 5.2 inch diameter would be required (for a metal duct) if the branch flow is equal to 130 CFM and the allowable velocity is equal to 900 FPM.

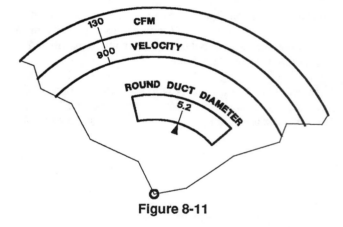

Figure 8-11

The duct sizing worksheet can be used to perform the sizing calculations that are associated with branch ducts. Figure 8-12 provides examples (sheet metal supply ducts) that show the final duct sizes are based on the CFM and the friction rate value — when the velocity is acceptable. (The velocities that are associated with branch runouts will always be acceptable if the friction rate value falls inside the "wedge" that is defined by the 0.06 and 0.18 lines on the friction rate chart.)

FR Value = 0.12 and Maximum Velocity = 900 FPM			
Dsn CFM	Round Size	Velocity	Final Size
120	6.0"	620 ok	6"
90	5.4" (use 6")	460	6"
140	6.4" (use 7")	540	7"

Figure 8-12

8-12 Trunk Sizing (Supply or Return)

Once the design values for the friction rate and the trunk CFM are known, a preliminary size for a section of trunk duct can be determined by using a duct slide rule or a friction chart. For example, if the design value for the friction rate is equal to 0.10 IWC/100, the duct slide rule shows that a 15.5 inch diameter would be associated with 1,300 CFM of air flow.

After the friction rate and CFM values are used to establish a tentative trunk size, it is necessary to verify that the velocity that is associated with the trunk does not exceed the recommended limit. (Maximum velocities are listed in Table 3-1, on page 3-6). If this velocity exceeds the recommended value, the trunk must be resized. In this case, the new size is based on the flow rate and the allowable velocity.

For example, it already has been demonstrated that a 15.5 inch (metal) duct is compatible with a 1,300 CFM flow rate and a 0.10 IWC/100 friction rate, but the velocity that is associated with this size is somewhat high. (The duct slide rule indicates that the velocity is equal to 1,020 FPM.) In this case, the size of the supply trunk will be based on the 1,300 CFM flow rate and a 900 FPM velocity. The duct slide rule indicates that the corresponding size is equal to 16.5 inches.

The duct sizing worksheet can be used to perform the sizing calculations that are associated with trunk ducts. Figure 8-13 provides two examples (sheet metal supply ducts). The first line shows that when the velocity is acceptable, the size is based on the friction rate and CFM. The second line shows that when the velocity is too high, the size must be based on the CFM and the maximum allowable velocity.

FR Value = 0.12 & Maximum Velocity = 900 FPM			
Dsn CFM	Round Size	Velocity	Final Size
500	10.3" (use 11')	790 ok	11"
1100	14.0"	1050	15"

Figure 8-13

8-13 Equivalent Rectangular Sizes

If square or rectangular shapes are required, the duct slide rule or a round-to-square conversion table can be used to find the equivalent rectangular size. This size should be entered into the column that is located on the far right side of the duct sizing worksheet.

> Equivalent rectangular sizes may vary, depending on the slide rule, because two (slightly different) equations are used to convert round sizes to equivalent rectangular sizes.

> The equivalent rectangular size will have the same resistance (friction rate) as the corresponding round size, but the velocity that is associated with the equivalent rectangular size will be lower than the velocity that is associated with the round shape.
>
> • The velocity that is associated with any shape can be calculated by dividing the CFM by the square feet of cross-sectional area.
>
> • The velocity that is associated with a round shape can be read off of any duct slide rule.
>
> • The velocity that is associated with a rectangular duct shape must be calculated or it can be read off of the "Auxiliary Calculations" side of the ACCA Duct Sizing Slide Rule.

8-14 Air Distribution Hardware

The air distribution devices must be selected in accordance with the procedures and recommendations that are found in **Manual T**. After these devices have been selected, the locations and sizes of the supply and return hardware can be recorded on a sketch of the duct system.

Section 9
Constant Volume Rigid Duct Systems

This section provides detailed examples of the calculations that are associated with constant volume duct systems that utilize rigid duct materials. These examples include a simple extended plenum system, a reducing trunk system, a complex trunk and branch system and a radial system.

9-1 Simple Extended Plenum System

Figure 9-1 provides an example of a simple extended plenum system that is fabricated out of galvanized metal. In this case the equipment is located near the center of the duct system and the flow of supply air is routed through two trunk ducts. The advantage of this configuration is that it minimizes the size of the trunk ducts (each duct carries about one-half of the required air flow). Also note that all of the air is collected at a single return that is located near the unit. (A single return is acceptable, providing that there is an unrestricted circulation path between each room and the return.)

Effective Length Calculation
Effective length estimates are critical to the duct sizing calculation procedure. The objective of this work is to identify the longest supply run and the longest return run. This information can be obtained in two ways: by using the brute force method (calculate the effective length of each run and compare the answers); or by thoughtfully selecting candidates for the longest run and ignoring the other runs (calculate the effective length of a few candidate runs and compare the

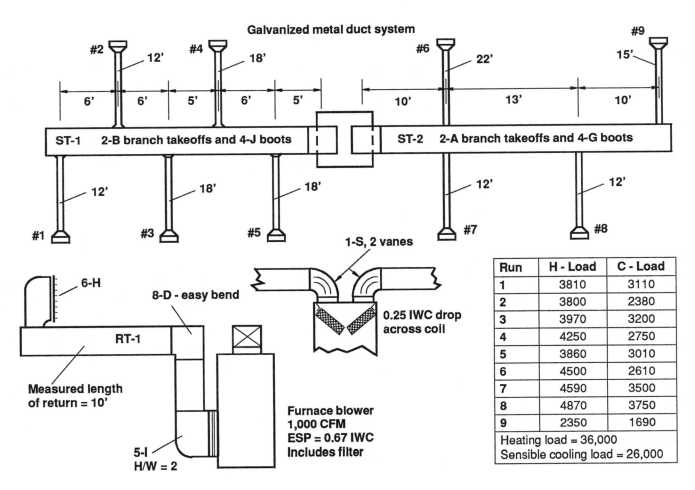

Run	H - Load	C - Load
1	3810	3110
2	3800	2380
3	3970	3200
4	4250	2750
5	3860	3010
6	4500	2610
7	4590	3500
8	4870	3750
9	2350	1690
Heating load = 36,000		
Sensible cooling load = 26,000		

Figure 9-1

answers). If the calculations are made by hand, the second method is preferred because it takes less time. In this example, runs 1, 5, 6 and 9 were selected as "longest run" candidates because:

- All of the branch runouts are about the same length, so this information can be discounted.

- Runs 1 and 9, which are furthest from the air handler, have the longest measured lengths and the smallest branch takeoff equivalent length values.

- Runs 5 and 6, which are closest to the air handler, have the shortest measured lengths and the largest branch takeoff equivalent length values.

- The other runs can be ignored because the distances between the branch takeoff fittings are smaller than the differences in the branch takeoff equivalent length values.

In other words, the measured lengths can be balanced against the equivalent lengths that are associated with the branch takeoff fittings. If the differences in the measured lengths are relatively small compared with the differences in the branch takeoff equivalent lengths, the longest run will be the run that

has a takeoff near the air handler. If the differences in the measured lengths are relatively large compared with the differences in the branch takeoff equivalent lengths, the longest run will be the one that has a takeoff that is far away from the air handler.

It also is necessary to compare the efficiency of the fittings that are associated with each run. For this particular example, one would expect to find the longest run on the right side of the system (run 6 or 9) because the fittings that are associated with the right trunk are considerably less efficient than the fittings associated with the left trunk. (Normally, the same types of fittings would be used on both sides of the system. The fittings that are used in this example were selected to illustrate a point.)

- The equivalent length of a 4G boot is equal to 80 feet and the equivalent length of a 4J boot is equal to 30 feet.

- The base equivalent length (no downstream branches) for the 2A takeoff is equal to 35 feet and the base equivalent length value for the 2B takeoff is equal to 20 feet.

Based on the observations that are listed above, one might speculate (without making a single calculation) that the run

Effective Length Calculation Sheet									
Element	Supply Run ID Number				Element	Return Run ID Number			
	# 1	# 5	# 6	# 9		# 1	#	#	#
Trunk Length	28	5	10	33	Trunk Length	10			
Trunk Length					Trunk Length				
Trunk Length					Trunk Length				
Runout Length	12	18	22	15	Runout Length				
Group 1 (S)	30	30	30	30	Group 5 (I)	30			
Group 2 (A)			65	35	Group 6 (H)	15			
Group 3					Group 7				
Group 4 (G)			80	80	Group 8 (D)	65	(easy bend)		
Group 8					Group 10				
Group 9					Group 11				
Group 11					Group 12				
Group 12					Group 13				
Other					Other				
Other (2B)	20	45			Other				
Other (4J)	30	30			Other				
Other					Other				
Total Length	120	128	207	193	Total Length	120			

Figure 9-2

Friction Rate Worksheet

Step 1) Manufacturer's Blower Data

External static pressure (ESP) = ___0.67___ IWC   CFM = ___1000___

Step 2) Device Pressure Losses

Direct expansion refrigerant coil . . . . ___0.25___
Electric resistance heating coil . . . . . _____
Hot water coil . . . . _____
Heat exchanger . . . . _____
Low efficiency filter . . . . _____
High or mid-efficiency filter . . . . _____
Electronic filter . . . . _____
Humidifier . . . . _____
Supply outlet . . . . ___0.03___
Return grille . . . . ___0.03___
Balancing damper . . . . ___0.03___
Other device . . . . _____

Total device losses (DPL) . . . . ___0.34___ IWC

Step 3) Available Static Pressure

ASP = (ESP - DPL) = (___0.67___ - ___0.34___) = ___0.33___ IWC

Step 4) Total Effective Length (TEL)

Supply-side TEL + Return-side TEL = (___207___ + ___120___) = ___327___ FEET

Step 5) Friction Rate Design Value (FR)

FR value from friction rate chart = ___0.10___ IWC/100

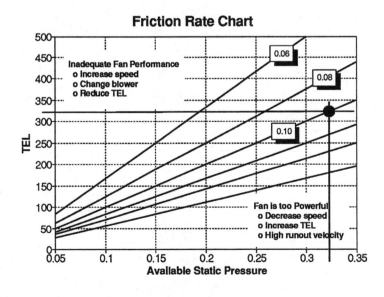

Friction Rate Chart

Figure 9-3

Duct Sizing Worksheet

HF = Blower CFM / Manual J Heat Loss = (1000) / (36000) = 0.0278

CF = Blower CFM / Manual J Sensible Heat Gain = (1000) / (26000) = 0.0385

FR Value 0.10

Supply Duct System

Run - Trunk	H-BTUH	C-BTUH	H-CFM	C-CFM	Dsn CFM	Round Size	Velocity	Final Size
1 — ST1	3810	3110	106	120	120	6	ok	6
2 — ST1	3800	2380	106	92	106	6	ok	6
3 — ST1	3970	3200	110	123	123	6	ok	6
4 — ST1	4250	2750	118	106	118	6	ok	6
5 — ST1	3860	3010	107	116	116	6	ok	6
6 — ST2	4500	2610	125	100	125	6	ok	6
7 — ST2	4590	3500	128	135	135	7	ok	7
8 — ST2	4870	3750	135	144	144	7	ok	7
9 — ST2	2350	1690	65	65	65	5	ok	5
10 —								
11 —								
12 —								
13 —								
14 —								
15 —								
	Trunk ST1		547	557	557	11	870	11
	Trunk ST2		453	444	453	11	720	11
	Trunk							
	Trunk							

Return Duct System

Run - Trunk	Associated Supply Runs	H-CFM	C-CFM	Dsn CFM	Round Size	Velocity	Final Size
1 —							
2 —							
3 —							
4 —							
5 —							
6 —							
7 —							
8 —							
9 —							
10 —							
11 —							
	Trunk RT1	1000	1000	1000	14	970	17
	Trunk						
	Trunk						

1) H-BTUH and C-BTUH from the **Manual J** room load calculation procedure

2) H-CFM = HF x H-BTUH and C-CFM = CF x C--BTUH

3) Dsn CFM = larger of the H-CFM or C-CFM values (runout ducts) . . . or . . . total downstream CFM (trunk ducts)

4) Round size based on FR value. Final size based on FR value (if the velocity is acceptable) or the maximum allowable velocity value

Figure 9-4

number 6 is the longest supply run. Figure 9-2 (previous page) confirms this assumption. In this case the effective length of the longest supply run is 207 feet and the effective length of the return run is 120 feet. Therefore the total effective length of the longest circulation path is equal to 327 feet.

Note: When two branch runout ducts are directly across from each other, count the opposing runout as a downstream branch. For example, refer to Figure 9-1. In this arrangement, run 6 has three downstream branches and run 7 has three downstream branches.

Design Friction Rate Calculation
In this example, the blower data indicates that the fan can deliver 1,000 CFM when it operates against 0.67 IWC of external resistance. Since the resistance that is associated with the A-coil (0.25 IWC), the supply outlet (0.03 IWC), the return (0.30 IWC) and a hand damper (0.03 IWC) is equal to 0.34 IWC; the available static pressure is equal to 0.33 IWC. Therefore, the design value for the friction rate will be based on 0.33 IWC of pressure and 327 feet of effective length. These calculations are summarized on page 9-3 by Figure 9-3, which indicates that the design value for the friction rate is equal to 0.10 IWC/100.

Duct Sizing Calculations
Figure 9-4 (see page 9-4) summarizes the duct sizing calculations, which begin with the heating factor and cooling factor calculations; followed by the supply runout sizing calculations, the supply trunk sizing calculations and the return duct sizing calculations. The following comments apply to these calculations.

- All of the values in the "round size" column were determined by using the "Galvanized Metal Duct" scale (refer to the ACCA Duct Sizing Slide Rule).

- Supply runs 1 through 5 are associated with trunk ST-1 and supply runs 6 through 9 are associated with trunk ST-2.

- The final sizes of supply runouts are based on the friction rate design value (0.10 IWC/100) because the corresponding velocities are less than 900 FPM. (The runout velocities are always less than 900 FPM when the design friction rate value falls inside the "wedge" that is associated with the friction rate chart.)

- The final sizes of supply trunks (ST-1 and ST-2) are based on the friction rate design value (0.10 IWC/100) because the corresponding velocities are less than 900 FPM.

- The final size of return trunk (RT-1) is based on the allowable velocity (700 FPM) because the velocity that is associated with the friction rate design value (0.10 IWC/100) exceeds the recommended maximum.

Equivalent Rectangular Sizes
The ACCA Duct Sizing Slide Rule can be used to convert round sizes into equivalent rectangular sizes. These rectangular shapes are equivalent because they produce the same resistance (to air flow) as the round shapes. (Note that the velocities that are associated with the round and the equivalent rectangular shapes will not be equal. But, this poses no problem because the velocities that are associated with the equivalent rectangular shapes will always be less than the velocities that are associated with the round shapes.)

9-2 Simple Reducing Plenum System

On the next page, Figure 9-5 provides an example of a simple reducing plenum system that is fabricated out of galvanized metal. (Refer to Section 1-6 for more information about the location of the trunk reducer fitting.) Note that the geometry that is associated with this example is very similar to the geometry that is associated with example 1. The only difference between the two layouts is that the equipment has been moved to one end of the duct system. However, there are other differences. This arrangement requires a different type of plenum takeoff fitting at the air handler and an electronic filter has been added to the system.

Effective Length Calculation
As explained previously (see example 1), thoughtful observations will minimize that amount of work that is associated with the effective length circulations. Based on these observations, one would select runs 1, 6 and 9 as candidates for the longest supply run. On the next page, Figure 9-6 shows the effective length calculations that are associated with these supply runs and the return run. This figure shows that the effective length of the longest supply run is 255 feet and the effective length of the return run is 120 feet. Therefore, the total effective length of the longest circulation path is equal to 375 feet.

Design Friction Rate Calculation
In this example, the blower data indicates that the fan can deliver 1,000 CFM when it operates against 0.67 IWC of external resistance. Since the resistance that is associated with the A-coil (0.25 IWC), electronic filter (0.10 IWC), the supply outlet (0.03 IWC), the return (0.03 IWC) and a hand damper (0.03 IWC) is equal to 0.44 IWC, the available static pressure is equal to 0.23 IWC. Therefore, the design value for the friction rate will be based on 0.23 IWC of pressure and 375 feet of effective length. These calculations are summarized on page 9-7 by Figure 9-7, which indicates that the design value for the friction rate is equal to 0.06 IWC/100.

Duct Sizing Calculations
Figure 9-8 (see page 9-8) summarizes the duct sizing calculations. The following comments apply to these calculations.

- All of the values in the "round size" column were determined by using the "Galvanized Metal Duct" scale (refer to the ACCA Duct Sizing Slide Rule).

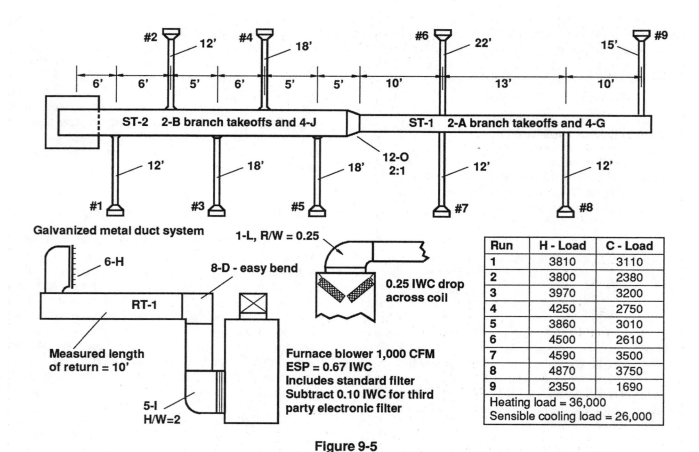

Galvanized metal duct system

Furnace blower 1,000 CFM
ESP = 0.67 IWC
Includes standard filter
Subtract 0.10 IWC for third
party electronic filter

Run	H - Load	C - Load
1	3810	3110
2	3800	2380
3	3970	3200
4	4250	2750
5	3860	3010
6	4500	2610
7	4590	3500
8	4870	3750
9	2350	1690
Heating load = 36,000		
Sensible cooling load = 26,000		

Figure 9-5

Effective Length Calculation Sheet									
Element	**Supply Run ID Number**				**Element**	**Return Run ID Number**			
	# 1	# 6	# 9			# 1			
Trunk Length	6	43	66		Trunk Length	10			
Trunk Length					Trunk Length				
Trunk Length					Trunk Length				
Runout Length	12	22	15		Runout Length				
Group 1 (1L)	40	40	40		Group 5 (I)	30			H/W=2
Group 2 (B, A)	45	65	35		Group 6 (H)	15			
Group 3					Group 7				
Group 4 (J, G)	30	80	80		Group 8 (D)	65	(easy bend)		
Group 8					Group 10				
Group 9					Group 11				
Group 11					Group 12				
Group 12 (O)		5	5		Other				
Other					Other				
Other					Other				
Total Length	133	255	241		Total Length	120			

Figure 9-6

Friction Rate Worksheet

Step 1) Manufacturer's Blower Data

External static pressure (ESP) = ___0.67___ IWC   CFM = ___1000___

Step 2) Device Pressure Losses

Direct expansion refrigerant coil 0.25
Electric resistance heating coil . . . . .
Hot water coil . . . .
Heat exchanger . . . .
Low efficiency filter . . . .
High or mid-efficiency filter . . . .
Electronic filter 0.10
Humidifier . . . .
Supply outlet 0.03
Return grille 0.03
Balancing damper 0.03
Other device . . . .

Total device losses (DPL) . . . .   ___0.44___   IWC

Step 3) Available Static Pressure

ASP = (ESP - DPL) = (___0.67___ - ___0.44___) = ___0.23___   IWC

Step 4) Total Effective Length (TEL)

Supply-side TEL + Return-side TEL = (___255___ + ___120___) = ___375___   FEET

Step 5) Friction Rate Design Value (FR)

FR value from friction rate chart = ___0.06___   IWC/100

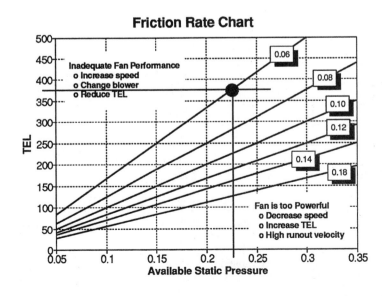

Figure 9-7

Duct Sizing Worksheet

HF = Blower CFM / Manual J Heat Loss = (1000) / (36000) = 0.0278

CF = Blower CFM / Manual J Sensible Heat Gain = (1000) / (26000) = 0.0385

FR Value 0.06

Supply Duct System

Run - Trunk	H-BTUH	C-BTUH	H-CFM	C-CFM	Dsn CFM	Round Size	Velocity	Final Size
1 — ST2	3810	3110	106	120	120	7	ok	7
2 — ST2	3800	2380	106	92	106	7	ok	7
3 — ST2	3970	3200	110	123	123	7	ok	7
4 — ST2	4250	2750	118	106	118	7	ok	7
5 — ST2	3860	3010	107	116	116	7	ok	7
6 — ST1	4500	2610	125	100	125	7	ok	7
7 — ST1	4590	3500	128	135	135	7	ok	7
8 — ST1	4870	3750	135	144	144	8	ok	8
9 — ST1	2350	1690	65	65	65	6	ok	6
10 —								
11 —								
12 —								
13 —								
14 —								
15 —								
		Trunk ST1	453	444	453	12	590	12
		Trunk ST2	1000	1000	1000	16	730	16
		Trunk						
		Trunk						

Return Duct System

Run - Trunk	Associated Supply Runs	H-CFM	C-CFM	Dsn CFM	Round Size	Velocity	Final Size
1 —							
2 —							
3 —							
4 —							
5 —							
6 —							
7 —							
8 —							
9 —							
10 —							
11 —							
	Trunk RT1	1000	1000	1000	16	730	17
	Trunk						
	Trunk						

1) H-BTUH and C-BTUH from the **Manual J** room load calculation procedure

2) H-CFM = HF x H-BTUH and C-CFM = CF x C--BTUH

3) Dsn CFM = larger of the H-CFM or C-CFM values (runout ducts) ... or ... total downstream CFM (trunk ducts)

4) Round size based on FR value. Final size based on FR value (if the velocity is acceptable) or the maximum allowable velocity value

Figure 9-8

- Supply runs 1 through 5 are associated with trunk ST-2 and supply runs 6 through 9 are associated with trunk ST-1.

- The final sizes of supply runouts are based on the friction rate design value (0.06 IWC/100) because the corresponding velocities are less than 900 FPM. (The runout velocities are always less than 900 FPM when the design friction rate value falls inside the "wedge" that is associated with the friction rate chart.)

- The final sizes of supply trunks (ST-1 and ST-2) are based on the friction rate design value (0.06 IWC/100) because the corresponding velocities are less than 900 FPM.

- The final size of return trunk (RT-1) is based on the allowable velocity (700 FPM) because the velocity that is associated with the friction rate design value (0.06 IWC/100) exceeds the recommended maximum.

- The ACCA Duct Slide Rule can be used to convert round sizes into equivalent rectangular sizes.

Comments and Observations

The duct systems that are described by examples 1 and 2 are similar, except for the position of the furnace and the addition of an electronic filter. The net effect of these two changes was to reduce the design friction rate from the 0.10 IWC/100 value (example 1) to the 0.06 IWC/100 value (example 2). This reduction in the design friction rate value is associated with the increase in the total effective length value (375 feet versus 327 feet) and the decrease in the available static pressure value (0.23 IWC versus 0.33 IWC). And, since the duct sizes depend on the design friction rate, the 0.06 IWC/100 value caused a 1-inch increase in the runout duct sizes and a 1- or 2-inch increase in the supply trunk duct sizes (in both cases, the return ducts were sized to satisfy the 700 FPM velocity limit).

Note that the 0.06 friction rate value is barely within the "wedge" that is associated with the friction rate chart. This friction rate value could be increased by selecting a higher fan speed or by reducing the total effective length of the duct system. In this regard, it would be logical to change the inefficient branch takeoff and boot fittings that are associated with trunk 2. Figure 9-9 shows that if 2B branch takeoff and 4J boot fittings are substituted for the 2A and 4G fittings, the total effective length can be reduced by 75 feet (300 feet versus 375 feet).

If the total effective length is decreased, there will be a corresponding increase in the design friction rate value. As indicated on the next page by Figure 9-10, the new friction rate value (0.075 IWC/100 approximate) is well inside the "wedge" that is associated with the friction rate chart.

Effective Length Calculation Sheet									
Element	Supply Run ID Number				Element	Return Run ID Number			
	# 1	# 6	# 9	#		# 1	#	#	#
Trunk Length	6	43	66		Trunk Length	10			
Trunk Length					Trunk Length				
Trunk Length					Trunk Length				
Runout Length	12	22	15		Runout Length				
Group 1 (L)	40	40	40		Group 5 (I)	30			H/W=2
Group 2 (B)	45	40	20		Group 6 (H)	15			
Group 3					Group 7				
Group 4 (J)	30	30	30		Group 8 (D)	65	(easy bend)		
Group 8					Group 10				
Group 9					Group 11				
Group 11					Group 12				
Group 12 (J)		5	5		Other				
Other					Other				
Other					Other				
Total Length	133	180	176		Total Length	120			

Figure 9-9

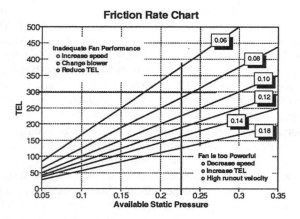

Figure 9-10

9-3 Primary and Secondary Trunk System

Figure 9-11 provides a schematic drawing of a 1500 CFM system that is fabricated out of duct board, except for the supply runout ducts, which are sheet metal. This system has a primary, reducing, supply trunk and two secondary supply trunks. The return system consists of four return runs and two return trunks. Figure 9-12 summarizes the heating and cooling loads that are associated with the various runout ducts and Figure 9-13 (see next page) presents the manufacturer's blower data and accessory device pressure drop data.

Runout	Length - FT	H-BTUH	C-BTUH
1	16	4250	2750
2	14	3860	3010
3	16	3970	3200
4	14	2780	2130
5	17	3800	2380
6	16	4440	3420
7	17	4590	3500
8	16	4620	3510
9	12	2350	1690
10	12	3020	2590
11	8	3810	3110
12	12	3430	2400
13	8	4500	2610
Heating Load = 49,420		Cooling Load = 36,300	

Figure 9-12

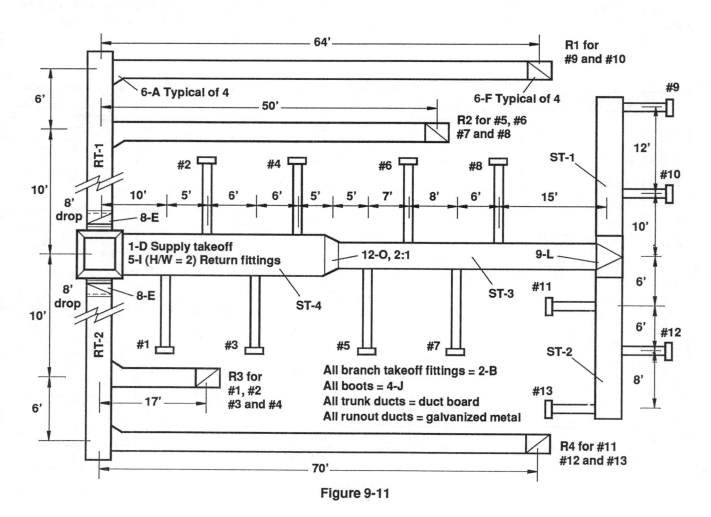

Figure 9-11

Blower Data — Example 3			
CFM	External Resistance — IWC		
	High	Medium	Low
1200			0.58
1300		0.62	0.43
1400	0.68	0.47	0.27
1500	0.53	0.32	0.12
1600	0.38	0.15	
1700	0.20		

Unit tested with wet coil and low efficiency filter in place. If an auxiliary heating coil is required, subtract 0.08 IWC from the values that are listed in this table.

Figure 9-13

Effective Length Calculation

After reflecting on the geometry and the fittings that are associated with this duct system, it appears that runs 1, 5, 9 and 11 are candidates for the longest supply run and that the corresponding return runs are R3, R2, R1 and R4. Figure 9-14 documents the effective length calculations that are associated with these runs. The following summary shows that the effective length of the critical circulation path is 451 feet. This path is defined by the #9 supply run (192 feet) and the R4 return run (259 feet).

Run	#1	#5	#9	#11
Supply TEL	106	139	192	187
Run	R1	R2	R3	R4
Return TEL	253	201	133	259

Summary

Design Friction Rate Calculation

In this example, heating and cooling is provided by an air-to-air heat pump and the blower data indicates that at medium speed, the fan can deliver 1,500 CFM when it operates against 0.32 IWC of external resistance. Since the resistance that is associated with the auxiliary heating coil (0.08 IWC), the supply outlet (0.03 IWC), the return (0.03 IWC) and a hand damper (0.03 IWC) is equal to 0.17 IWC, the available static pressure is equal to 0.15 IWC. Therefore, the design value for the friction rate will be based on 0.15 IWC of pressure and 451 feet of effective length. These calculations are summarized on the next page by Figure 9-15, which indicates that, at medium speed, the blower cannot produce enough static pressure.

There are two ways to deal with inadequate fan performance: increase the fan speed or reduce the total effective length of the longest circulation path. The second option is normally preferred, but the first option (increase the blower speed) will be applied to this example because the proposed fittings are reasonably efficient.

Effective Length Calculation Sheet									
Element	Supply Run ID Number				Element	Return Run ID Number			
	# 1	# 5	# 9	# 11		# R-1	# R-2	# R-3	# R-4
Trunk Length	10	37	95	79	Trunk Length	24	18	18	24
Trunk Length					Trunk Length				
Trunk Length					Trunk Length				
Runout Length	16	17	12	8	Runout Length	64	50	17	70
Group 1 (D)	10	10	10	10	Group 5 (I)	30	30	30	30
Group 2 (B)	40	40	20	35	Group 6 (A br)	75	68	33	75
Group 3					Group 7				
Group 4 (J)	30	30	30	30	Group 8 (E)	10	10	10	10
Group 8					Group 10				
Group 9 (L)			20	20	Group 11				
Group 11					Group 12				
Group 12 (O)		5	5	5	Other (6A main)	25			25
Other					Other (6F)	25	25	25	25
Other					Other				
Total Length	106	139	192	187	Total Length	253	201	133	259

Figure 9-14

Friction Rate Worksheet

Step 1) Manufacturer's Blower Data

External static pressure (ESP) = ~~0.32~~ 0.53   IWC   CFM = __1500__

Step 2) Device Pressure Losses

Direct expansion refrigerant coil . . .
Electric resistance heating coil 0.08
Hot water coil . . . .
Heat exchanger . . . .
Low efficiency filter . . . .
High or mid-efficiency filter . . . .
Electronic filter . . . .
Humidifier . . . .
Supply outlet 0.03
Return grille 0.03
Balancing damper 0.03
Other device . . . .

Total device losses (DPL) . . . .   __0.17__   IWC

Step 3) Available Static Pressure

ASP = (ESP - DPL) = (~~0.32~~ 0.53 - __0.17__) = ~~0.15~~ 0.36   IWC

Step 4) Total Effective Length (TEL)

Supply-side TEL + Return-side TEL = (__192__ + __259__) = __451__   FEET

Step 5) Friction Rate Design Value (FR)

FR value from friction rate chart = ~~NA~~ 0.08   IWC/100

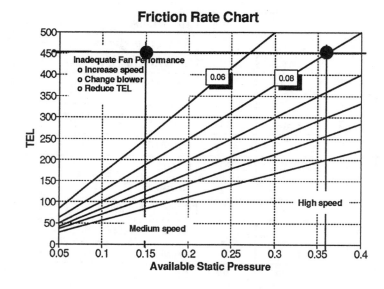

Friction Rate Chart

Figure 19-15

Duct Sizing Worksheet

HF = Blower CFM / Manual J Heat Loss = (1500) / (49420) = 0.0304

CF = Blower CFM / Manual J Sensible Heat Gain = (1500) / (36300) = 0.0413

FR Value 0.08

Supply Duct System

Run - Trunk	H-BTUH	C-BTUH	H-CFM	C-CFM	Dsn CFM	Round Size	Velocity	Final Size
1 — ST4	4250	2750	129	114	129	7	ok	7
2 — ST4	3860	3010	117	124	124	7	ok	7
3 — ST4	3970	3200	120	132	132	7	ok	7
4 — ST4	2780	2130	84	88	88	6	ok	6
5 — ST3	3800	2380	115	98	115	7	ok	7
6 — ST3	4440	3420	135	141	141	7	ok	7
7 — ST3	4590	3500	139	145	145	7	ok	7
8 — ST3	4620	3510	140	145	145	7	ok	7
9 — ST1	2350	1690	71	70	71	6	ok	6
10 — ST1	3020	2590	92	107	107	6	ok	6
11 — ST2	3810	3110	116	129	129	7	ok	7
12 — ST2	3430	2400	104	99	104	6	ok	6
13 — ST2	4500	2610	137	108	137	7	ok	7
14 —								
15 —								
Trunk ST1			163	177	177	8	510	8
Trunk ST2			357	336	357	10	670	10
Trunk ST3			1049	1042	1049	16	770	16
Trunk ST4			1500	1500	1500	18	870	18

Return Duct System

Run - Trunk	Associated Supply Runs	H-CFM	C-CFM	Dsn CFM	Round Size	Velocity	Final Size
1 — RT1	#9, #10	163	177	177	8	510	8
2 — RT1	#5, #6, #7, #8	529	529	529	12	690	12
3 — RT2	#1, #2, #3, #4	450	458	458	11	705	11
4 — RT2	#11, #12, #13	357	336	357	10	660	10
5 —							
6 —							
7 —							
8 —							
9 —							
10 —							
11 —							
Trunk RT1		692	706	706	13	790	14
Trunk RT2		807	794	807	14	780	15
Trunk							

1) H-BTUH and C-BTUH from the **Manual J** room load calculation procedure
2) H-CFM = HF x H-BTUH and C-CFM = CF x C--BTUH
3) Dsn CFM = larger of the H-CFM or C-CFM values (runout ducts) . . . or . . . total downstream CFM (trunk ducts)
4) Round size based on FR value. Final size based on FR value (if the velocity is acceptable) or the maximum allowable velocity value

Figure 9-16

At high speed, the blower data indicates that the fan can deliver 1,500 CFM when it operates against 0.53 IWC of external resistance. Therefore, when 0.17 IWC is subtracted from this value, the design value for the friction rate will be based on 0.36 IWC of pressure and 451 feet of effective length. These revisions, which are also summarized by Figure 9-15, indicate that the design friction rate value will be equal to 0.08 IWC/100.

Duct Sizing Calculations

On the preceding page, Figure 9-16 summarizes the duct sizing calculations that are associated with this example. The following comments apply to these calculations:

- All of the supply branch runout sizes were determined by using the "Galvanized Metal Duct" scale (refer to the ACCA Duct Sizing Slide Rule).

- All of the supply trunk sizes and the return duct sizes were determined by using the "Duct Board" scale (refer to the ACCA Duct Sizing Slide Rule).

- Supply runs 1 through 4 are associated with primary trunk ST-4, supply runs 5 through 8 are associated with primary trunk ST-3, supply runs 11 through 13 are associated with secondary trunk ST-2, and supply runs 9 and 10 are associated with secondary trunk ST-1.

- Supply runs 9 and 10 are associated with return R1, supply runs 5 through 8 are associated with return R2, supply runs 1 through 4 are associated with return R3 and supply runs 11 through 13 are associated with return R4.

- Return runs R1 and R2 feed into return trunk RT-1, and return runs R3 and R4 feed into return trunk RT-2.

- The final sizes of supply runouts are based on the friction rate design value (0.08 IWC/100) because the corresponding velocities are less than 900 FPM. (The runout velocities are always less than 900 FPM when the design friction rate value falls inside the "wedge" that is associated with the friction rate chart.)

- The final sizes of the supply trunks (ST-1, ST-2, ST-3 and ST-4) are based on the friction rate design value (0.08 IWC/100) because the corresponding velocities are less than 900 FPM.

- The final sizes of the return branch ducts (R1, R2, R3 and R4) are based on the friction rate design value (0.08 IWC/100) because the corresponding velocities are acceptable (700 FPM or less).

- The final sizes of the return trunks (RT-1 and RT-2) are based on the maximum allowable velocity (700 FPM) because the velocity that is associated with the friction rate value (0.08 IWC/100) exceeds 700 FPM.

- A summary of the calculations that are associated with the group 6A equivalent length values is provided below.

Summary	R1	R2	R3	R4
CFM1/CFM2	1.00	0.75	0.56	1.00
Branch EL	75	68	33	75
Main EL	0	25	25	0

- The ACCA Duct Slide Rule can be used to convert round sizes into equivalent rectangular sizes.

Comments and Observations

This example is characterized by marginal blower performance and a substantial total effective length value. But as demonstrated above, there was enough blower capacity (at the high speed setting) to provide the required air flow.

This example also is characterized by an absence of accessory devices, which made a viable design possible. If a simple device, such as an electronic filter, is added to the system, the blower would have marginal ability (even at the high speed setting) to deliver the desired air flow.

For example, if an electronic filter adds 0.10 IWC to the device pressure loss calculation, the available static pressure would be equal to 0.26 IWC instead of 0.36 IWC. Under these circumstances (refer to Figure 9-17) the design friction rate would be equal to 0.06 IWC/100, which is slightly outside the "wedge." This problem could be corrected by using equipment that has a more powerful blower.

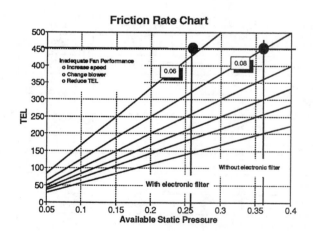

Figure 9-17

9-4 Radial Duct System

Figures 9-18 and 9-19 illustrate an 800 CFM radial duct system that features below-the-slab supply ducts and above-

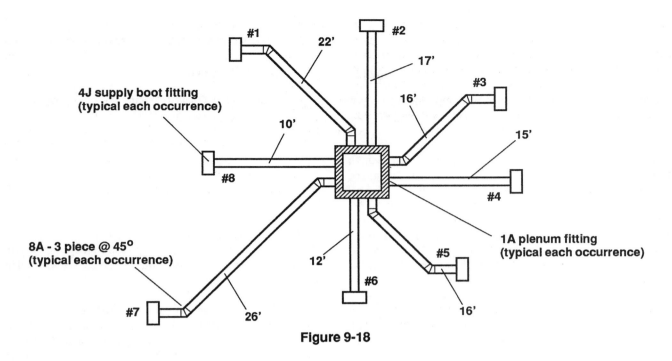

Figure 9-18

the-ceiling return ducts. The below-grade ducts are fabricated out of plastic and the return ducts are sheet metal. Heating and cooling is supplied by a heat pump. Figure 9-20 summarizes the heating and cooling loads that are associated with the various supply air outlets and Figure 9-21 presents the manufacturer's blower data and accessory device pressure drop data.

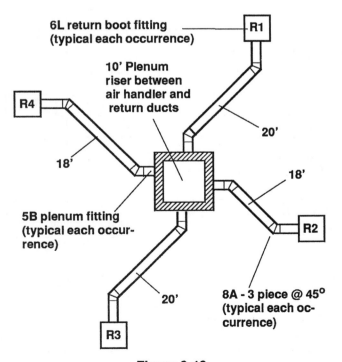

Figure 9-19

Runout	Length - FT	H-BTUH	C-BTUH
1	22	4250	2750
3	17	3970	3200
5	16	3800	2380
7	15	4590	3500
8	16	2350	1690
10	12	3020	2590
12	26	3430	2400
13	10	4500	2610
Heating Load = 29,910		Cooling Load = 21,120	

Figure 9-20

Blower Data — Example 4			
CFM	External Resistance — IWC		
	High	Medium	Low
600			0.48
650		0.66	0.33
725	0.67	0.51	0.17
800	0.51	0.36	
875	0.36	0.19	
950	0.17		

Figure 9-21

Effective Length Calculation

After surveying the geometry and the fittings that are associated with this duct system, it appears that the longest circulation path is defined by supply run 7 and return run R3. (Since the same fittings are used the supply runs and the return runs, the longest runs can be determined by comparing the lengths that are associated with the straight sections.) Figure 9-22 summarizes the effective length calculations that are associated with this circulation path. This summary shows that the effective length of run # 7 is 111 feet and the effective length of run R3 is 110 feet. Therefore, the total effective length of the critical circulation path is equal to 221 feet.

Design Friction Rate Calculation

In this example, heating and cooling is provided by an air-to-air heat pump and the blower data indicates that at medium speed, the fan can deliver 800 CFM when it operates against 0.36 IWC of external resistance. Since an electronic filter will be used, the resistance that is associated with the accessory filter (0.11 IWC), the supply outlet (0.03 IWC), the return (0.03 IWC) and a hand damper (0.03 IWC) is equal to 0.20 IWC; the available static pressure is equal to 0.16 IWC. Therefore, the design value for the friction rate will be based on 0.16 IWC of pressure and 221 feet of effective length. These calculations are summarized on the next page by Figure 9-23, which indicates that the design value for the friction rate is equal to 0.07 IWC/100.

Duct Sizing Calculations

On page 9-18, Figure 9-24 summarizes the duct sizing calculations that are associated with this example. The following comments apply to these calculations:

- Since the ACCA Duct Slide Rule does not provide information about plastic ducts, the supply duct sizes were determined by using the "Galvanized Metal Duct" scale. (The galvanized metal scale will yield conservative answers because plastic is smoother than galvanized metal.)

- All of the return duct sizes were determined by using the "Galvanized Metal Duct" scale.

- Supply runs 2 and 3 are associated with return R1, supply runs 4 and 5 are associated with return R2, supply runs 6 and 7 are associated with return R3 and supply runs 8 and 1 are associated with return R4.

- The final sizes of supply runs are based on the friction rate design value (0.07 IWC/100) because runout velocities are always less than 900 FPM when the friction rate value falls inside the "wedge" that is found on the friction rate chart.

- The final sizes of the return runs are based on the friction rate design value (0.07 IWC/100) because the corresponding velocities are less than 700 FPM.

Effective Length Calculation Sheet									
Element	**Supply Run ID Number**				**Element**	**Return Run ID Number**			
	# 7					# R3			
Trunk Length					Trunk Length	10			
Trunk Length					Trunk Length				
Trunk Length					Trunk Length				
Runout Length	26				Runout Length	20			
Group 1 (A)	35				Group 5 (B)	40			
Group 2					Group 6 (L)	20			
Group 3					Group 7				
Group 4 (J)	30				Group 8 (A)	20	(2 @ 10)		
Group 8 (A)	20	(2 @ 10)			Group 10				
Group 9					Group 11				
Group 11					Group 12				
Group 12					Group 13				
Group 13					Other				
Other					Other				
Total Length	111				Total Length	110			

Figure 9-22

Friction Rate Worksheet

Step 1) Manufacturer's Blower Data

External static pressure (ESP) = ___0.36___ IWC   CFM = ___800___

Step 2) Device Pressure Losses

Direct expansion refrigerant coil . . . .
Electric resistance heating coil . . . . .
Hot water coil . . . .
Heat exchanger . . . .
Low efficiency filter . . . .
High or mid-efficiency filter . . . .
Electronic filter 0.11
Humidifier . . . .
Supply outlet 0.03
Return grille 0.03
Balancing damper 0.03
Other device . . . .

Total device losses (DPL) . . . .   0.20   IWC

Step 3) Available Static Pressure

ASP = (ESP - DPL) = (___0.36___ - ___0.20___) = ___0.16___   IWC

Step 4) Total Effective Length (TEL)

Supply-side TEL + Return-side TEL = (___111___ + ___110___) = ___221___   FEET

Step 5) Friction Rate Design Value (FR)

FR value from friction rate chart = ___0.07___   IWC/100

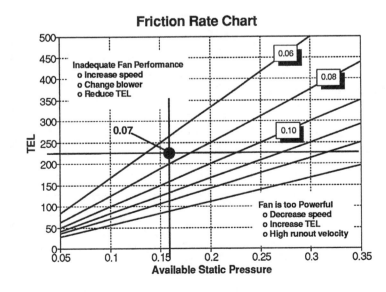

Figure 9-23

Duct Sizing Worksheet

HF = Blower CFM / Manual J Heat Loss = (800) / (29910) = 0.0267	FR Value
CF = Blower CFM / Manual J Sensible Heat Gain = (800) / (21120) = 0.0379	0.07

Supply Duct System

Run - Trunk	H-BTUH	C-BTUH	H-CFM	C-CFM	Dsn CFM	Round Size	Velocity	Final Size
1 —	4250	2750	114	104	114	7	ok	7
2 —	3970	3200	106	121	121	7	ok	7
3 —	3800	2380	102	90	102	6	ok	6
4 —	4590	3500	123	133	133	7	ok	7
5 —	2350	1690	63	64	64	6	ok	6
6 —	3020	2590	81	98	98	6	ok	6
7 —	3430	2400	92	91	92	6	ok	6
8 —	4500	2610	120	99	120	7	ok	7
9 —								
10 —								
11 —								
12 —								
13 —								
14 —								
15 —								
		Trunk						
		Trunk						
		Trunk						
		Trunk						

Return Duct System

Run - Trunk	Associated Supply Runs	H-CFM	C-CFM	Dsn CFM	Round Size	Velocity	Final Size
1 —	#2, #3	208	211	211	9	495	9
2 —	#4, #5	186	197	197	8	575	8
3 —	#6, #7	173	189	189	8	542	8
4 —	#8, #1	234	203	234	9	550	9
5 —							
6 —							
7 —							
8 —							
9 —							
10 —							
11 —							
	Trunk						
	Trunk						
	Trunk						

1) H-BTUH and C-BTUH from the **Manual J** room load calculation procedure
2) H-CFM = HF x H-BTUH and C-CFM = CF x C--BTUH
3) Dsn CFM = larger of the H-CFM or C-CFM values (runout ducts) . . . or . . . total downstream CFM (trunk ducts)
4) Round size based on FR value. Final size based on FR value (if the velocity is acceptable) or the maximum allowable velocity value

Figure 9-24

Section 10
Flexible Duct Systems

This section presents the calculations that are associated with constant volume duct systems that utilize flexible duct materials. These examples include an extended plenum system that combines a rigid trunk duct with flexible runout ducts and a flexible duct system that features junction boxes.

10-1 Extended Plenum System with Flex Runouts

Figure 10-1 provides an example of an extended plenum that is fabricated out of duct board and flexible runout ducts. In this case, heating and cooling is provided by a furnace that is equipped with a DX cooling coil and a standard throw away filter. Figure 10-2 summarizes the heating and cooling loads that are associated with the various supply runs and on the next page, Figure 10-3 summarizes the manufacturer's blower performance data.

Run	Length - FT	H - Load	C - Load
1	22	3810	3110
2	15	3800	2380
3	12	3970	3200
4	15	4250	2750
5	12	3860	3010
6	15	4500	2610
7	22	4590	3500
8	16	4870	3750
9	15	2350	1690
R1	For supply runs 1, 2, 3, 4 and 5		
R2	For supply runs 6 and 9		
R3	For supply runs 7 and 8		

Figure 10-2

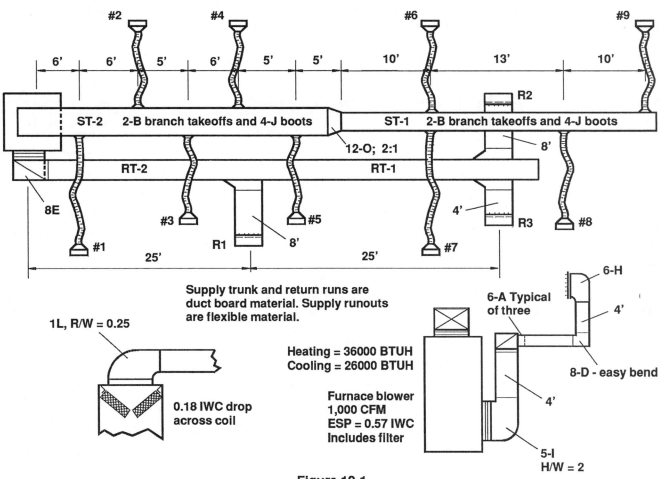

Figure 10-1

Blower Data — Example 1			
CFM	External Resistance — IWC		
	High	Medium	Low
800			0.53
900		0.65	0.45
1000	0.63	0.57	0.37
1100	0.48	0.49	0.29
1200	0.33	0.41	
1250	0.17		
Furnace tested with low efficiency filter in place. If a DX cooling coil is required, subtract 0.18 IWC (wet coil) from the values that are listed in this table.			

Figure 10-3

Effective Length Calculation

An inspection of the geometry and fittings that characterize this example indicates that supply runs 1, 7 and 9 could be associated with the longest circulation path. Also note that the R1 return run is associated with supply run 1, the R2 return run is associated with supply run 9 and the R3 return run is associated with supply run 7.

Figure 10-4 shows the equivalent length calculations that pertain to these duct runs. The following summary shows that the effective length of the longest circulation path is 427 feet.

This path combines supply run 7 (180 feet) with the R3 return run (247 feet).

Run	#1	#7	#9
Supply TEL	143	180	176
Run	R1	R2	R3
Return TEL	194	221	247

Design Friction Rate Calculation

In this example, the blower data indicates that the fan can deliver 1,000 CFM when it operates against 0.57 IWC of external resistance. Since the resistance that is associated with the A-coil (0.18 IWC), the supply outlet (0.03 IWC), the return (0.03 IWC) and a hand damper (0.03 IWC) is equal to 0.27 IWC, the available static pressure is equal to 0.30 IWC. Therefore, the design value for the friction rate will be based on 0.30 IWC of pressure and 427 feet of effective length. These calculations are summarized on page 10-3 by Figure 10-5, which indicates that the design value for the friction rate is equal to 0.07 IWC/100.

Duct Sizing Calculations

On page 10-4, Figure 10-6 summarizes the duct sizing calculations that are associated with this example. The following comments apply to these calculations:

Effective Length Calculation Sheet								
Element	Supply Run ID Number				Element	Return Run ID Number		
	# 1	# 7	# 9			# R-1	# R-2	# R-3
Trunk Length	6	43	66		Trunk Length	29	54	54
Trunk Length					Trunk Length			
Trunk Length					Trunk Length			
Runout Length	22	22	15		Runout Length	12	12	8
Group 1 (L)	40	40	40		Group 5 (I)	30	30	30 (H/W = 2)
Group 2 (B)	45	40	20		Group 6 (H)	15	15	15
Group 3					Group 7			
Group 4 (J)	30	30	30		Group 8 (D)	65	65	65 (ez bend)
Group 8					Group 10			
Group 9					Group 11			
Group 11					Group 12			cfm1/cfm2
Group 12 (O)		5	5		Other (6A br)	33	10	40 / 0.56 (R1) 0.41 (R2)
Other					Other (6A m)		25	25 / 0.59 (R3)
Other					Other (8E)	10	10	10
Total Length	143	180	176		Total Length	194	221	247

Figure 10-4

Friction Rate Worksheet

Step 1) Manufacturer's Blower Data

External static pressure (ESP) = __0.57__ IWC   CFM = __1000__

Step 2) Device Pressure Losses

Direct expansion refrigerant coil	__0.18__
Electric resistance heating coil	_____
Hot water coil	_____
Heat exchanger	_____
Low efficiency filter	_____
High or mid-efficiency filter	_____
Electronic filter	_____
Humidifier	_____
Supply outlet	__0.03__
Return grille	__0.03__
Balancing damper	__0.03__
Other device	_____

Total device losses (DPL) . . . . __0.27__   IWC

Step 3) Available Static Pressure

ASP = (ESP - DPL) = (__0.57__ - __0.27__) = __0.30__   IWC

Step 4) Total Effective Length (TEL)

Supply-side TEL + Return-side TEL = (__180__ + __247__) = __427__   FEET

Step 5) Friction Rate Design Value (FR)

FR value from friction rate chart = __0.07__   IWC/100

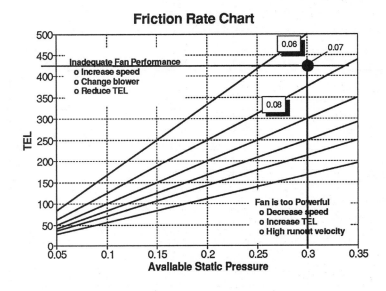

Figure 10-5

Duct Sizing Worksheet

HF = Blower CFM / Manual J Heat Loss = (1000   ) / (36000   ) = __0.0278__

CF = Blower CFM / Manual J Sensible Heat Gain = (1000   ) / (26000   ) = __0.0385__

FR Value
0.07

Supply Duct System

Run - Trunk	H-BTUH	C-BTUH	H-CFM	C-CFM	Dsn CFM	Round Size	Velocity	Final Size
1 — ST2	3810	3110	106	120	120	8	ok	8
2 — ST2	3800	2380	106	92	106	7	ok	7
3 — ST2	3970	3200	110	123	123	8	ok	8
4 — ST2	4250	2750	118	106	118	8	ok	8
5 — ST2	3860	3010	107	116	116	8	ok	8
6 — ST1	4500	2610	125	100	125	8	ok	8
7 — ST1	4590	3500	128	135	135	8	ok	8
8 — ST1	4870	3750	135	144	144	8	ok	8
9 — ST1	2350	1690	65	65	65	6	ok	6
10 —								
11 —								
12 —								
13 —								
14 —								
15 —								
Trunk ST1			453	444	453	12	600	12
Trunk ST2			1000	1000	1000	16	735	17
Trunk								
Trunk								

Return Duct System

Run - Trunk	Associated Supply Runs	H-CFM	C-CFM	Dsn CFM	Round Size	Velocity	Final Size
1 — RT2	#1, #2, #3, #4 and #5	547	557	557	13	610	13
2 — RT1	#6 and #9	190	165	190	8	550	8
3 — RT1	#7 and #8	263	279	279	10	515	10
4 —							
5 —							
6 —							
7 —							
8 —							
9 —							
10 —							
11 —							
Trunk RT1		453	444	453	12	595	12
Trunk RT2		1000	1000	1000	16	735	17
Trunk							

1) H-BTUH and C-BTUH from the **Manual J** room load calculation procedure
2) H-CFM = HF x H-BTUH and C-CFM = CF x C--BTUH
3) Dsn CFM = larger of the H-CFM or C-CFM values (runout ducts) . . . or . . . total downstream CFM (trunk ducts)
4) Round size based on FR value. Final size based on FR value (if the velocity is acceptable) or the maximum allowable velocity value

Figure 10-6

- All of the supply branch runout sizes were determined by using the "Wire Helix Flexible Duct" scale (refer to the ACCA Duct Sizing Slide Rule).

- All of the supply trunk sizes and the return duct sizes were determined by using the "Duct Board" scale (refer to the ACCA Duct Sizing Slide Rule).

- Supply runs 1 through 5 are associated with supply trunk ST-2 and supply runs 6 through 9 are associated with supply trunk ST-1.

- Return runs R2 and R3 feed into secondary return trunk RT-1.

- Return run R1 and return trunk RT-1 feed into primary return trunk RT-2.

- The final sizes of supply runouts are based on the friction rate design value (0.07 IWC/100) because the corresponding velocities are less than 900 FPM. (The runout velocities are always less than 900 FPM when the design friction rate value falls inside the "wedge" that is associated with the friction rate chart.)

- The final sizes of the supply trunks (ST-1 and ST-2) are based on the design friction rate (0.07 IWC/100) because the corresponding velocities are less than 900 FPM.

- The final sizes of the return branch ducts (R1, R2 and R3) are based on the design friction rate value (0.07 IWC/100) because the corresponding velocities are less than recommended maximum (700 FPM).

- The final size of return trunk RT-1 is based on the friction rate design value (0.07 IWC/100) because the corresponding velocity is less than 700 FPM.

- The final size of return trunk RT-2 is based on the maximum allowable velocity (700 FPM) because the velocity that is associated with the design friction rate slightly exceeds the recommended maximum.

- The R3 return run is longer than the R2 return run because the group 6A (branch) equivalent length value that is associated with the R3 run is 30 feet more than the equivalent length value that is associated with the R2 run.

- The ACCA Duct Slide Rule can be used to convert round sizes into equivalent rectangular sizes.

Comments and Observations

This example is characterized by an absence of accessory devices, which made a viable design possible. If a simple device, such as an electronic filter, had been included in the original design, the blower would have marginal ability (at the medium speed setting) to deliver the desired air flow.

Therefore, if accessories were desired, the design would have been based on the high speed blower setting. Also note that the effective length of the duct system can be reduced by 55 feet if the 8-D elbow fittings that are associated with the return branches (EL = 65) are replaced with elbow fittings that have turning vanes (EL = 10).

10-2 Flexible Duct System

On the next page, Figures 10-7, -8 and -9 provide an example of a 900 CFM air distribution system (supply and return) that is fabricated out of flexible duct materials and duct board junction boxes. In this case, heating and cooling is provided by a heat pump that is equipped with a supplemental electric resistance heater and a standard throw away filter. (Figure 10-7 shows the geometry of the duct system. Figure 10-8 lists the heating and cooling loads that are associated with the various duct runs. Figure 10-9 summarizes the manufacturer's blower performance data and provides information about the pressure drop that is associated with the heater.)

Effective Length Calculation

An inspection of the geometry and fittings that are associated with this example indicates that supply outlets 7 and 8 are associated with the longest supply path and that return R3 is associated with the longest return path. Therefore, these duct runs define the critical circulation path.

Figure 10-10 (see page 10-7) shows the equivalent length calculations that are associated with these duct runs. This figure shows that the effective length of the longest supply run is 316 feet and the effective length of the longest return run is 188 feet. Therefore, the total effective length of the critical circulation path is equal to 504 feet.

> When junction boxes are involved, the equivalent length values that are associated with these boxes depend on a reference velocity (see Appendix 3, page A3-25). Therefore, before proceeding with the effective length calculations, the designer must select a value for the maximum velocity that will be associated with the duct system. Note that if the designer decides to limit the velocity to 600 FPM, the equivalent length value for a junction box will be equal to 75 feet.

Design Friction Rate Calculation

In this example, the blower data indicates that at medium speed, the fan can deliver 900 CFM when it operates against 0.42 IWC of external resistance. Since the resistance that is associated with the electric resistance heaters (0.12 IWC), the supply outlet (0.03 IWC), the return (0.03 IWC) and a hand damper (0.03 IWC) is equal to 0.21 IWC, the available static

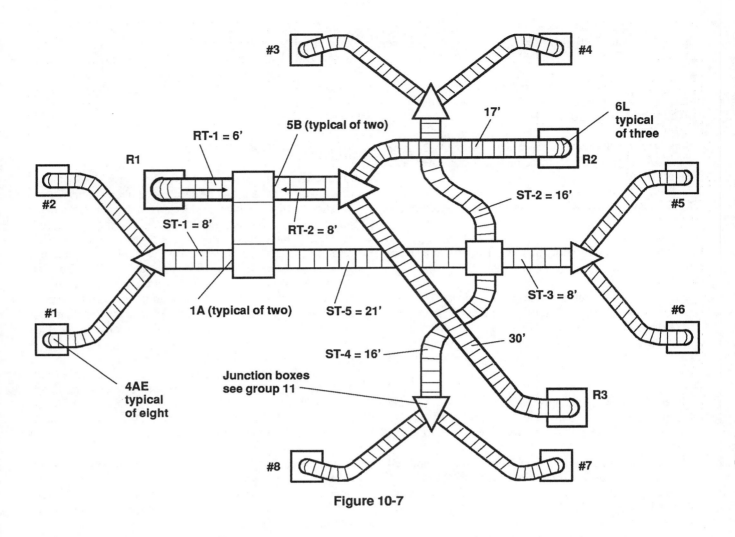

Figure 10-7

pressure is equal to 0.21 IWC. Therefore, the design value for the friction rate will be based on 0.21 IWC of pressure and 504 feet of effective length. These calculations, which are summarized on page 10-8 by Figure 10-11, indicate that the design friction rate value is less than 0.06 IWC/100 and that the fan cannot produce enough pressure.

Run	Length - FT	H - Load	C - Load
1	16	3800	2380
2	16	3970	3200
3	14	4250	2750
4	14	3860	3010
5	14	4500	2610
6	14	4590	3500
7	14	4870	3750
8	14	2350	1690
R1	For supply runs 1 and 2	Heat = 32190 Cool = 22890	
R2	For supply runs 3, 4 and 5		
R3	For supply runs 6, 7 and 8		

Figure 10-8

Blower Data — Example 2			
CFM	External Resistance — IWC		
	High	Medium	Low
750			0.49
800		0.58	0.41
850	0.65	0.50	0.33
900	0.60	0.42	0.25
950	0.45	0.34	
1000	0.29		

Unit tested with low efficiency filter in place. If resistance heating coils are required, subtract 0.12 IWC from the values that are listed in this table.

Figure 10-9

Effective Length Calculation Sheet									
Element	**Supply Run ID Number**				**Element**	**Return Run ID Number**			
	# 7 or #8					# R-3			
Trunk Length	37				**Trunk Length**	8			
Trunk Length					**Trunk Length**				
Trunk Length					**Trunk Length**				
Runout Length	14				**Runout Length**	30			
Group 1 (A)	35				**Group 5 (B)**	40			
Group 2					**Group 6 (L)**	20			
Group 3					**Group 7**				
Group 4 (AE)	55				**Group 8**				
Group 8					**Group 10**				
Group 9					**Group 11**	75	(1 @ 75 FT @ 600 FPM)		
Group 11	150	(2 @ 75 FT @ 600 FPM)			**Group 12**				
Group 12					**Other**				
Other					**Other (11)**	5	(one 45 degree bend)		
Other (11)	15	(three 45 degree bends)			**Other (11)**	10	(one 90 degree bend)		
Other (11)	10	(one 90 degree bend)			**Other**				
Total Length	316				**Total Length**	188			

Figure 10-10

There are two ways to deal with inadequate blower performance: increase the fan speed or reduce the total effective length of the longest circulation path. In this example, the second option (reduce the effective length) will be explored because 225 feet of equivalent length is associated with the junction boxes.

If the maximum allowable velocity is reduced to 500 FPM, the equivalent length that is associated with a single junction box will be reduced by 25 feet (from 75 feet to 50 feet). Therefore, this change will reduce the total effective length of the longest circulation path by 75 feet (for three boxes). Unfortunately, this option is not practical because, as indicated by Figure 10-11, the design friction rate value will still be less than 0.06 IWC/100 when the effective length is reduced to 425 feet. The next option is to retain the original 600 FPM velocity limit and to increase the fan speed.

At high speed, the blower data indicates that the fan can deliver 900 CFM when it operates against 0.60 IWC of external resistance. Therefore, when the pressure drop that is associated with the external devices (0.21 IWC) is subtracted from this value, the design value for the friction rate will be based on 0.39 IWC of pressure and 504 feet of effective length. These revisions, which are also summarized by Figure 10-11, indicate that the design friction rate value will be equal to 0.077 IWC/100 (round-off to 0.08 IWC/100).

Duct Sizing Calculations
On page 10-9, Figure 10-12 summarizes the duct sizing calculations that are associated with this example. The following comments apply to these calculations:

• All of the duct sizes were determined by using the "Wire Helix Flexible Duct" scale (refer to the ACCA Duct Sizing Slide Rule).

• Supply runs 3 and 4 are associated with secondary trunk ST-2; supply runs 5 and 6 are associated with secondary trunk ST-3; and supply runs 7 and 8 are associated with secondary trunk ST-4.

• Supply runs 1 and 2 are associated with primary supply trunk ST-1; supply runs 3, 4, 5, 6, 7 and 8 are associated with primary supply trunk ST-5.

• Return branches R2 and R3 feed into return trunk RT-2 and return R1 feeds directly to the air handler through RT-1.

• The final sizes of supply runouts are based on the friction rate design value (0.08 IWC/100) because the corresponding velocities are less than 600 FPM. (The 600 FPM velocity limit was selected because a higher value would have produced a significant increase in the equivalent length that is associated with the junction box fittings.)

Friction Rate Worksheet

Step 1) Manufacturer's Blower Data

External static pressure (ESP) = ~~0.42~~ 0.60 IWC   CFM = 900

Step 2) Device Pressure Losses

Direct expansion refrigerant coil . . .
Electric resistance heating coil 0.12
Hot water coil . . . .
Heat exchanger . . . .
Low efficiency filter . . . .
High or mid-efficiency filter . . . .
Electronic filter . . . .
Humidifier . . . .
Supply outlet 0.03
Return grille 0.03
Balancing damper 0.03
Other device . . . .

Total device losses (DPL) . . . .   0.21   IWC

Step 3) Available Static Pressure

ASP = (ESP - DPL) = (~~0.42~~ 0.60 - 0.21) = ~~0.21~~ 0.39   IWC

Step 4) Total Effective Length (TEL)

Supply-side TEL + Return-side TEL = (316 + 188) = 504   FEET

Step 5) Friction Rate Design Value (FR)

FR value from friction rate chart = 0.08   IWC/100

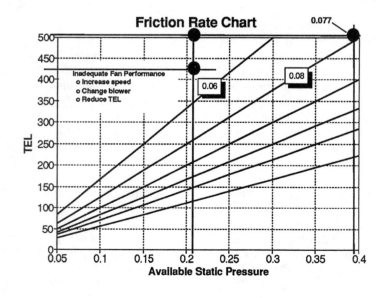

Figure 10-11

Duct Sizing Worksheet

HF = Blower CFM / Manual J Heat Loss = (900) / (32190) = ___0.0280___

CF = Blower CFM / Manual J Sensible Heat Gain = (900) / (22890) = ___0.0393___

FR Value
0.08

Supply Duct System

Run - Trunk	H-BTUH	C-BTUH	H-CFM	C-CFM	Dsn CFM	Round Size	Velocity	Final Size
1 — ST1	3800	2380	106	94	106	7	below 600	7
2 — ST1	3970	3200	111	126	126	8	below 600	8
3 — ST2	4250	2750	119	108	119	8	below 600	8
4 — ST2	3860	3010	108	118	118	8	below 600	8
5 — ST3	4500	2610	126	103	126	8	below 600	8
6 — ST3	4590	3500	128	138	138	8	below 600	8
7 — ST4	4870	3750	136	147	147	8	below 600	8
8 — ST4	2350	1690	66	66	66	6	below 600	6
9 —								
10 —								
11 —								
12 —								
13 —								
14 —								
15 —			Trunk ST1	217	220	220	10	below 600	10
			Trunk ST2	227	226	227	10	below 600	10
			Trunk ST3	254	241	254	10	below 600	10
			Trunk ST4	202	213	213	10	below 600	10
			Trunk ST5	683	680	683	15	below 600	15

Return Duct System

Run - Trunk	Associated Supply Runs	H-CFM	C-CFM	Dsn CFM	Round Size	Velocity	Final Size
1 — RT1	#1 and #2	217	220	220	See RT1	See RT1	See RT1
2 — RT2	#3, #4 and #5	353	329	353	11	below 600	11
3 — RT2	#6, #7 and #8	330	351	351	11	below 600	11
4 —							
5 —							
6 —							
7 —							
8 —							
9 —							
10 —							
11 —							
	Trunk RT1	217	220	220	10	below 600	10
	Trunk RT2	683	680	683	15	below 600	15
	Trunk						

1) H-BTUH and C-BTUH from the **Manual J** room load calculation procedure
2) H-CFM = HF x H-BTUH and C-CFM = CF x C--BTUH
3) Dsn CFM = larger of the H-CFM or C-CFM values (runout ducts) . . . or . . . total downstream CFM (trunk ducts)
4) Round size based on FR value. Final size based on FR value (if the velocity is acceptable) or the maximum allowable velocity value

Figure 10-12

- The final sizes of the supply trunks (ST-1, ST-2, ST-3, ST-4 and ST-5) are based on the friction rate design value (0.08 IWC/100) because the corresponding velocities are less than 600 FPM.

- The final sizes of the return branch ducts (R2 and R3) are based on the friction rate design value (0.08 IWC/100) because the corresponding velocities are less than 600 FPM.

- The final sizes of the return trunks (RT-1 and RT-2) are based on the friction rate design value (0.08 IWC/100) because the corresponding velocities are less than 600 FPM.

- The final size of some runs (trunk ducts) may have to be increased by 1-inch in order to conform with the standard sizes that are associated with this product.

Comments and Observations

This example is characterized by a long effective length, but a relatively powerful fan (operating at high speed) and an absence of accessory devices made a viable design possible. If a simple device, such as an electronic filter, had been included in the original design, the blower would have had marginal ability to deliver the desired air flow.

Note that if the blower was less powerful or if an accessory device was required, the length of the critical path would have to be reduced. This could be accomplished by modifying the basic layout (geometry) and by reducing the maximum allowable velocity.

- The geometry could be revised so that the critical path does not pass through more than one junction box.

- The velocity limit could be reduced to 500 FPM.

Section 11
Variable Volume Systems

As explained below, the calculation procedures that are used to design variable air volume (VAV) systems are somewhat different from the procedures that are associated with constant volume systems. The most obvious difference is associated with the way the room loads are calculated, which has a direct effect on the room air flow requirements. (Also refer to Section 1 of this manual for additional information about designing zoned systems.)

11-1 Room Temperature Variations

As explained in Section 1, temperature variations within the structure can be attributed to variations in solar gains and internal loads or to differences in the density (buoyancy) of air. For example, during the cooling season, variations in solar gains can cause an east-facing room to overheat in the morning and to be somewhat cool in the afternoon. Conversely, a west-facing room may be too cold in the morning and a little warm in the afternoon. Or, in multilevel homes, cooler air tends to accumulate in the lower levels and warmer air tends to migrate to the upper levels.

Room-to-room temperature variations also depend on the openness of the floor plan. If two or more rooms share a common area or if there are large openings between adjacent rooms, the air will be free to circulate throughout the space and the room-to-room temperature differences will be minimized. Conversely, objectionable temperature differences may occur in rooms that are isolated from the room where the thermostat is located.

When room-to-room temperature variations occur, continual fan operation may solve the problem, but there is no guarantee that this strategy will work in every case. Also note that continual fan operation increases the cost of operation and may cause humidity problems in the conditioned space. (When the compressor is off and the fan is running, the humidity in the conditioned space increases because the water that is on the cooling coil and in the drip pan evaporates into the supply air.)

11-2 VAV Systems

The comfort problems that are associated with single zone systems can be avoided by installing a variable volume system. This type of system uses multiple thermostats (one per zone) and flow control dampers (one or more per thermostat) to control the temperature in the zones (which may consist of one or more rooms) that are associated with the house.

Usually, the air distribution system features a single blower unit, but two or more blower units could be required for a large house. In any case, air is delivered (from the blower unit to the zone) through a duct that is equipped with a control damper, which opens or closes in response to a signal from a zone thermostat.

Change-over from heating to cooling may be automatic or manual. If change-over is manual, the system will shut down when all the thermostats are satisfied. If change-over is automatic, the system will operate in the mode (heating or cooling) that satisfies the greatest number of zone thermostats.

Normally, when a VAV system shuts down (because the zone thermostats have been satisfied), the zone dampers are in the closed position. However, some manufacturers provide controls that drive the zone dampers to the full open position when the central heating-cooling equipment is not active. This feature allows continuous air circulation (blower energized) when there is no call for heat or cooling. (As noted above, continuous fan operation reduces room-to-room temperature differences, but it increases the operating cost and it can have an adverse effect on the indoor humidity during the cooling season.)

11-3 Zoning VAV Systems

If the floor plan partitions the house into separate but contiguous living and sleeping areas, the simplest and least expensive way to zone the house is to establish a living zone and a sleeping zone. This strategy maintains comfort in the occupied zone and allows setup and setback control in the unoccupied zone. (If this two-zone strategy is used, the rooms that are associated with either zone should be "open" to each other or they must have similar load patterns.)

A two-zone VAV system also can be used to improve comfort in a two-story home. In this case, one zone includes all of the rooms on the lower level and a second zone is associated with all of the rooms on the upper level. This zoning arrangement minimizes the floor-to-floor temperature control problems that are created when warmer air floats to the upper level and cooler air sinks to the lower level.

Note that two-zone designs have limited ability to improve room-to-room temperature control. Most modern homes, especially the larger structures, require more than two zones. Three or more zones will be required when the floor plan cannot be easily divided into two groups of contiguous rooms that have similar load profiles. In extreme cases there may be almost as many zones as there are rooms.

11-4 Load Calculations

There are two sizing issues associated with VAV systems. One pertains to sizing the terminal components of the air distribution system (branch ducts, dampers and air outlets), and the other pertains to sizing the components that are associated with the central unit (fuel conversion equipment, blower and trunk ducts). In some cases sizes are based on a peak load estimate and in other cases they are based on the average load.

Loads Associated with Terminal Components

When a variable volume system is involved, the flow of supply air that is delivered to a room or zone should be capable of neutralizing the peak cooling load that is associated with the room or zone. For residential applications, these load peaks are (mostly) caused by hourly variations in the solar gain. Therefore, the load calculation procedure must be capable of addressing this time-of-day issue.

Since the standard **Manual J** load calculation procedure is based on average solar gains (for the whole day), it underestimates the peak solar load that is associated with a room or zone. Therefore, the standard **Manual J** load estimating procedure must be modified so that it can be used to design a variable air volume system. This is accomplished by using a set of "sensible load correction factors" that convert the standard **Manual J** loads into peak room or peak zone loads. This is all documented in **Manual J**, Appendix A2.

A zone may consist of a single room or it may include two or more rooms. When two or more rooms are involved, the loads should peak at approximately the same time. In this case the peak zone load is equal to the sum of the peak room loads.

Loads Associated with Central Components

In some cases, the sizing calculations that are associated with the central components are based on the average load for the whole house (the standard **Manual J** load) and in other cases, these calculations are based on the sum of the peak zone loads. The determining factor is diversity. Diversity is created when the loads that are associated with the various zones do not peak simultaneously. In this case, the sizing calculations can be based on the block load. If there is no diversity (the zone loads peak at approximately the same time-of-day), the sizing calculations must be based on the sum of the peak zone loads.

Diversity is created when three or four exposures (north, south, east, west) are associated with the zones that are served by the central equipment. In this case, the traditional (uncorrected) **Manual J** load for the "entire house" can be used to size the central components because this load is equivalent to the peak block load.

There is no diversity when a single exposure is associated with the zones that are served by the central equipment, and there may not be a significant amount of diversity when two exposures are involved. (This concept can apply to equipment that is associated with multifamily dwellings. It also can apply when two or more central units are associated with a single-family home.) In this case, the size of the central components should be based on the sum of the peak zone loads. (For additional information, refer to **Manual J**, Appendix A3.)

11-5 Design Considerations

The components that are associated with a residential VAV distribution system will be subject to a wide range of air flow rates. These components include blowers, refrigerant coils, electric resistance coils, heat exchangers, filters, duct runs, supply outlets and return grilles. It is the designer's responsibility to make sure that the operating range that is associated with the system (the minimum and the maximum air flow rates) is compatible with the operating range that is associated with each component.

- Maximum air flow through a blower, coil, heat exchanger, filter or primary trunk duct occurs when all of the zone thermostats are calling for supply air. (The system resistance is minimized when all of the control dampers are open.)

- Maximum air flow through a supply outlet or branch duct occurs when just one or two zone thermostats are calling for supply air. (More air is forced through the open runs when the other runs are throttled.)

- Minimum air flow through a blower, coil, heat exchanger, filter or primary trunk duct occurs when all but one or two zone thermostats are satisfied. (The system resistance is maximized when most of the zone control dampers are closed.)

- Minimum air flow through a supply outlet or branch duct occurs when all of the zone thermostats are calling for supply air. (The blower CFM is shared by the maximum number of the outlets when all of the control dampers are open.)

Operating Characteristics — Constant-speed Blower

As the zone dampers open and close, the total CFM delivered by a constant-speed blower will vary as the operating point rides the fan curve. This behavior is demonstrated by Figure 11-1 (see the next page), which illustrates how a simple two-zone system interacts with a constant-speed blower. Note that when both zone dampers are open, the system resistance is equal to 0.42 IWC and 1,200 CFM is delivered by the fan (point A). Also notice that 500 CFM is routed through zone 1 (point B) and 700 CFM is delivered through zone 2 (point C).

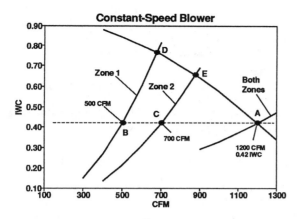

Figure 11-1

When one of the two zone dampers closes, all the air leaving the blower will be forced through the open run. If the zone 2 damper is closed, the system will operate at point D (about 670 CFM). If the zone 1 damper is closed, the system will operate at point E (about 880 CFM). In either case, the blower CFM is reduced and the zone CFM (and branch duct velocity) is increased when one of the zone dampers is closed. The following table summarizes the system performance as the zone dampers open and close.

Configuration	Blower CFM	Zone 1 CFM	Zone 2 CFM	Blower IWC
Two zones open	1200	500	700	0.42
Zone 2 closed	670	670	0	0.90
Zone 1 closed	880	0	880	0.80

This example indicates that there are four potential problems associated with adding zone dampers to a conventional air distribution system. (A conventional system is a single-zone system that features a constant-speed blower.)

- The blower may be forced to operate at a condition which is outside of the range that is recommended by the manufacturer. (The fan will stall if it is forced to operate at a low flow rate and a relatively high pressure. Refer to Section 5 for more information about blower performance.)

- The air flow through the coil (refrigerant or electric resistance) or the heat exchanger (furnace) may fall below the minimum value that is recommended by the manufacturer. (Refer to the manufacturer's engineering data for more information about operating ranges and safety controls.)

- The velocity in a branch duct may exceed the recommended maximum value and undesirable noise might be generated.

- If an excessive flow of air is forced through a supply air terminal, the face velocity may exceed the recommended value. If this happens, the outlet may generate undesirable noise and produce a "throw" that causes drafts.

In general, these problems will become more severe as the number of zones is increased. If, in the example above, the number of zones is increased from two to four, the zone flows would be smaller and the corresponding duct sizes and air terminals would be smaller. Now, if three of four zone dampers were to close, the entire blower CFM would be forced through one relatively small branch duct. This would cause severe throttling at the blower and excessive velocities would be associated with the open run.

Bypass Duct

A bypass duct is necessary if flow control dampers are added to a traditional HVAC system (constant-speed blower, on-off capacity control). This bypass circuit is required to maintain adequate flow through critical components (fan, coil or heat exchanger) when the system air flow is vigorously throttled by the zone dampers. If a bypass loop is installed, it should be equipped with a control damper; and when this damper is open, the bypass duct should be able to accommodate at least 80 percent of the design air flow. (The response characteristic of the bypass damper will be more linear if the resistance that is associated with an open damper is 20 to 30 percent of the resistance that is associated with the critical circulation path. Also note that the control system must synchronize the operation of the zone dampers and the bypass damper.)

Operating Characteristics — Variable-speed Blower

As the zone dampers open and close, the CFM delivered by a variable-speed blower can be adjusted to match the system air flow requirements. This behavior is demonstrated by Figure 11-2, which illustrates how a simple two-zone system interacts with a variable-speed blower. This figure shows that when both zone dampers are open, the system resistance is equal to 0.42 IWC and 1,200 CFM is delivered by the fan (point A). The figure also shows that 500 CFM is routed to zone 1 (point B) and 700 CFM is delivered to zone 2 (point C).

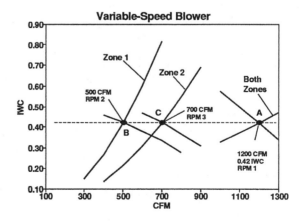

Figure 11-2

When one of the zone dampers closes, all the air leaving the blower will be forced through the open run, but the flow through that run will not change if the blower RPM is reduced. For example, if the zone 2 damper is closed, the blower RPM can be adjusted so that the flow through zone 1 will hold steady at point B (500 CFM). Or, if the zone 1 damper is closed, the blower RPM can be adjusted so that the flow through zone 1 will hold steady at point C (700 CFM). Therefore, a variable-speed fan provides more control over the air flow that is associated with the open run. The following table compares the performance of a constant speed fan and a variable speed fan.

Constant-speed Blower	Blower CFM	Zone 1 CFM	Zone 2 CFM
Two zones open	1200	500	700
Zone 2 closed	670	670	0
Zone 1 closed	880	0	880

Variable-speed Blower	Blower CFM	Zone 1 CFM	Zone 2 CFM
Two zones open	1200	500	700
Zone 2 closed	500	500	0
Zone 1 closed	700	0	700

This example indicates that fan modulation improves the performance of a multizone system. The following characteristics are associated with a system that features speed control:

• The blower is less likely to operate under a condition that is outside of the range that is recommended by the manufacturer. (Fan stall is still possible if a part load operating condition is too adverse.)

• The velocity that is associated with a branch duct or a supply outlet will hold steady if fan speed adjustments maintain a constant flow through the branch run.

• The air flow through a coil (refrigerant or electric) or a heat exchanger (furnace) *still can* fall below the minimum value that is recommended by the equipment manufacturer.

11-6 Supply Air Outlets

The supply air outlets that are traditionally installed in residential systems are designed for constant flow applications. Therefore, the performance of these devices will be compromised when they are used in a system that features a variable volume control strategy. For example, throws will be less than optimum when a zone operates at a minimum flow rate and throws will be greater than optimum when a zone operates at maximum flow rate. Therefore, if standard (constant-volume) supply air outlets are used, they should be carefully sized so that the problems that are associated with pockets of stagnant air, drafts and noise are minimized.

• Size the supply air outlets to operate in the mid-range of the flow rates that are associated with the outlets.

• Check the throws and face velocities that are associated with the maximum flow rates.

• Check the throws and face velocities that are associated with the minimum flow rates.

Supply air outlets that are specifically designed for variable volume applications will be required if constant volume outlets cannot provide satisfactory performance. These types of outlets are not commonly associated with residential systems, but they are always found on commercial VAV systems that are properly designed.

11-7 Control Dampers

The number of control dampers will be equal to the number of zones. These devices may be installed in a branch runout duct (if a single supply outlet is involved) or in a secondary trunk duct (if multiple supply outlets serve the zone).

If the control dampers modulate, they should feature an elliptical blade (in a round duct). This type of blade is desirable because the performance characteristic (percent flow versus percent open) is fairly linear. Also note that controllability and sensitivity are affected by the pressure drop that is associated with an open damper. In this regard, an adequate pressure drop will be obtained if the control dampers are sized so that the velocity of the flow (through an open damper) ranges between 800 FPM and 1,000 FPM.

Elliptical blades are not required if simple open-shut control dampers are used. In this case a round or rectangular blade will suffice. These dampers can be sized so that the velocity of the air passing through an open damper is compatible with the velocity of the air that is associated with the upstream duct.

Installation details also are important. Use gradual transitions between the damper section and the upstream-downstream duct runs, and place the control dampers as far from the supply air outlet as possible. (Control dampers generate noise when they are in the throttled position.)

11-8 Balancing Dampers

Hand operated balancing dampers are required so that the full operating range of the control dampers can be used to maintain the temperature in the conditioned space. Adjust these dampers so that when the control dampers are in the open position, the same resistance (approximately) is associated with the various circulation paths.

11-9 Duct Sizing

The sizing procedure that was used for constant-volume systems (Sections 9 and 10) also can be used for a variable volume system, but there are some differences. These differences (which can be traced to how the cooling loads are calculated) affect the equipment sizing calculations (which determine the design value for the blower CFM) and the system flow rate calculations (supply CFM values).

- The supply CFM that is associated with each room must be based on the corrected (peak) room load. (It follows that the CFM value that is associated with any branch runout will be based on the peak room load.)

- Two or more rooms can be combined into a zone, providing that the room loads peak simultaneously. (It follows that the CFM value that is associated with a zone trunk duct is equal to the sum of the corresponding room CFM values.)

- If a main trunk duct is characterized by diversity (the associated rooms or zones do not peak simultaneously), the CFM value that is associated with the duct is equal to the sum of the corresponding room CFM values — but in this case, the room CFM values should be based on the traditional **Manual J** room loads (no peak load adjustment).

- If a main trunk duct is characterized by a lack of diversity (the associated rooms or zones do peak simultaneously), the CFM value that is associated with the duct is equal to the sum of the corresponding room CFM values — but in this case, the room CFM values should be based on the peak room loads.

- If the VAV system is characterized by diversity (rooms or zones do not peak simultaneously), the equipment size (and the associated blower CFM) can be based on the standard **Manual J** load calculation for the entire house, which is equivalent to a peak block load.

- If the VAV system is characterized by a lack of diversity (zones peak simultaneously), the equipment size (and the associated blower CFM) should be based on the sum of the peak room loads.

- Return ducts should be sized to accommodate the maximum flow rate that might be encountered during any operating condition.

11-10 Example — System that Features Diversity

On the next page, Figure 11-3 provides a schematic drawing of a 1300 CFM sheet metal VAV system that features a conventional heat pump and a constant-speed blower. This air distribution system consists of four zones, primary trunk ducts, secondary trunk ducts and branch runout ducts; the return air system consists of four return runs and two return trunks. (Figure 11-6 on page 11-7 shows the geometry and the fittings that are associated with the return duct system.)

The following table provides information about the orientation, the percentage of glass and the sensible load correction factors (SLCF) that are associated with each of the four zones. This information is required to estimate the peak cooling loads that are associated with each runout duct. Also refer to Figure 11-4, which summarizes the load calculations that are associated with the various runout ducts and to Figure 11-5, which presents the manufacturer's blower data and provides information regarding the pressure drops that are associated with accessory devices.

	Exposure	Percent Glass	SLCF
Zone 1	South	15	1.20
Zone 2	West	10	1.25
Zone 3	East	15	1.0
Zone 4	North	10	1.0
SLCF — Refer to Table A2, Appendix 2, **Manual J**			

Effective Length Calculation
Based on an inspection of the geometry and the fittings that characterize this duct system, it appears that the zone 2, 3 and 4 loops are candidates for the longest circulation path. Figure 11-7 on page 11-7 presents the effective length calculations that pertain to the associated supply and return runs. The following summary shows that the effective length of the longest circulation path is 192 + 163 = 355 feet.

Run	#3	#9	#10
Supply TEL	179	192	173
Run	R2	R3	R4
Return TEL	162	139	163

Design Friction Rate Calculation
In this example, the blower data indicates that at medium speed, the fan can deliver 1,300 CFM when it operates against 0.55 IWC of external resistance. Since the resistance that is associated with the auxiliary heating coil (0.13 IWC), the supply outlet (0.03 IWC), the return (0.03 IWC), an open control damper (0.05 IWC) and an open hand damper (0.03 IWC) is equal to 0.27 IWC, the available static pressure is equal to 0.28 IWC. Therefore, the design value for the friction rate will be based on 0.28 IWC of pressure and 355 feet of effective length. These calculations are summarized on page 11-8 by Figure 11-8.

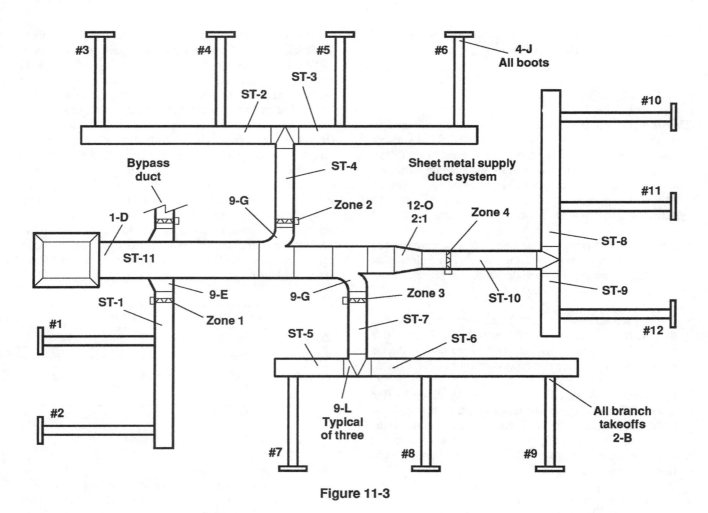

Figure 11-3

Run	Trunks (Feet)	Branch (Feet)	Heat BTUH	Cool BTUH	SLCF	Peak BTUH
1	14	12	4250	2750	1.20	3300
2	24	12	3860	3010	1.20	3612
3	54	10	3970	3200	1.25	4000
4	40	10	2780	2130	1.25	2663
5	40	10	3800	2380	1.25	2975
6	54	10	4440	3420	1.25	4275
7	46	10	4590	3500	1.0	3500
8	48	10	4620	3510	1.0	3510
9	62	10	2350	1690	1.0	1690
10	66	12	3020	2590	1.0	2590
11	54	12	3810	3110	1.0	3110
12	56	12	·3430	2400	1.0	2400

Heating Load = 44920   Block Cooling Load = 33690

SLCF = Sensible Load Correction Factor

Figure 11-4

Manufacturer's Data Blower Performance and Device Pressure Drop			
CFM	External Resistance — IWC		
	High	Medium	Low
1150			0.53
1200			0.45
1250		0.65	0.37
1300		0.55	0.29
1350	0.59	0.45	
1400	0.48	0.34	
1450	0.37		
1500	0.26		

Heat pump unit tested with a wet DX coil and a low efficiency filter in place. If auxiliary heating coils are required, subtract 0.13 IWC from the values that are listed in this table. If zone control damper is installed in the circulation path, subtract 0.05 IWC (for an open damper) from the values that are listed in this table.

Figure 11-5

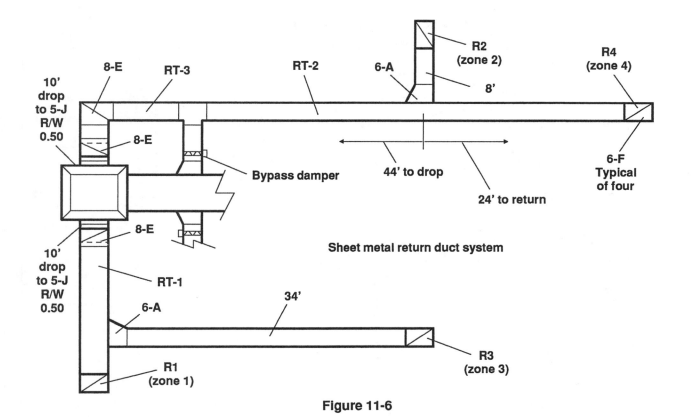

Figure 11-6

Effective Length Calculation Sheet									
Element	**Supply Run ID Number**				**Element**	**Return Run ID Number**			
	# 3	# 9	# 10			# R2	# R3	# R4	
Trunk Length	54	62	66		**Trunk Length**	54	22	78	
Trunk Length					**Trunk Length**				
Trunk Length					**Trunk Length**				
Runout Length	10	10	12		**Runout Length**	8	34		
Group 1 (D)	10	10	10		**Group 5** (J)	15	15	15	(R/W=0.5)
Group 2 (B)	20	20	20		**Group 6** (F)	25	25	25	
Group 3					**Group 7**				
Group 4 (J)	30	30	30		**Group 8** (E)	20	10	20	
Group 8					**Group 10**				
Group 9 (G)	35	35		(branch)	**Group 11**				
Group 11					**Group 12**				
Group 12 (O)			5		**Group 13**				
Group 13					**Other** (6A br)	40	33		cfm1/cfm2 R2 & R4 0.63 or 0.56 (R4)
Other (9G)		5	10	(main)	**Other** (6A m)			25	
Other (9L)	20	20	20		**Other**				
Other					**Other**				
Total Length	179	192	173		**Total Length**	162	139	163	

Figure 11-7

Friction Rate Worksheet

Step 1) Manufacturer's Blower Data

External static pressure (ESP) = _____0.55_____ IWC   CFM = _____1300_____

Step 2) Device Pressure Losses

Direct expansion refrigerant coil . . .
Electric resistance heating coil 0.13
Hot water coil . . . .
Heat exchanger . . . .
Low efficiency filter . . . .
High or mid-efficiency filter . . . .
Electronic filter . . . .
Humidifier . . . .
Supply outlet 0.03
Return grille 0.03
Balancing damper 0.03
Other device 0.05

Total device losses (DPL) . . . .   _____0.27_____   IWC

Step 3) Available Static Pressure

ASP = (ESP - DPL) = (_____0.55_____ - _____0.27_____) = _____0.28_____   IWC

Step 4) Total Effective Length (TEL)

Supply-side TEL + Return-side TEL = (_____192_____ + _____163_____) = _____355_____   FEET

Step 5) Friction Rate Design Value (FR)

FR value from friction rate chart = _____0.08_____   IWC/100

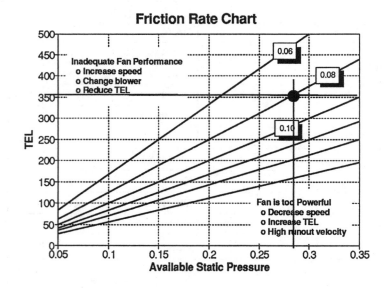

Friction Rate Chart

Figure 11-8

Duct Sizing Worksheet

HF = Blower CFM / Manual J Heat Loss = (1300) / (44920) = 0.0289

CF = Blower CFM / Manual J Sensible Heat Gain = (1300) / (33690) = 0.0386

FR Value 0.08

Supply Duct System

Run - Trunk	H-BTUH	C-BTUH	H-CFM	C-CFM	Dsn CFM	Round Size	Velocity	Final Size
1 — ST-1	4250	3300	123	127	127	7	ok	7
2 — ST-1	3860	3612	112	139	139	7	ok	7
3 — ST-2	3970	4000	115	154	154	7	ok	7
4 — ST-2	2780	2663	80	103	103	6	ok	6
5 — ST-3	3800	2975	110	115	115	7	ok	7
6 — ST-3	4440	4275	128	165	165	8	ok	8
7 — ST-5	4590	3500	133	135	135	7	ok	7
8 — ST-6	4620	3510	134	135	135	7	ok	7
9 — ST-6	2350	1690	68	65	68	5	ok	5
10 — ST-8	3020	2590	87	100	100	6	ok	6
11 — ST-8	3810	3110	110	120	120	7	ok	7
12 — ST-9	3430	2400	99	93	99	8	ok	8
Trunk ST-1			235	266	266	9	610	9
Trunk ST-2			195	257	257	9	600	9
Trunk ST-3			238	280	280	9	645	9
Trunk ST-4			433	537	537	12	705	12
Trunk ST-5			133	135	135	7	520	7
Trunk ST-6			202	200	202	8	595	8
Trunk ST-7			335	335	335	10	630	10
Trunk ST-8			197	220	220	8	645	8
Trunk ST-9			99	93	99	6	505	6
Trunk ST-10			296	313	313	10	610	10
Trunk ST-11			1300	1300	1300	16	950	17

Return Duct System

Run - Trunk	Associated Supply Runs	H-CFM	C-CFM	Dsn CFM	Round Size	Velocity	Final Size
1 — RT-1	#1, #2	235	266	266	9	630	9
2 — RT-2	#3 , #4, #5, #6	433	537	537	12	705	12
3 — RT-1	#7 , #8, #9	335	335	335	10	640	10
4 — RT-2	#10, #11,#12	296	313	313	10	610	10
5 —							
6 —							
Trunk RT1		570	601	601	12	790	13
Trunk RT2		729	850	850	14	800	15
Trunk RT3		1040	1040	1040	15	875	17
Trunk BP		1040	1040	1040	15	875	17

1) H-BTUH and C-BTUH from the **Manual J** room load calculation procedure
2) H-CFM = HF x H-BTUH and C-CFM = CF x C--BTUH
3) Dsn CFM = larger of the H-CFM or C-CFM values (runout ducts) . . . or . . . total downstream CFM (trunk ducts)
4) Round size based on FR value. Final size based on FR value (if the velocity is acceptable) or the maximum allowable velocity value

Figure 11-9

Duct Sizing Calculations

On page 11-9, Figure 11-9 summarizes the duct sizing calculations that are associated with this example. The following comments apply to these calculations:

- The duct sizes were determined by using the ACCA Duct Sizing Slide Rule (refer to the "Galvanized Metal Duct" scale).

- Supply runs 1 and 2 are associated with zone 1 and return R1; supply runs 3 through 6 are associated with zone 2 and return R2; supply runs 7 through 9 are associated with zone 3 and return R3; and supply runs 10 through 12 are associated with zone 4 and return R4.

- Supply runs 1 and 2 are associated with secondary trunk ST-1; supply runs 3 through 6 are associated with secondary trunks ST-2, ST-3 and ST-4; supply runs 7 through 9 are associated with secondary trunks ST-5, ST-6 and ST-7; and supply runs 10 through 12 are associated with secondary trunks ST-8, ST-9 and ST-10.

- Return runs R1 and R3 feed into primary return trunk RT-1, and return runs R2 and R4 feed into primary return trunk RT-2.

- Primary return trunk RT-2 and the bypass duct feed into primary return trunk RT-3.

- The sizes of the supply runout ducts are based on the CFM values that are associated with the peak loads.

- The final sizes of the supply runouts are based on the friction rate design value (0.08 IWC/100) because the corresponding velocities are less than 900 FPM. (The runout velocities are always less than 900 FPM when the design friction rate value falls inside the "wedge" that is associated with the friction rate chart.)

- The sizes of secondary trunk ducts ST-1 through ST-10 are based on the CFM values that are associated with the peak loads.

- The final sizes of the secondary supply trunks ST-1 through ST-10 are based on the friction rate design value (0.08 IWC/100) because the corresponding velocities are less than 900 FPM.

- The size of primary trunk duct ST-11 is based on the 1,300 CFM value that is associated with the **Manual J** load for the entire house. (The **Manual J** load for the entire house — which is equivalent to the peak block load — was used because the zone loads do not peak simultaneously.)

- The final size of primary supply trunk ST-11 is based on the maximum allowable velocity (900 FPM) because the velocity that is associated with the friction rate value (0.08 IWC/100) exceeds 900 FPM.

- The sizes of the zone return runs (R1, R2, R3 and R4) are based on the CFM values that are associated with the peak zone loads.

- The final sizes of the zone return ducts (R1, R2, R3 and R4) are based on the friction rate design value (0.08 IWC/100) because the corresponding velocities are acceptable (700 FPM or less).

- The sizes of primary return trunks RT-1 and RT-2 are based on the CFM values that are associated with the peak zone loads.

- The final sizes of primary return trunks RT-1 and RT-2 are based on the maximum allowable velocity (700 FPM) because the velocity that is associated with the friction rate value (0.08 IWC/100) exceeds 700 FPM.

- The final sizes of the bypass duct and primary return trunk RT-3 are based on 80 percent of the design air flow rate (1,040 CFM = 0.80 x 1,300 CFM).

- The final sizes of the bypass duct and primary return trunk RT-3 are based on the maximum allowable velocity (700 FPM) because the velocity that is associated with the friction rate value (0.08 IWC/100) exceeds 700 FPM

- The ACCA duct slide rule can be used to convert round sizes into equivalent rectangular sizes.

Comments and Observations

Since this example is characterized by zone loads that do not peak simultaneously, the capacity of the central fuel conversion equipment and the design value for the blower CFM were based on the (standard) **Manual J** load for the entire house. Diversity was also applied to the sizing calculation that is associated with the main supply trunk. Therefore, as far as the central components are concerned, the sizing calculations are identical to the calculations that would be used to design a conventional (constant-volume) system. But, as far as the rest of the air distribution system is concerned, the design procedure has some noticeable differences.

- The duct layout features a system of secondary trunk ducts. This geometry is preferred because a minimum number of control dampers are required when the duct arrangement is used to establish the zones. (If an extended plenum design was used, each branch runout would have required a control damper.)

- The secondary trunk and runout duct sizes were based on the CFM values that are associated with the peak loads.

This example also is characterized by equipment that does not provide capacity control or fan control. Therefore, a bypass duct (and the associated control damper) is required to assure that an adequate flow of air is maintained through each air-side component during any part-load operating condition. (A bypass duct would still be required if a variable speed blower is used in conjunction with HVAC equipment that does not have capacity control because a minimum flow of air is required for a refrigerant coil or heat exchanger.)

11-11 Example — System with No Diversity

Figure 11-10 provides a sketch of an 1050 CFM variable air volume system that features a heat pump that is equipped with a variable speed compressor and a variable-speed blower. This sketch shows a two-zone, sheet metal, supply air duct system that includes a primary trunk duct, secondary trunk ducts and branch runout ducts. On the next page, Figure 11-13 shows the geometry and the fittings that are associated with the return duct system. This system consists of two branch runs and one return trunk.

Figure 11-10 also contains a table that provides information about the orientation, the percentage of glass and the sensible load correction factors that are associated with each zone. This information is required to estimate the peak cooling loads that are associated with the runout ducts. Also refer to Figure

Run	Trunks (Feet)	Branch (Feet)	Heat BTUH	Cool BTUH	SLCF	Peak BTUH
1	48	10	4250	2750	1.20	3300
2	36	10	3860	3010	1.20	3612
3	36	10	3970	3200	1.20	3840
4	48	10	2780	2130	1.20	2556
5	62	12	3800	2380	1.25	2975
6	48	12	4440	3420	1.25	4275
7	48	12	4590	3500	1.25	4375
8	62	12	4620	3510	1.25	4388
Totals			32310	23900		29331
SLCF = sensible load correction factor						

Figure 11-11

11-11, which summarizes the load calculations that are associated with the various runout ducts and to Figure 11-12 (next page), which presents the manufacturer's blower data and provides information regarding the test stand configuration and the pressure drops that are associated with accessory components and flow control devices.

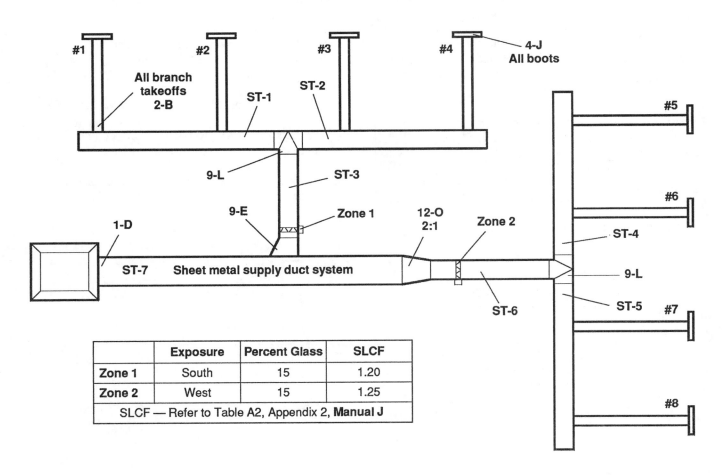

	Exposure	Percent Glass	SLCF
Zone 1	South	15	1.20
Zone 2	West	15	1.25
SLCF — Refer to Table A2, Appendix 2, **Manual J**			

Figure 11-10

Manufacturer's Data Blower Performance and Device Pressure Drop			
Speed	CFM	ESP (IWC)	MAX RPM
TAP - 1	800	0.22 - 0.40	500
TAP - 2	900	0.23 - 0.45	600
TAP - 3	1000	0.24 - 0.50	700
TAP - 4	1100	0.24 - 0.60	850
TAP - 5	1200	0.23 - 0.70	1000
TAP - 6	1300	0.19 - 0.75	1200

Heat pump unit tested with a wet DX coil and a low efficiency filter in place. If auxiliary heating coils are required, subtract 0.12 IWC from the values that are listed in this table. If zone control damper is installed in the circulation path, subtract 0.05 IWC (for an open damper) from the values that are listed in this table.

Figure 11-12

Effective Length Calculation

On the next page, Figure 11-14 summarizes the effective length calculations that are associated with all of the supply runs and return runs. (A cursory inspection of the geometry and the fittings that are associated with this example does not suggest an obvious candidate for the longest circulation path.) The following summary shows that the effective length of the critical circulation path is equal to 188 + 167 = 355 feet. In this case, return R1 is associated with the zone 1 supply runs (outlets 1 through 4) and return R2 is associated with the zone 2 supply runs (outlets 5 through 8).

Run	#1	#2	#5	#6
Supply TEL	188	186	164	160
Run	R1	R2		
Return TEL	149	167		

Design Friction Rate Calculation

In this example the blower data indicates that if speed tap 4 is selected, the fan can deliver 1,100 CFM when it operates against a resistance that ranges between 0.24 and 0.60 IWC of external resistance. Therefore, it is reasonable to assume that 0.60 IWC of pressure will be available when the fan delivers the system air flow requirements (1,050 CFM). Since the resistance that is associated with the auxiliary heating coil (0.12 IWC), the supply outlet (0.03 IWC), the return (0.03 IWC), an open balancing damper (0.05 IWC) and an open hand damper (0.03 IWC) is equal to 0.26 IWC, the available static pressure is equal to 0.34 IWC. Therefore, the design value for the friction rate will be based on 0.34 IWC of pressure and 355 feet of effective length. These calculations are summarized on page 11-14 by Figure 11-15.

Duct Sizing Calculations

On page 11-15, Figure 11-16 summarizes the duct sizing calculations that are associated with this example. The following comments apply to these calculations:

- All of the duct sizes were determined by using the ACCA Duct Sizing Slide Rule ("Galvanized Metal Duct" scale.)

- Supply runs 1 through 4 are associated with zone 1 and return R1; supply runs 5 through 8 are associated with zone 2 and return R2.

- Supply runs 1 through 4 are associated with secondary trunks ST-1, ST-2 and ST-3; supply runs 5 through 8 are associated with secondary trunks ST-4, ST-5 and ST-6.

- Return runs R1 and R2 feed into primary return trunk RT-1.

- The sizes of the supply runouts are based on the CFM values that are associated with the peak loads.

- The final sizes of supply runouts are based on the friction rate design value (0.10 IWC/100) because the correspond-

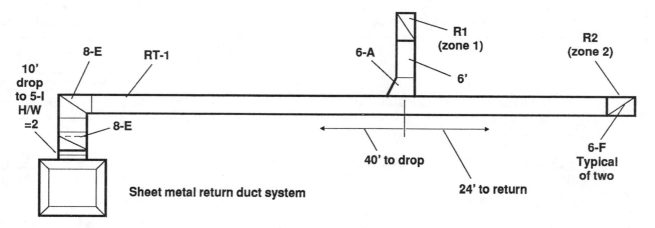

Figure 11-13

	Effective Length Calculation Sheet								
Element	**Supply Run ID Number**				**Element**	**Return Run ID Number**			
	# 1 or #4	#2 or #3	#5 or #8	#6 or #7		# R1	# R2	#	#
Trunk Length	48	36	62	48	**Trunk Length**	40	40		
Trunk Length					**Trunk Length**	10	10		
Trunk Length					**Trunk Length**				
Runout Length	10	10	12	12	**Runout Length**	6	24		
Group 1 (D)	10	10	10	10	**Group 5 (I)**	30	30	(H/W = 2)	
Group 2 (B)	20	30	20	30	**Group 6 (F)**	25	25		
Group 3					**Group 7**				
Group 4 (J)	30	30	30	30	**Group 8 (E)**	10	10		
Group 8					**Group 10**				
Group 9 (L)	20	20	20	20	**Group 11**				
Group 11					**Group 12**				
Group 12 (O)			5	5	**Group 13**				
Group 13					**Other (6A br)**	18		(cfm1/cfm2 = 0.45)	
Other (9E)	50	50	5	5	**Other (6A m)**		18		
Other					**Other (8E)**	10	10		
Other					**Other**				
Total Length	188	186	164	160	**Total Length**	149	167		

Figure 11-14

ing velocities are less than 900 FPM. (The runout velocities are always less than 900 FPM when the design friction rate value falls inside the "wedge" that is associated with the friction rate chart.)

- The sizes of secondary supply trunks ST-1 through ST-6 are based on the CFM values that are associated with the peak zone loads.

- The final sizes of the secondary supply trunks ST-1 through ST-6 are based on the friction rate design value (0.10 IWC/100) because the corresponding velocities are less than 900 FPM.

- The size of primary trunk ST-7 is based on the sum of the CFM values that are associated with the peak room loads. (The **Manual J** load for the entire house — which is equivalent to the peak block load — does not apply because the zone loads peak simultaneously.)

- The final size of primary supply trunk ST-7 is based on the friction rate design value (0.10 IWC/100) because the corresponding velocity is less than 900 FPM.

- The sizes of zone return ducts R1 and R2 are based on the CFM values that are associated with the peak zone loads.

- The final sizes of zone return ducts R1 and R2 are based on the maximum allowable velocity (700 FPM) because the velocity that is associated with the friction rate value (0.10 IWC/100) exceeds 700 FPM.

- The size of primary return trunk RT-1 is based on the sum of the CFM values that are associated with the peak zone loads. (The CFM value that is associated with the **Manual J** load for the entire house — the peak block load — does not apply because the zone loads peak simultaneously.)

- The final sizes of primary return trunk RT-1 is based on the maximum allowable velocity (700 FPM) because the velocity that is associated with the friction rate value (0.10 IWC/100) exceeds 700 FPM.

- The ACCA Duct Sizing Slide Rule can be used to convert round sizes into equivalent rectangular sizes.

Comments and Observations
Since this example is characterized by a west exposure and a south exposure, the peak zone loads will not occur at exactly the same time of day, but they will occur at approximately the same time of day (3 P.M. to 6 P.M.). Because there is not a substantial amount of diversity associated with this example,

Friction Rate Worksheet

Step 1) Manufacturer's Blower Data

External static pressure (ESP) = ___0.60___ IWC   CFM = ___1050___

Step 2) Device Pressure Losses

Direct expansion refrigerant coil ...

Electric resistance heating coil 0.12

Hot water coil ....

Heat exchanger ....

Low efficiency filter ....

High or mid-efficiency filter ....

Electronic filter ....

Humidifier ....

Supply outlet 0.03

Return grille 0.03

Balancing damper 0.03

Other device 0.05

Total device losses (DPL) .... ___0.26___ IWC

Step 3) Available Static Pressure

ASP = (ESP - DPL) = (___0.60___ - ___0.26___) = ___0.34___ IWC

Step 4) Total Effective Length (TEL)

Supply-side TEL + Return-side TEL = (___188___ + ___167___) = ___355___ FEET

Step 5) Friction Rate Design Value (FR)

FR value from friction rate chart = ___0.10___ IWC/100

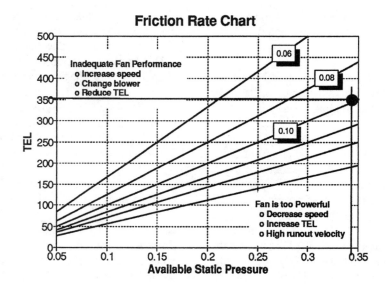

Figure 11-15

Duct Sizing Worksheet								
HF = Blower CFM / Manual J Heat Loss = (1050) / (32310) = 0.0325							FR Value	
CF = Blower CFM / Manual J Sensible Heat Gain = (1050) / (29321) = 0.0358							0.10	
Supply Duct System								
Run - Trunk	H-BTUH	C-BTUH	H-CFM	C-CFM	Dsn CFM	Round Size	Velocity	Final Size
1 — ST-1	4250	3300	138	118	138	7	ok	7
2 — ST-1	3860	3612	125	129	129	7	ok	7
3 — ST-2	3970	3840	129	138	138	7	ok	7
4 — ST-2	2780	2556	90	92	92	6	ok	6
5 — ST-4	3800	2975	123	107	107	7	ok	7
6 — ST-4	4440	4275	144	153	153	7	ok	7
7 — ST-5	4590	4375	149	157	157	7	ok	7
8 — ST-5	4620	4388	150	157	157	7	ok	7
9 —								
10 —								
11 —								
12 —								
13								
14								
15								
		Trunk ST-1	263	247	263	9	610	9
		Trunk ST-2	219	230	230	8	670	8
		Trunk ST-3	482	477	482	11	760	11
		Trunk ST-4	267	260	267	9	610	9
		Trunk ST-5	299	314	314	9	760	9
		Trunk ST-6	566	574	574	12	750	12
		Trunk ST-7	1050	1050	1050	15	870	15
Return Duct System								
Run - Trunk	Associated Supply Runs	H-CFM	C-CFM	Dsn CFM	Round Size	Velocity	Final Size	
1 — RT-1	#1, #2, #3, #4	482	477	482	11	780	12	
2 — RT-2	#5, #6, #7, #8	566	574	574	12	750	13	
3 —								
4 —								
5 —								
6 —								
7 —								
8 —								
	Trunk RT1	1050	1050	1050	15	930	17	
	Trunk							
	Trunk							

1) H-BTUH and C-BTUH from the **Manual J** room load calculation procedure

2) H-CFM = HF x H-BTUH and C-CFM = CF x C--BTUH

3) Dsn CFM = larger of the H-CFM or C-CFM values (runout ducts) . . . or . . . total downstream CFM (trunk ducts)

4) Round size based on FR value. Final size based on FR value (if the velocity is acceptable) or the maximum allowable velocity value

Figure 11-16

the capacity of the central equipment and the design value for the blower CFM were based on the sum of the peak zone loads. This type of load analysis also applies to the sizing calculations that are associated with the primary trunk ducts, the secondary ducts and the runout ducts. Therefore, all of the design calculations (equipment sizing, blower CFM requirement, duct sizing and air terminal sizing) were based on the adjusted **Manual J** loads. The following comments also apply to the calculations that are associated with this example:

- The standard **Manual J** load for the entire house is equal to 23,900 BTUH, but since there is no diversity, the design value for the sensible cooling load is equal to 29,331 BTUH, which represents the sum of the peak zone loads. (This 29,331 design load also would be used to design a constant volume system because the standard **Manual J** load calculation procedure does not apply to dwellings that are characterized by a lack of diversity.)

- The duct layout features a system of secondary trunk ducts. This geometry is preferred because a minimum number of control dampers are required when the duct arrangement is used to establish the zones. (If an extended plenum design was used, each branch runout would have been equipped with a control damper.)

This example also is characterized by conditioning equipment that features a variable-speed compressor and blower. Therefore, a bypass duct is not required because the capacity of the major mechanical components can be adjusted to match the part-load operating conditions. (A bypass duct would still be required if a variable-speed blower is used in conjunction with cooling and heating equipment that does not have capacity control because a minimum flow of air is required for a refrigerant coil or heat exchanger.)

11-12 Flexible Duct VAV System

Figure 11-17 provides a sketch of a 900 CFM flexible duct system that is geometrically similar to the sheet metal system that was analyzed in example 1. Both of these systems use an arrangement of primary trunk ducts, secondary trunk ducts and branch runout ducts to create four zones; but in this example, there are only three returns. (A transfer grille completes the circulation path between zone four and the return grilles (R2 and R3). A bypass duct is not required for this system because the central equipment consists of a heat pump that features a variable-speed compressor, a variable-speed blower and minimum air flow controls.

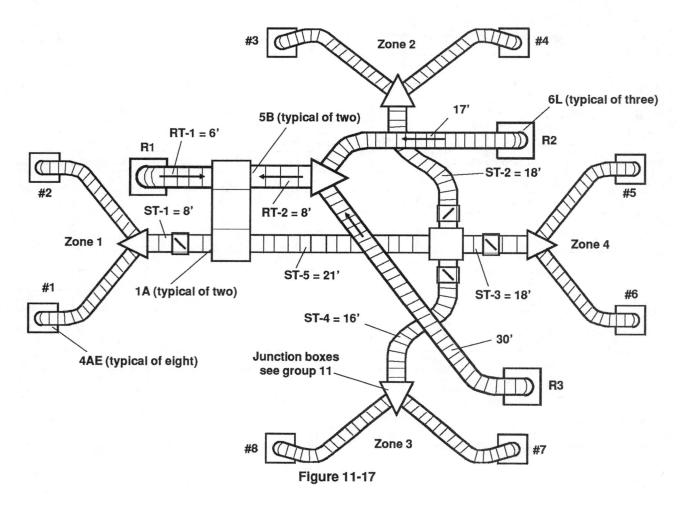

Figure 11-17

Sizing Calculations

The sizing calculations that are required to design a flexible duct system are basically the same as calculations that are associated with sheet metal VAV systems. These calculations are based on the following concepts, which pertain to all types of VAV systems:

- Zones are defined by rooms that have similar load characteristics.

- Room CFM values are based on the peak room load.

- The peak room load can be estimated by multiplying the traditional **Manual J** load by the sensible load correction factors that are found in **Manual J**, Appendix A2.

- The concept of diversity applies to the sizing calculations that are associated with the central components.

- If the zone loads are characterized by diversity, the sizes of the central components are based on the **Manual J** load for the entire house.

- If the zone loads are not characterized by diversity, the sizes of the central components are based on the sum of the peak zone loads.

- The pressure drop that is associated with a VAV control damper must be subtracted from the pressure that is produced by the blower.

- There must be an unobstructed free return path for every supply air outlet.

The following table provides information about the orientation, the percentage of glass and the sensible load correction factors that are associated with each of the four zones. This information is required to estimate the peak cooling loads that are associated with each runout duct. Also refer to Figure 11-18, which summarizes the load calculations that are associated with the various runout ducts and to Figure 11-19, which presents the manufacturer's blower data and provides information regarding the pressure drops that are associated with accessory devices.

	Exposure	Percent Glass	SLCF
Zone 1	South	15	1.20
Zone 2	West	10	1.25
Zone 3	East	15	1.0
Zone 4	North	10	1.0
SLCF — Refer to Table A2, Appendix 2, **Manual J**			

Effective Length Calculation

Based on an inspection of the geometry and the fittings that are associated with this duct system, it appears that the zone 2

Run	Runout	H-Load	C-Load	SLCF	P-Load
1	16'	3800	1983	1.2	2380
2	16'	3970	2667	1.2	3200
3	14'	4250	2200	1.25	2750
4	14'	3860	2408	1.25	3010
5	14'	4500	2610	1.0	2610
6	14'	4590	3500	1.0	3500
7	14'	4870	3750	1.0	3750
8	14'	2350	1690	1.0	1690
Heating Load = 32190			Block Cooling Load = 20808		
R1	For supply runs 1 and 2				
R2	For supply runs 3, 4 and 5				
R3	For supply runs 6, 7 and 8				

Figure 11-18

loop (supply run #7 or supply run # 8 and return run R3), is the longest circulation path. On the next page, Figure 11-20 summarizes the effective length calculations that are associated with this circulation path. This summary shows that the effective length of the longest supply run is 316 feet and the effective length of the longest return run is 188 feet. Therefore, the total effective length of the critical circulation path is equal to 504 feet.

Manufacturer's Data			
Blower Performance and Device Pressure Drop			
Speed	**CFM**	**ESP (IWC)**	**MAX RPM**
TAP - 1	700	0.23 - 0.50	600
TAP - 2	800	0.24 - 0.55	700
TAP - 3	1000	0.24 - 0.65	850
TAP - 5	1150	0.23 - 0.70	1000
TAP - 6	1300	0.19 - 0.75	1200
Heat pump unit tested with a wet DX coil and a low efficiency filter in place. If auxiliary heating coils are required, subtract 0.10 IWC from the values that are listed in this table. If zone control damper is installed in the circulation path, subtract 0.05 IWC (for an open damper) from the values that are listed in this table.			

Figure 11-19

Design Friction Rate Calculation

In this example, the blower data indicates that if speed tap 3 is selected, the fan can deliver 1,000 CFM when it operates against a resistance that ranges between 0.24 and 0.65 IWC. Therefore, it is reasonable to assume that 0.60 IWC of pressure will be available when the fan delivers the system air flow requirements (900 CFM). Since the resistance that is associated with the auxiliary heating coil (0.10 IWC), the supply outlet (0.03 IWC), the return (0.03 IWC), an open balancing

Effective Length Calculation Sheet											
Element	**Supply Run ID Number**				**Element**	**Return Run ID Number**				
	# 7 or 8					# R3	#	#	#
Trunk Length	37				**Trunk Length**	8			
Trunk Length					**Trunk Length**				
Trunk Length					**Trunk Length**				
Runout Length	14				**Runout Length**	30			
Group 1 (A)	35				**Group 5 (B)**	40			
Group 2					**Group 6 (L)**	20			
Group 3					**Group 7**				
Group 4 (AE)	55				**Group 8**				
Group 8					**Group 10**				
Group 9					**Group 11**	75	(1 @ 75 FT @ 600 FPM)		
Group 11	150	(2 @ 75 FT @ 600 FPM)			**Group 12**				
Group 12					**Group 13**				
Group 13					**Other (11)**	5	(one 45 degree bend)		
Other (11)	15	(three 45 degree bends)			**Other (11)**	10	(one 90 degree bend)		
Other (11)	10	(one 90 degree bend)			**Other**				
Total Length	316				**Total Length**	188			

Figure 11-20

damper (0.05 IWC) and an open hand damper (0.03 IWC) is equal to 0.24 IWC, the available static pressure is equal to 0.36 IWC. Therefore, the design value for the friction rate will be based on 0.36 IWC of pressure and 504 feet of effective length. These calculations are summarized on the next page by Figure 11-21.

Duct Sizing Calculations
On page 11-20, Figure 11-22 summarizes the duct sizing calculations that are associated with this example. The following comments apply to these calculations:

- All of the duct sizes were determined by using the ACCA Duct Sizing Slide Rule ("Wire Helix Duct" scale.)

- Supply runs 3 and 4 are associated with secondary trunk ST-2, supply runs 5 and 6 are associated with secondary trunk ST- 3 and supply runs 7 and 8 are associated with secondary trunk ST- 4.

- Supply runs 1 and 2 are associated with primary supply trunk ST-1, supply runs 3, 4, 5, 6, 7 and 8 are associated with primary supply trunk ST-5.

- Return branches R2 and R3 feed into return trunk RT-2 and return R1 feeds directly to the air handler through return trunk RT-1.

- The sizes of the supply runouts are based on the CFM values that are associated with the peak loads.

- The final sizes of supply runouts are based on the friction rate design value (0.07 IWC/100) because the corresponding velocities are less than 600 FPM. (The 600 FPM velocity limit was selected because a higher value would have produced a significant increase in the equivalent length that is associated with the junction box fittings.)

- The sizes of secondary supply trunks ST-1 through ST-4 are based on the CFM values that are associated with the peak zone loads.

- The size of primary trunk duct ST-5 is based on the 698 CFM value that is associated with the standard (uncorrected) **Manual J** loads. (The standard **Manual J** loads were used because the loads that are associated with zones 2, 3 and 4 do not peak simultaneously.)

- The final sizes of the supply trunks (ST-1, ST-2, ST-3, ST-4 and ST-5) are based on the friction rate design value (0.07 IWC/100) because the corresponding velocities are less than 600 FPM.

- The sizes of return runs R2 and R3 are based on the CFM values that are associated with the peak zone loads.

Friction Rate Worksheet

Step 1) Manufacturer's Blower Data

External static pressure (ESP) = _____0.60_____ IWC   CFM = _____900_____

Step 2) Device Pressure Losses

Direct expansion refrigerant coil . . . .
Electric resistance heating coil 0.10
Hot water coil . . . .
Heat exchanger . . . .
Low efficiency filter . . . .
High or mid-efficiency filter . . . .
Electronic filter . . . .
Humidifier . . . .
Supply outlet 0.03
Return grille 0.03
Balancing damper 0.03
Other device 0.05

Total device losses (DPL) . . . . _____0.24_____ IWC

Step 3) Available Static Pressure

ASP = (ESP - DPL) = (_____0.60_____ - _____0.24_____) = _____0.36_____ IWC

Step 4) Total Effective Length (TEL)

Supply-side TEL + Return-side TEL = (_____316_____ + _____188_____) = _____504_____ FEET

Step 5) Friction Rate Design Value (FR)

FR value from friction rate chart = _____0.07_____ IWC/100

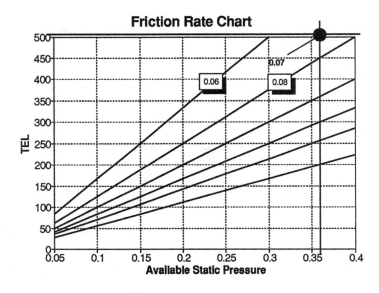

Figure 11-21

Duct Sizing Worksheet

HF = Blower CFM / Manual J Heat Loss = (900) / (32190) = <u>0.0280</u>

CF = Blower CFM / Manual J Sensible Heat Gain = (900) / (20808) = <u>0.0433</u>

FR Value
0.07

Supply Duct System

Run - Trunk	H-BTUH	C-BTUH	H-CFM	C-CFM	Dsn CFM	Round Size	Velocity	Final Size
1 — ST-1	3800	2380	106	103	106	7	ok	7
2 — ST-1	3970	3200	111	138	138	8	ok	8
3 — ST-2	4250	2750	119	119	119	8	ok	8
4 — ST-2	3860	3010	108	130	130	8	ok	8
5 — ST-3	4500	2610	126	113	126	8	ok	8
6 — ST-3	4590	3500	128	151	151	8	ok	8
7 — ST-4	4870	3750	136	162	162	9	ok	9
8 — ST-4	2350	1690	66	73	73	6	ok	6
9 —	(Supply #3)	2200	<Std. J>	95	<-- For ST-5			
10 —	(Supply #4)	2408	<Std. J>	104	<-- For ST-5			
11 —	(Supply #5)	2610	<Std. J>	113	<-- For ST-5			
12 —	(Supply #6)	3500	<Std. J>	151	<-- For ST-5			
13 —	(Supply #7)	3750	<Std. J>	162	<-- For ST-5			
14 —	(Supply #8)	1690	<Std. J>	73	<-- For ST-5			
15 —								
		Trunk ST-1	217	241	241	10	450	10
		Trunk ST-2	227	249	249	10	450	10
		Trunk ST-3	254	264	264	11	405	11
		Trunk ST-4	202	235	235	10	420	10
		Trunk ST-5	683	698	698	15	580	15

Return Duct System

Run - Trunk	Associated Supply Runs	H-CFM	C-CFM	Dsn CFM	Round Size	Velocity	Final Size
1 — RT-1	#1, #2	217	241	241	See RT1	See RT1	See RT1
2 — RT-2	#3, #4, #5	353	362	362	10	675	11
3 — RT-2	#6, #7, #8	330	386	386	11	605	11
4 —							
5 —							
6 —							
7 —							
8 —							
9 —							
	Trunk RT-1	217	241	241	9	565	9
	Trunk RT-2	683	698	698	15	580	15
	Trunk						
	Trunk						

1) H-BTUH and C-BTUH from the **Manual J** room load calculation procedure
2) H-CFM = HF x H-BTUH and C-CFM = CF x C--BTUH
3) Dsn CFM = larger of the H-CFM or C-CFM values (runout ducts) . . . or . . . total downstream CFM (trunk ducts)
4) Round size based on FR value. Final size based on FR value (if the velocity is acceptable) or the maximum allowable velocity value

Figure 11-22

- The final size of the return duct R2 is based on the design velocity (600 FPM) because the velocity that is associated with the friction rate value exceeds 600 FPM.

- The final size of the return duct R3 is based on the friction rate design value (0.07 IWC/100) because the corresponding velocity is close to 600 FPM.

- The size of return run trunk RT-1 is based on the CFM value that is associated with the peak zone load.

- The size of primary return trunk RT-2 is based on the 698 CFM value that is associated with the standard (uncorrected) **Manual J** loads. (The standard **Manual J** loads were used because the loads that are associated with zones 2, 3 and 4 do not peak simultaneously.)

- The final sizes of return trunks RT-1 and RT-2 are based on the friction rate design value (0.07 IWC/100) because the corresponding velocities are either less than 600 FPM.

- The final size of some trunk ducts may have to be increased by 1-inch in order to conform with the standard sizes that are associated with the wire helix product.

Comments and Observations

Since this example is characterized by zone loads that do not peak simultaneously, the capacity of the central heating and cooling unit and the design value for the blower CFM were based on the (standard) **Manual J** load for the entire house. Diversity also applied to the sizing calculations that are associated with primary supply trunk ST-5 and primary return trunk RT-2. Therefore, as far as the central components are concerned, the sizing calculations are identical to the calculations that would be used to design a conventional (constant volume) system. But, as far as the rest of the air distribution system is concerned, the design procedure is noticeably different.

- The duct layout features a system of secondary trunk ducts. This geometry is preferred because a minimum number of control dampers are required when the duct arrangement is used to establish the zones. (If an extended plenum design was used, each branch runout would have been equipped with a control damper.)

- The sizes of the secondary trunk and runout ducts were based on the CFM values that are associated with the peak zone loads.

This example also is characterized by equipment that features a variable-speed compressor and blower. Therefore, a bypass duct is not required because the capacity of the major mechanical components can be adjusted to match the part-load operating conditions. (A bypass duct would still be required if a variable speed blower is used in conjunction with cooling and heating equipment that does not have capacity control because

a minimum flow of air is required for a refrigerant coil or heat exchanger.)

11-13 Bilevel Zoning with Central Equipment

On the next page, Figures 11-23 and 11-24 provide sketches of a two-zone system that serves the upper and lower levels of a two-story dwelling. This 1300 CFM duct system features two distribution systems (one for each floor), primary trunk ducts (supply and return), zone control dampers and one central air handling unit. A bypass duct may or may not be required for this system, depending on the control strategy that is used to adjust the capacity of the central equipment (on-off controls versus modulating or staged controls).

Design Concept

The most common zoning problem that is associated with two-story homes is that the upper level tends to be too warm and the lower level tends to be too cool. This problem can be minimized by installing two separate systems (one for each level), or by fitting a central system with hardware (flow control dampers and "intelligent" controls) that provide a two-zone capability. (This hardware and the associated operating controls may be packaged with the central equipment or it may be provided by an independent vendor.)

One advantage associated with the two-zone VAV system is that it has the ability to shift capacity from level to level. For example, if additional cooling capacity is required for the second level, the flow control dampers can route a greater percentage of the supply CFM to the second floor. Or, if more heating capacity is required for the lower level, the flow control dampers can direct a greater percentage of the supply CFM to the first floor. Therefore, both of the distribution systems (first and second floor) should be designed to accommodate a 20 percent increase in the flow rate that is associated with each supply air outlet.

Control Dampers

The control dampers may be characterized by a modulating action or by an open-close action. In either case, it is important to know something about the minimum flow rate that is associated with the damper. If the damper is equipped with a stop, some flow will be associated with a fully modulated damper. If the damper is not equipped with a stop, the flow will be completely throttled.

System Controls

One thermostat is required for each zone. These thermostats must be programmed to sequence the operation of the VAV dampers and the central equipment in response to the simultaneous demand that is associated with both zones. The details of the control strategy will vary, depending on the product or vendor. In any case, it is important to know how the controls affect the maximum and minimum flow rates that are associated with each zone and how they affect the minimum flow rate that is associated with the central equipment.

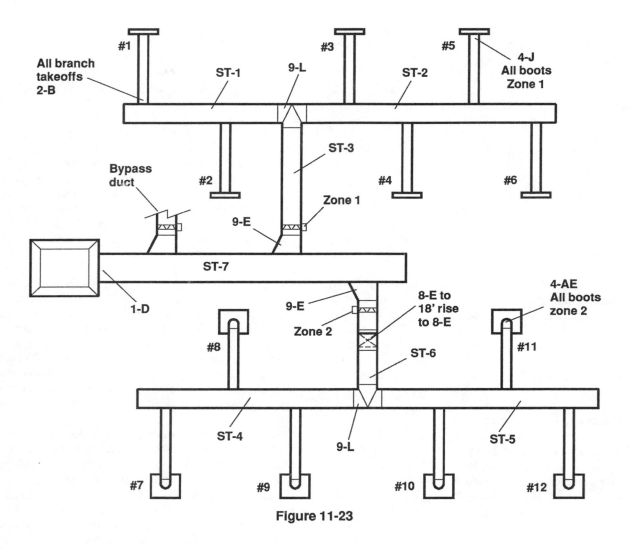

Figure 11-23

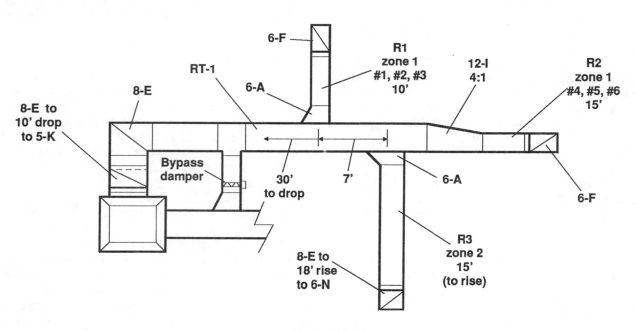

Figure 11-24

Bypass Duct

A bypass duct and a bypass damper will be required if the primary components of the HVAC system (blower, compressor or heat exchanger) are not equipped with some type of capacity control (speed control, for example). If a bypass duct is required, the design value for the air flow through the bypass will depend on the minimum flow rates that are associated with the zone dampers. If both of the zone dampers can be driven to the closed position (when the blower is operating), the bypass duct should be sized to handle at least 80 percent of the design air flow rate. If the zone dampers are equipped with minimum position stops, the bypass duct can be sized to handle the difference between the design air flow rate and the minimum flow rate that can be routed through the supply duct system.

The bypass damper may be equipped with a mechanical operator or it may be a pressure-activated (counter balanced) device. In either case, the pressure drop that is associated with the bypass loop should be comparable to the pressure drop that is associated with the critical circulation path.

Returns

A comprehensive return system should be provided for each level. If a central return is used (for either level), transfer grilles will be required to establish a circulation path between each isolated room and the central return.

Sizing Calculations

This example emphasizes sheet metal construction, but this system could be fabricated from any combination of sheet metal, duct board or flexible wire helix materials. In any case, the sizing calculations that are required to design this particular type of two-zone system can be based on the following concepts:

- The capacity of the central equipment, the design value for the blower CFM and the flow rates that are associated with the primary trunk ducts are based on the standard **Manual J** load for the entire house. (The concept of diversity applies to the central components because four exposures are associated with both zones.)

- Since air flow is not controlled on a room-by-room basis, the room CFM calculations are based on the standard **Manual J** loads. (The sensible load correction factors do not apply to this type of zoned system).

- Since the flow control dampers can be used to increase the percentage of the blower CFM that is routed to either level, the CFM values that are associated with each supply outlet, runout duct and secondary trunk duct should be increased by 20 percent. (This adjustment does not apply to the central components.)

- The pressure drop that is associated with a VAV control damper must be subtracted from the pressure that is produced by the blower.

- There must be a low resistance return path for every supply air outlet.

The information that is required to proceed with this example is provided by Figure 11-25, which summarizes the **Manual J** load information. Also refer to Figure 11-26, which presents the manufacturer's blower data table and notes that document the test stand configuration and the pressure drops that are associated with accessory devices.

Run	Trunks (Feet)	Branch (Feet)	Heat BTUH	Cool BTUH
1	52	10	4250	2750
2	44	8	3860	3010
3	42	10	3970	3200
4	48	8	2780	2130
5	56	10	3800	2380
6	64	8	4440	3420
7	80	10	4590	3500
8	74	8	4620	3510
9	66	10	2350	1690
10	66	10	3020	2590
11	74	8	3810	3110
12	80	10	3430	2400
Heating Load = 44920			Block Cooling Load = 33690	

Figure 11-25

Manufacturer's Data Blower Performance and Device Pressure Drop			
CFM	External Resistance — IWC		
	High	Medium	Low
1150			0.53
1200			0.45
1250		0.67	0.37
1300		0.59	0.29
1350	0.59	0.47	
1400	0.48	0.36	
1450	0.37		
1500	0.26		

Heat pump unit tested with a wet DX coil and a low efficiency filter in place. If auxiliary heating coils are required, subtract 0.08 IWC from the values that are listed in this table. If zone control damper is installed in the circulation path, subtract 0.05 IWC (for an open damper) from the values that are listed in this table.

Figure 11-26

Effective Length Calculation Sheet									
Element	Supply Run ID Number				Element	Return Run ID Number			
	# 3	# 6	# 7 or 12	# 9 or 10		# R1	# R2	# R3	
Trunk Length	42	64	80	66	Trunk Length	10	10	10	
Trunk Length					Trunk Length	30	30	30	
Trunk Length					Trunk Length		7	7	
Runout Length	10	8	10	10	Runout Length	10	15	33	
Group 1 (D)	10	10	10	10	Group 5 (k)	10	10	10	
Group 2 (B)	40	20	20	35	Group 6 (F)	25	25		
Group 3					Group 7				
Group 4 (J, AE)	30	30	55	55	Group 8 (E all)	20	20	30	(10 each)
Group 8(2@E)			20	20	Group 10				
Group 9 (E br)	50	50	50	50	Group 11				
Group 11					Group 12 (I)		10		(4:1)
Group 12					Group 13				
Group 13					Other (6A br)	10		60	cfm1/cfm2
Other (9L)	20	20	20	20	Other (6A m)		35	10	0.32 (R1) 0.67 (R3)
Other (9E main)			5	5	Other				35 = 25+10
Other					Other (6N)			10	
Total Length	202	202	270	271	Total Length	115	162	200	

Figure11-27

Effective Length Calculation

Based on an inspection of the geometry and the fittings that are associated with this duct system, it appears that supply runs 3, 6, 7 (or 12) and 9 (or 8) could be associated with the longest circulation path. Also note that return R1 is associated with supply run 3, that return run R2 is associated with supply run 6, and that return run R3 is associated with all of the upper-level supply runs.

Figure 11-27 summarizes the effective length calculations that are associated with the selected duct runs. In this example, a supplemental calculation is required because the effective length of the longest supply run must be combined with the effective length of the longest return run. These calculations are summarized below. This summary shows that the effective length of the longest circulation path is 471 feet. This path is defined by supply run 9 (or 10) , which has a 271 foot length and return run R3, which has a 200 foot length.

Run	#3	#6	#7	#9
Supply TEL	202	202	270	271
Run	R1	R2	R3	
Return TEL	115	162	200	

Design Friction Rate Calculation

In this example, the blower data indicates that the fan can deliver 1,300 CFM when it operates against 0.59 IWC of external resistance. Since the resistance that is associated with the auxiliary heating coil (0.08 IWC), the supply outlet (0.03 IWC), the return (0.03 IWC), an open balancing damper (0.05 IWC) and an open hand damper (0.03 IWC) is equal to 0.22 IWC, the available static pressure is equal to 0.37 IWC. Therefore, the design value for the friction rate will be based on 0.37 IWC of pressure and 471 feet of effective length. These calculations are summarized by Figure 11-28 (on the next page).

Duct Sizing Calculations

On page 11-26, Figure 11-29 summarizes the duct sizing calculations that are associated with this example. The following comments apply to these calculations:

- All of the duct sizes were determined by using the ACCA Duct Sizing Slide Rule (refer to the "Galvanized Metal Duct" scale.)

- Zone 1 includes all the supply runs that are associated with the lower level and Zone 2 includes all the supply runs that are associated with the upper level.

Friction Rate Worksheet

Step 1) Manufacturer's Blower Data

External static pressure (ESP) = ___0.59___ IWC   CFM = ___1300___

Step 2) Device Pressure Losses

Direct expansion refrigerant coil . . . .
Electric resistance heating coil 0.08
Hot water coil . . . .
Heat exchanger . . . .
Low efficiency filter . . . .
High or mid-efficiency filter . . . .
Electronic filter . . . .
Humidifier . . . .
Supply outlet 0.03
Return grille 0.03
Balancing damper 0.03
Other device 0.05

Total device losses (DPL) . . . .   ___0.22___   IWC

Step 3) Available Static Pressure

ASP = (ESP - DPL) = (___0.59___ - ___0.22___) = ___0.37___ IWC

Step 4) Total Effective Length (TEL)

Supply-side TEL + Return-side TEL = (___271___ + ___200___) = ___471___ FEET

Step 5) Friction Rate Design Value (FR)

FR value from friction rate chart = ___0.08___ IWC/100

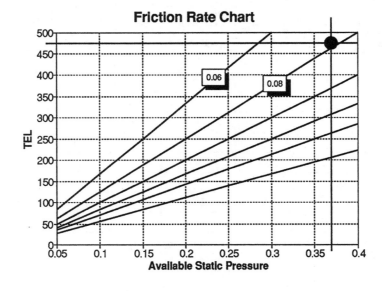

Figure 11-28

Duct Sizing Worksheet

HF = Blower CFM / Manual J Heat Loss = (1300) / (44920) = 0.0289

CF = Blower CFM / Manual J Sensible Heat Gain = (1300) / (33690) = 0.0386

FR Value 0.08

Supply Duct System   (Dsn CFM = 1.2 x larger of the two CFM values)

Run - Trunk	H-BTUH	C-BTUH	H-CFM	C-CFM	Dsn CFM	Round Size	Velocity	Final Size
1 — ST-1	4250	2750	123	106	148	7	ok	7
2 — ST-1	3860	3010	112	116	139	7	ok	7
3 — ST-2	3970	3200	115	123	148	7	ok	7
4 — ST-2	2780	2130	80	82	99	6	ok	6
5 — ST-2	3800	2380	110	92	132	7	ok	7
6 — ST-2	4440	3420	128	132	158	8	ok	8
7 — ST-4	4590	3500	133	135	162	8	ok	8
8 — ST-4	4620	3510	134	135	163	8	ok	8
9 — ST-4	2350	1690	68	65	82	6	ok	6
10 — ST-5	3020	2590	87	100	120	7	ok	7
11 — ST-5	3810	3110	110	120	144	7	ok	7
12 — ST-5	3430	2400	99	93	119	7	ok	7
13 —								
14 —								
15 —					(Dsn CFM = 1.2 x larger of the two CFM values)			
Trunk ST- 1			235	222	282	9	675	9
Trunk ST- 2			433	429	520	12	685	12
Trunk ST- 3			668	651	802	14	760	14
Trunk ST- 4			335	335	402	11	615	11
Trunk ST- 5			296	313	376	10	690	10
Trunk ST- 6			631	648	778	14	750	14
					(1.2 adjustment does not apply to primary duct			
Trunk ST- 7			1300	1300	1300	16	940	17

Return Duct System   (Dsn CFM = 1.2 x larger of the two CFM values)

Run - Trunk	Associated Supply Runs	H-CFM	C-CFM	Dsn CFM	Round Size	Velocity	Final Size
1 — RT-1	#1, #2, #3	350	345	420	11	660	11
2 — RT-1	#4, #5, #6	318	306	382	10	700	10
3 — RT-1	#7 , #8, #9, #10, #11, #12	631	648	778	14	770	15
4 —							
5 —							
6 —					(1.2 adjustment does not apply to primary duct		
Trunk RT1	1300	1300	1300	16	940	19
Trunk						
Trunk BP	1040	1040	1040	15	875	15
Trunk						

1) H-BTUH and C-BTUH from the **Manual J** room load calculation procedure

2) H-CFM = HF x H-BTUH and C-CFM = CF x C--BTUH

3) Dsn CFM = larger of the H-CFM or C-CFM values (runout ducts) . . . or . . . total downstream CFM (trunk ducts)

4) Round size based on FR value. Final size based on FR value (if the velocity is acceptable) or the maximum allowable velocity value

Figure 11-29

- Supply runs 1, 2 and 3 are associated with zone 1 and return R1; supply runs 4, 5 and 6 are associated with zone 1 and return R2; supply runs 7 through 12 are associated with zone 2 and return R3.

- Supply branches 1 through 6 are associated with secondary trunks ST-1, ST-2 and ST-3; and supply branches 7 through 9 are associated with secondary trunks ST-4, ST-5 and ST-6.

- Secondary supply trunks ST-3 and ST-6 are associated with primary supply trunk ST-7.

- Return runs R1, R2 and R3 feed into primary return trunk RT-1.

- The air flow rate that is associated with the central equipment (blower CFM) is based on the traditional **Manual J** load for the entire house. (The concept of diversity applies to central equipment that serves a single-family, detached, home.)

- The basic air flow requirements (CFM values) that are associated with either zone are based on the traditional **Manual J** load calculation procedures. (Zone correction factors are not required because each zone has four exposures.)

- The CFM values that are used to size the branch ducts and the secondary trunk ducts (both zones, supply and return) are 20 percent larger than the CFM values that are associated with the traditional (single-zone) duct sizing procedures. (This system has the ability to shift some capacity from the lower level to the upper level and vice versa.)

- The final sizes of the supply runouts and the secondary supply trunks (ST-1 trough ST-6) are based on the friction rate design value (0.08 IWC/100) because the corresponding velocities are less than 900 FPM. (The runout velocities are always less than 900 FPM when the design friction rate value falls inside the "wedge" that is associated with the friction rate chart.)

- The size of primary supply trunk ST-7 is based on the 1,300 CFM value that is associated with the **Manual J** load for the entire house. (The CFM value that is used to size the primary supply trunk is not increased by 20 percent because the total air flow does not change when capacity is diverted from one floor to another.)

- The final size of primary supply trunk ST-7 is based on the maximum allowable velocity (900 FPM) because the velocity that is associated with the friction rate value (0.08 IWC/100) exceeds 900 FPM.

- The sizes of the zone return runs (R1, R2 and R3) are based on the adjusted CFM values that are associated with the supply ducts.

- The final sizes of the zone return ducts (R1 and R2) are based on the friction rate design value (0.08 IWC/100) because the corresponding velocities are acceptable (700 FPM or less).

- The final size of zone return duct R3 is based on the maximum allowable velocity (700 FPM) because the velocity that is associated with the friction rate value (0.08 IWC/100) exceeds 700 FPM.

- The size of primary return trunk RT-1 is based on the 1,300 CFM value that is associated with the **Manual J** load for the entire house. (The CFM value that is used to size the primary supply trunk is not increased by 20 percent because the total air flow does not change when capacity is diverted from one floor to another.)

- The final size of primary return trunk RT-1 is based on the maximum allowable velocity (700 FPM) because the velocity that is associated with the friction rate value (0.08 IWC/100) exceeds 700 FPM.

- The final size of the bypass duct is based on 80 percent of the design air flow rate (1,040 CFM = 0.80 x 1,300 CFM) because the zone dampers do not have minimum air flow stops.

- The final sizes of the bypass duct is based on the maximum allowable velocity (700 FPM) because the velocity that is associated with the friction rate value (0.08 IWC/100) exceeds 700 FPM

- The ACCA Duct Sizing Slide Rule can be used to convert round sizes into equivalent rectangular sizes.

Comments and Observations

This example is characterized by a zoning arrangement that has a limited objective, which is to reduce the temperature control problems that are caused by the buoyancy of warm air. It can divert a little more of the blower CFM to the level that is too warm (upper level) or the level that is too cool (lower level), but it does not have the ability to control space temperatures on a room-by-room basis. (Note that the capabilities of this system will be reduced if the supply outlets are improperly sized or if the return paths are inadequate.)

Since the concept of peak room loads does not apply, the capacity of the central heating and cooling unit and the design value for the blower CFM were based on the standard **Manual J** load for the entire house. The concept of diversity also applied to the sizing calculations that were associated with primary supply trunk (ST-1) and primary return trunk (RT-1). Therefore, as far as the central components are concerned, the sizing calculations are identical to the calculations that would be used to design a conventional (constant volume) system. But, as far as the rest of the air distribution system is concerned, the design CFM values were increased by 20 percent so that the duct runs could accommodate the level-to-level capacity shifts.

This example also is characterized by equipment that features a constant-speed blower and zone dampers that do not have minimum flow stops. Therefore, an 80 percent bypass duct is required because the capacity of the major mechanical components cannot be adjusted to match the part-load operating conditions. (If the zone dampers had been equipped with minimum position stops, the bypass duct could have been sized to handle the difference between the design air flow rate and the minimum flow rate that can be routed through the supply duct system. Or, the bypass duct might have been eliminated if the central equipment featured a variable-speed blower and staged or modulating capacity controls.)

11-14 VAV Retrofit System

Figure 11-30 provides a sketch of a central (single-zone) air distribution system that is a candidate for retrofit work that will convert the system into a five-zone variable air volume system. (At this point, the contractor is speculating that these zones can be created by installing VAV control dampers in the branch runout ducts.) This duct system features an extended plenum supply trunk, branch runout ducts, three return runs, a primary return trunk duct and a central air handling unit. In addition, this duct system is characterized by good workmanship, which means that all of the ducts are properly installed and carefully sealed.

Zone Control Hardware

This system was not originally designed as a VAV system, so it does not have an arrangement of secondary trunk ducts that segregate the zones. (Secondary trunk ducts are desirable because they produce a one-to-one relationship between the zone thermostats and the zone control dampers). Since the zones cannot be created at the trunk duct level, they must be created by installing dampers in the branch runout ducts. Therefore, (in this example) two control dampers are associated with four of five zones. This means that the zone thermostat (and the associated control hardware) must be capable of controlling two dampers — which may be in different rooms. (If necessary, three or more dampers could be associated with a zone or a zone thermostat.)

Bypass Duct

A bypass duct and a bypass damper will be required if the primary components of the HVAC system (blower, compressor or heat exchanger) are not equipped with some type of capacity control (speed control, for example). If a bypass duct is required, the design value for the air flow through the bypass will depend on the minimum flow rates that are associated with the zone dampers. If the zone dampers can be driven to the closed position (when the blower is operating), the bypass duct should be sized to handle at least 80 percent of the design air flow rate. If the zone dampers are equipped with minimum position stops, the bypass duct can be sized to handle the difference between the design air flow rate and the minimum flow rate that can be routed through the supply duct system.

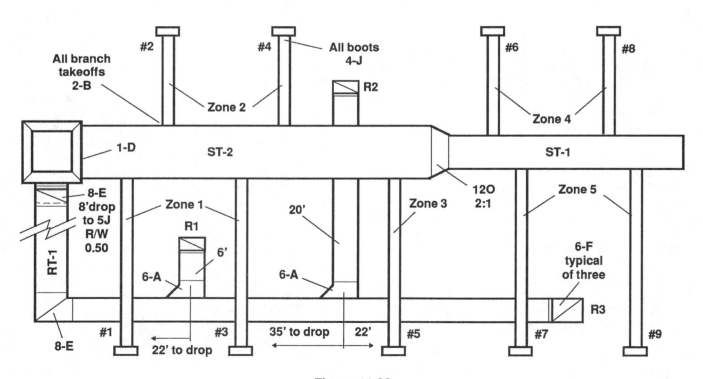

Figure 11-30

The bypass damper may be equipped with a mechanical operator or it may be a pressure-activated (counterbalanced) device. In either case, the pressure drop that is associated with the bypass loop should be comparable to the pressure drop that is associated with the critical circulation path.

Returns
A low-resistance return path is required for each zone. If any room is isolated from one of the returns, transfer grilles can be used to establish a circulation path between the isolated room and the return.

Data Collection
The designer must verify that the existing blower and duct system is compatible with the proposed modification. This work begins with a **Manual J** load calculation. (Assuming that the designer does not have access to the original design calculations and equipment performance data.)

The **Manual J** calculations are required because the loads determine the air flow rates that are associated with each room and the proposed zones. Figure 11-31 summarizes the information that pertains to this example. This data includes the orientation of the primary exposure, the percentage of glass (compared to the wall area), the **Manual J** loads and the peak cooling load that is associated with each room.

Run	Glass faces	Glass %	Heat BTUH	Cool BTUH	SHCF	Peak Cool
1	S	20	3810	3110	1.25	3888
2	W	15	3800	2380	1.25	2975
3	E	15	3970	3200	1.00	3200
4	W	10	4250	2750	1.25	3438
5	E	10	3860	3010	1.00	3010
6	W	15	4500	2610	1.25	3263
7	E	15	4590	3500	1.00	3500
8	N	10	4870	3750	1.00	3750
9	N	10	2350	1690	1.00	1690
Heating load = 36000			Cooling load = 26000			

Figure 11-31

The field survey is required to evaluate the air moving capability of the blower and the air conveyance abilities of the existing duct runs. This inspection should produce the following information:

• The airway sizes that are associated with the existing trunk ducts and runout ducts (supply and return).

• The measured length of each runout duct (supply and return).

• The measured length of each trunk run — from the branch runout fitting to the air handler (supply and return).

• An identification number (**Manual D** group number) for each fitting that is associated with the duct system.

• The system air flow rates (blower CFM) and the available static pressures (IWC) that are associated with each fan speed. (The available static pressure is the pressure that can be used to overcome the resistance of the air-side components that are external to the air handler cabinet.)

If the manufacturer's performance data is not available, air balancing equipment can be used to measure the flow rates and the external pressures that are associated with each fan speed. When these tests are conducted, all the hand dampers and registers should be in the wide open position and the filter (and coil) should be clean. Measure the system CFM values, the static pressure in the return plenum and the static pressure in the supply plenum. Note that the supply-side pressure measurements should be made at a position that is just downstream from the air handler (and the associated accessory components) and the return-side pressure measurements should be made at a position that is just upstream from the air handler (and the associated accessory components).

For this example, the information that is associated with a field survey is summarized by Figures 11-30 and 11-32. Figure 11-30 documents the system geometry and the fitting identification numbers. Figure 11-32 summarizes the dimensional data and presents the results of heat pump blower tests (flow and pressure measurements) that were made at each fan speed.

Supply Runs				Return Runs			
#	Size	Runout	Trunk	#	Size	Runout	Trunk
1	6"	24'	6'	R1	10"	6'	30'
2	6"	14'	12'	R2	12"	20'	43'
3	6"	24'	18'	R3	8"	22'	43'
4	6"	14'	24'	RT-1	16"	(20" x 10")	
5	6"	24'	34'				
6	6"	14'	43'	**Blower Test Data**			
7	6"	24'	58'	Speed	CFM	IWC	
8	6"	14'	63'	Low	840	0.20	
9	6"	24'	66'	Medium	920	0.31	
ST-1	11"	(12" x 8")		High	1060	0.36	
ST-2	14"	(20" x 8")		Includes filter, coil and heater			

Figure 11-32

Figure 11-33 compares the blower test data points with a graph that represents the system resistance curve (refer to Section 4-5). This type of diagram is useful because it can be used to certify the accuracy of the blower test. In this example there is a high level of confidence in the accuracy of the blower test because there is good correlation between all three test points and the system curve.

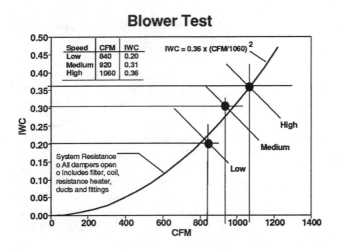

Blower Test

Speed	CFM	IWC
Low	840	0.20
Medium	920	0.31
High	1060	0.36

$IWC = 0.36 \times (CFM/1060)^2$

Figure 11-33

Sizing Calculations

This example emphasizes sheet metal construction, but this system could be fabricated from any combination of sheet

metal, duct board or flexible wire helix materials. In any case, the sizing calculations that are required to design this particular type of system can be based on the following concepts:

- Since flow control dampers will be added to the system, the pressure drop that is associated with an open damper must be subtracted from the available static pressure.

- The capacity of the central equipment and the flow rates that are associated with the primary trunk ducts (supply and return) can be based on the traditional **Manual J** load for the entire house. (The concept of diversity applies to the cooling loads that are associated with a single-family detached home.)

- Zones are defined by rooms that have similar load characteristics. In this example, the exposure and the amount of glass are the primary factors that affect zoning decisions.

- Room CFM values are based on the heating loads and the peak cooling loads. These load are summarized by Figure 11-31. Note that the peak cooling loads are estimated by multiplying the traditional **Manual J** cooling loads by the sensible load correction factors (SLCF values) that are found in **Manual J**, Appendix A2.

Effective Length Calculation

Figure 11-34 provides a sketch of the proposed modifications. This figure shows that supply runs 1 and 3 are associated with zone 1, supply runs 2 and 4 are associated with zone 2, supply run 3 is associated with zone 3, supply runs 6 and 8 are

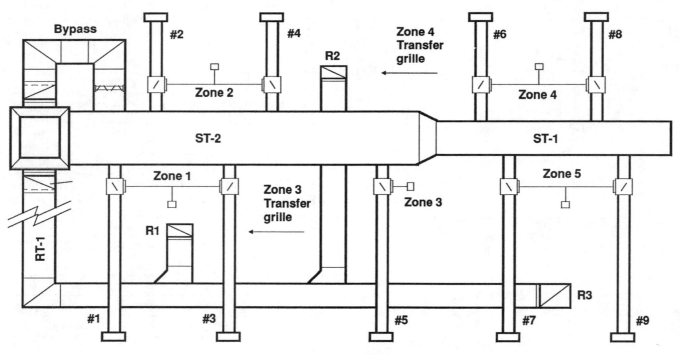

Figure 11-34

Effective Length Calculation Sheet

Element	Supply Run ID Number				Element	Return Run ID Number			
	# 1	# 6	# 9	#		# R1	# R2	# R3	#
Trunk Length	6	43	66		Trunk Length	22	35	35	
Trunk Length					Trunk Length	8	8	8	
Trunk Length					Trunk Length				
Runout Length	24	14	24		Runout Length	6	20	22	
Group 1 (D)	10	10	10		Group 5 (J)	15	15	15	(R/W = .5)
Group 2 (B)	45	40	20		Group 6 (F)	25	25	25	
Group 3					Group 7				
Group 4 (J)	30	30	30		Group 8 (E)	20	20	20	(2 @ 10')
Group 8					Group 10				
Group 9					Group 11				
Group 11					Group 12				
Group 12 (O)		5	5		Group 13				
Group 13					Other (6A br)	10	60		cfm1/cfm2
Other					Other (6A m)		10	35	0.39 (R1) 0.72 (R2)
Other					Other				35 = 25+10
Other					Other				
Total Length	115	142	155		Total Length	106	193	160	

Figure 11-35

associated with zone 4, and supply runs 7 and 9 are associated with zone 5. Also note that when the transfer grilles are installed, return R1 will be associated with zones 1 and 3, return R2 will be associated with zones 2 and 4 and return R3 will be associated with zone 5. Based on an inspection of the geometry and the fittings that are associated with this system, it appears that supply runs 1, 6, and 9 and returns R1, R2 and R3 could be associated with the longest circulation path.

Figure 11-35 summarizes the effective length calculations that are associated with the selected duct runs. In this example, a supplemental calculation is required because the effective length of the longest supply run must be combined with the effective length of the longest return run. These calculations are summarized below. This summary shows that the effective length of the longest circulation path is 348 feet. This path is defined by supply run 9, which has a 155 foot length and return run R2, which has a 193 foot length.

Run	#1	#6	#9
Supply TEL	115	142	155
Run	R1	R2	R3
Return TEL	106	193	160

Design Friction Rate Calculation

In this example, the blower test data indicates that the fan was able to move 1,060 CFM through a duct system that produces 0.36 IWC of external resistance (at high speed). Since there were no VAV dampers associated with the blower test, the resistance that is associated with an open control damper (0.05 IWC) must be subtracted from the 0.36 IWC value. Therefore, the design value for the friction rate will be based on 0.31 IWC of pressure and 348 feet of effective length. These calculations are summarized on the next page by Figure 11- 36.

Duct Sizing Calculations

On page 11-33, Figure 11-37 summarizes the duct sizing calculations that are associated with this example. The following comments apply to these calculations:

- All of the duct sizes were determined by using the ACCA Duct Sizing Slide Rule ("Galvanized Metal Duct" scale.)

- Supply runs 1 and 3 are associated with zone 1 and return R1; supply runs 2, and 4 are associated with zone 2 and return R2; supply run 5 is associated with zone 3 and return R1, supply runs 6, and 8 are associated with zone 4 and return R2; supply runs 7, and 9 are associated with zone 5 and return R3.

Friction Rate Worksheet

Step 1) Manufacturer's Blower Data (Field test data)

External static pressure (ESP) = __0.36__ IWC   CFM = __1060__

Step 2) Device Pressure Losses

Direct expansion refrigerant coil ...   included in test data
Electric resistance heating coil .....   included in test data
Hot water coil ....
Heat exchanger ....
Low efficiency filter ....   included in test data
High or mid-efficiency filter ....
Electronic filter ....
Humidifier ....
Supply outlet ....   included in test data
Return grille ....   included in test data
Balancing damper ....   included in test data
Other device ....   0.05 (VAV damper)

Total device losses (DPL) .... __0.05__   IWC

Step 3) Available Static Pressure

ASP = (ESP - DPL) = (__0.36__ - __0.05__) = __0.31__ IWC

Step 4) Total Effective Length (TEL)

Supply-side TEL + Return-side TEL = (__155__ + __193__) = __348__ FEET

Step 5) Friction Rate Design Value (FR)

FR value from friction rate chart = __0.09__ IWC/100

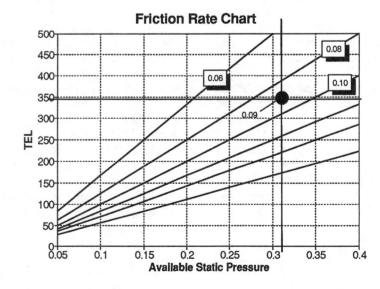

Figure 11-36

Duct Sizing Worksheet

HF = Blower CFM / Manual J Heat Loss = (1000) / (36000) = 0.0278

CF = Blower CFM / Manual J Sensible Heat Gain = (1000) / (26000) = 0.0385

FR Value
0.09

Supply Duct System

Run - Trunk	H-BTUH	C-BTUH	H-CFM	C-CFM	Dsn CFM	Round Size	Velocity	Final Size
1 — ST-1	3810	3888	106	150	150	7	ok	7
2 — ST-1	3800	2975	106	114	114	6	ok	6
3 — ST-1	3970	3200	110	123	123	7	ok	7
4 — ST-1	4250	3438	118	132	132	7	ok	7
5 — ST-1	3860	3010	107	116	116	6	ok	6
6 — ST-2	4500	3263	125	125	125	7	ok	7
7 — ST-2	4590	3500	128	135	135	7	ok	7
8 — ST-2	4870	3750	135	144	144	7	ok	7
9 — ST-2	2350	1690	65	65	65	5	ok	5
10 —								
11 —								
12 —								
13 —								
14 —								
15 —								
		Trunk						
		Trunk						
		Trunk						
		Trunk ST-1	453	469	469	11	710	11
		Trunk ST-2	1000	1000	1000	14	970	15

Return Duct System

Run - Trunk	Associated Supply Runs	H-CFM	C-CFM	Dsn CFM	Round Size	Velocity	Final Size
1 — RT-1	#1, #3, #5	323	389	389	10	740	11
2 — RT-1	#2, #4, #6, #8	484	515	515	11	800	12
3 — RT-1	#7 , #9	193	200	200	8	590	8
4 —							
5 —							
6 —							
7 —							
8 —							
9 —							
	Trunk RT1	1000	1000	1000	14	960	17
	Trunk						
	Trunk BP	800	800	800	13	880	15
	Trunk						

1) H-BTUH and C-BTUH from the **Manual J** room load calculation procedure
2) H-CFM = HF x H-BTUH and C-CFM = CF x C--BTUH
3) Dsn CFM = larger of the H-CFM or C-CFM values (runout ducts) . . . or . . . total downstream CFM (trunk ducts)
4) Round size based on FR value. Final size based on FR value (if the velocity is acceptable) or the maximum allowable velocity value

Figure 11-37

- Supply branches 1 through 5 are associated with supply trunk ST-2 and supply branches 6 through 9 are associated with supply trunk ST-1.

- Return runs R1, R2 and R3 feed into primary trunk RT-1.

- The sizes of the supply runout ducts are based on the CFM values that are associated with the heating loads and the peak cooling loads.

- The final sizes of the supply runout ducts are based on the friction rate design value (0.09 IWC/100) because the corresponding velocities are less than 900 FPM. (The runout velocities are always less than 900 FPM when the design friction rate value falls inside the "wedge" that is associated with the friction rate chart.)

- The size of supply trunk ST-1 is based on the CFM values that are associated with zones 4 and 5.

- The size of supply trunk ST-1 is based on the friction rate design value (0.09 IWC/100) because the corresponding velocity is less than 900 FPM.

- The size of supply trunk ST-2 is based on the 1,000 CFM value that is associated with the **Manual J** load for the entire house. (The **Manual J** load for the entire house was used because the zone loads do not peak simultaneously.)

- The final size of supply trunk ST-2 is based on the maximum allowable velocity (900 FPM) because the velocity that is associated with the friction rate value (0.09 IWC/100) exceeds 900 FPM.

- The sizes of the zone return runs (R1, R2 and R3) are based on the CFM values that are associated with the heating loads and the peak cooling loads.

- The final sizes of zone return ducts R1 and R2 are based on the maximum allowable velocity (700 FPM) because the velocities that are associated with the friction rate value (0.09 IWC/100) exceed 700 FPM.

- The final size of the zone return duct R3 is based on the friction rate design value (0.09 IWC/100) because the corresponding velocity is acceptable (700 FPM or less).

- The size of return trunk RT-1 is based on the 1,000 CFM value that is associated with the **Manual J** load for the entire house (the zone loads do not peak simultaneously).

- The final size of return trunk RT-1 is based on the maximum allowable velocity (700 FPM) because the velocity that is associated with the friction rate value (0.09 IWC/100) exceeds 700 FPM.

- The final size of the bypass duct is based on 80 percent of the design air flow rate (1,000 CFM = 0.80 x 800 CFM).

- The final size of the bypass duct is based on the maximum allowable velocity (700 FPM) because the velocity that is associated with the friction rate value (0.08 IWC/100) exceeds 700 FPM

- The ACCA Duct Sizing Slide Rule can be used to convert round sizes into equivalent rectangular sizes.

Comments and Observations

This example is characterized by two air distribution systems: the as-built system (which may not be properly designed or documented), and the desired system, which has been designed (on paper) to function as a five-zone VAV system. Geometrically, these systems are identical (except for the bypass duct), and they both share the same blower data, but there are differences associated with the duct sizes.

Figure 11-38 compares the round-duct sizes of the two systems. This comparison shows that some of the existing supply-side runout ducts are 1-inch smaller than the size that is associated with the desired system. As far as air delivery is concerned, this 1-inch difference is not critical unless the runout duct is associated with the critical path or a path that is nearly as long as the critical path. (The design value for the friction rate is dictated by the length of the critical circulation path.) Since runs 6, 7 and 8 are associated with a long circulation path (refer to page 11-31), the existing 6-inch ducts should be replaced with 7-inch ducts.

Run	Exsisting Size	Desired Size		Change Required
		For F/100	**For FPM**	
#1	6"	7"	7"	ok
#2	6"	6"	6"	ok
#3	6"	7"	7"	ok
#4	6"	7"	7"	ok
#5	6"	6"	6"	ok
#6	6"	7"	7"	new run
#7	6"	7"	7"	new run
#8	6"	7"	7"	new run
#9	6"	5"	5"	ok
ST-1	11"	11"	11"	ok
ST-2	14"	14"	15"	ok
R1	10"	10"	11"	ok
R2	12"	11"	12"	ok
R3	8"	8"	8"	ok
RT-1	16"	14"	17"	ok

The performance of the existing blower is acceptable , if operated at high speed.

Figure 11-38

Figure 11-38 also shows the existing supply-side trunk ducts and the return ducts are large enough to accommodate the flow rates that are associated with the desired system (based on the design value for the friction rate); but three of the runs (ST-2, R1 and RT-1) are 1-inch too small — if the size is based on the recommended velocity limit. Fortunately, modifications will not be required because a 1-inch discrepancy will not result in excessive velocities.

This example also is characterized by equipment that features a constant-speed blower (which is barely adequate) and zone dampers that do not have minimum flow stops. Therefore, an 80 percent bypass duct is required because the capacity of the major mechanical components cannot be adjusted to match the part-load operating conditions. (If the zone dampers had been equipped with minimum position stops, the bypass duct could have been sized to handle the difference between the design air flow rate and the minimum flow rate that can be routed through the supply duct system. Or, the bypass duct might have been eliminated if the central equipment featured a variable-speed blower and capacity controls.)

Note that the modifications that are associated with converting an existing single-zone system into a zoned VAV system (in addition to adding VAV dampers and controls) varies on a case-by-case basis. Some systems may not require any changes, some may require minor changes (as demonstrated by this example), some may require major sheet metal modifications, and, in extreme cases, sheet metal modifications and a new blower unit may be required.

Section 12
Duct System Efficiency

Duct system efficiency depends on the flow resistance that is associated with the duct runs, the heat transfer through the duct walls and the leakage that is associated with the seams and joints. The flow resistance that is associated with residential duct runs is not important as far as system efficiency is concerned, but it is pertinent to the duct sizing calculations. Conduction and leakage losses (or gains) can have a significant effect on the combined efficiency of the structural-mechanical system if uninsulated or marginally insulated ducts are exposed to the outdoor air or located in an unconditioned space. Conduction and leakage losses (or gains) also can degrade comfort, affect air quality and create health and safety problems.

12-1 Aerodynamic Efficiency

If the flow rate and the cross-sectional area are held constant, the aerodynamic efficiency of a duct depends on its shape. In this regard, round shapes are the most efficient because the friction rate (pressure drop per 100 feet of length) of a round duct will always be less than the friction rate that is associated with any other shape. Square shapes and rectangular shapes can be fairly efficient, but the aerodynamic efficiency decreases as the aspect ratio increases. (Oval shapes will be slightly more efficient than rectangular shapes that have the same aspect ratio.) A comparison of the aerodynamic efficiency of round, rectangular and oval shapes is provided by Figure 12-1.

The aerodynamic efficiency of a section of duct also depends on surface roughness of the airway material. Plastic and sheet metal surfaces are more efficient than fibrous glass surfaces (duct board and duct liner) and fibrous glass surfaces are more efficient than wire helix surfaces (flex duct). Figure 12-2 compares the aerodynamic efficiency of three popular duct materials.

Aerodynamic Efficiency of Duct Material				
CFM = 1000 Area = 1.25 SQ.FT. Velocity = 800 FPM				
Shape	Aspect	F/100 Value		
		SM	DB	Flex
Round	NA	0.066	0.080	0.120
Square	1:1	0.070	0.085	NA
Rectangular	2:1	0.075	0.092	NA
Rectangular	4:1	0.095	0.130	NA
Rectangular	8:1	0.130	0.180	NA
Friction rates from the ACCA Duct Sizing Slide Rule SM = Sheet Metal; DB = Duct Board; Flex = Flex Duct F/100 = IWC per 100 feet of duct				

Figure 12-2

Since the pressure that is available to move the air through the duct system is limited, the airway size must be increased to compensate for the efficiency differences that are associated with the duct shape and the airway material. Figure 12-3 demonstrates how the airway size can be used to compensate for aerodynamic inefficiencies. Note that the cross-sectional

Aerodynamic Efficiency of Duct Shapes			
CFM = 1000 Area = 1.25 SQ.FT. Velocity = 800 FPM			
Shape	Aspect	F/100	Size (inches)
Round	NA	0.066	15.14
Square	1:1	0.070	13.42 x 13.42
Rectangular	2:1	0.075	9.49 x 18.97
Oval	2:1	0.070	10.04 x 20.08
Rectangular	4:1	0.095	6.71 x 26.83
Oval	4:1	0.090	6.90 x 27.58
Rectangular	8:1	0.130	4.74 x 37.95
Oval	8:1	0.125	4.81 x 38.47
Friction rates from the ACCA Duct Sizing Slide Rule Sheet metal duct material F/100 = IWC per 100 feet of duct 1.25 SQ.FT. = 180 SQ.IN.			

Figure 12-1

Equal Resistance Designs			
CFM = 1000 Friction Rate = 0.10 IWC per 100 Feet			
Material	Size	Area	Velocity
Sheet Metal	14.0 Dia.	1.07	935
Duct Board	14.6 Dia	1.16	862
Sheet Metal	6.7 x 26.8	1.25	800
Duct Board	6.9 x 27.6	1.32	758
Flex Duct	15.7 Dia.	1.34	746
Sizes read from the ACCA Duct Sizing Slide Rule Sizes = Inches Area = SQ.FT. Velocity = FPM			

Figure 12-3

areas (and the amount of material) increase; and the velocities decrease as the aerodynamic inefficiencies get larger.

12-2 Conduction Losses

The conductive heat gains and losses that are created when ducts are exposed to the outdoor air or when ducts are located in an unconditioned space will degrade the performance of the HVAC system. However, the temperatures in the occupied space will be maintained if the duct wall conduction losses are included in the **Manual J** load estimates. But comfort is not the only consideration. Duct losses should be minimized because they degrade system efficiency and increase the annual cost of operation.

Duct Insulation Standards
Local codes and regulations may establish the minimum duct insulation requirements. These codes and regulations supersede any of the information that is provided in this manual.

Minimum duct insulation standards can be found in the CABO-MEC and in ASHRAE Standard 90.2. The information that is contained in these documents (1994 versions) is summarized on the next page by Figures 12-4 and 12-5. Duct materials must also meet certain fire hazard standards. Refer to the National Fire Protection Association Standard 90A and Standard 90B for this information.

Effective R-Values
There are many ways to obtain the desired duct insulation R-value. Some of the methods that can be used to satisfy a given R-value requirement are summarized below. Note that these suggestions recognize that it is difficult to install glass fiber blankets without causing some compression. Since some manufacturers suggest that 50 percent compression is typical, the recommended blanket thicknesses were adjusted for 50 percent compression. (A 50 percent compression translates into a 39 percent reduction in insulating efficiency.)

R-2 Duct Insulation
• 1 inch of 0.6 to 0.75 LB/CU.FT. glass fiber blanket
• 1/2 inch of 2 to 3 LB/CU.FT. glass fiber duct liner
• 1/2 inch of 3 to 10 LB/CU.FT. glass fiber board
• Flexible duct with 1 inch glass fiber jacket

R-4 Duct Insulation
• 2 inches of 0.6 to 0.75 LB/CU.FT. glass fiber blanket
• 1 inch of 1.5 to 3 LB/CU.FT. glass fiber duct liner
• 1 inch of 3 to 10 LB/CU.FT. glass fiber board
• Flexible duct with glass fiber jacket rated at R4

R-6 Duct Insulation
• 3 inches of 0.6 to 0.75 LB/CU.FT. glass fiber blanket
• 2-1/2 inches of 1.0 LB/CU.FT. glass fiber blanket
• 1-1/2 inches of 1.5 to 3.0 LB/CU.FT. glass fiber duct liner
• 1-1/2 inches of 3 to 10 LB/CU.FT. glass fiber board
• Flexible duct with glass fiber jacket rated at R6

R-8 Duct Insulation
• 1 inch duct liner plus 2 inches glass fiber blanket
• 1 inch duct board plus 2 inches glass fiber blanket
• 1-1/2 inches duct liner plus 1 inch glass fiber blanket
• 1-1/2 inches duct board plus 1 inch glass fiber blanket
• Flexible duct with glass fiber jacket rated at R8

Conduction Loss Estimates
Figure 12-6 (see page 12-4) can be used to estimate the temperature rise or the temperature drop of the air that flows through a duct that is installed in an unconditioned space. Note that this chart is designed for a bare metal duct that has a 2:1 aspect ratio. (The footnotes below the chart provide a method for making corrections for duct insulation and aspect ratio.)

Example
Calculate the temperature rise and heat gain if 1,000 CFM of 55 °F air flows through a 40-foot section of bare metal duct. The temperature of the air surrounding the duct is 130 °F, the flow velocity is equal to 900 FPM and the aspect ratio of the duct is 3:1. Also calculate the temperature rise and the heat gain if 1-inch duct board (R-4) is substituted for bare metal.

Gain factor from the chart = 0.34 (°F / °F / 100 FT)

Aspect multiplier = 1.10

Rise (metal) = 0.34 x 1.10 x (130-55) x 40/100 = 11.2 °F

Heat gain (metal) = 1.1 x 1000 x 11.2 = 12,320 BTUH

R-value multiplier = 0.17

Rise (duct board) = 0.17 x 11.2 = 1.9 °F

Heat gain (duct board) = 1.1 x 1000 x 1.9 = 2,090 BTUH

Vapor Retarders
In humid climates, duct board or external wrap may not provide enough insulation to prevent condensation on the duct walls. Facings and wraps that have a perm rating of 0.50 or less are recommended when the average cooling season outdoor dewpoint exceeds 60 °F. Figure 12-7 (page 12-5) shows the areas of the country that have an average cooling season (July/August) dewpoint that exceeds 60 °F.

12-3 Leakage Losses

A small amount of leakage *to or from the conditioned space* is acceptable, providing that it does not have an adverse effect on equipment loads, comfort or operating costs. However, duct sealing may be required if this type of leakage is significant and localized because it produces room-to-room pressure differences that amplify the envelope infiltration loads and disrupt the balance of the air distribution system.

CABO-MEC — Table No. 503.9.1 Minimum Duct Insulation				1994
Duct location	Cooling		Heating	
Exterior of building	**CDD** Below 500 501 to 1150 1151 to 2000 Above 2000	**R-Value** 3.3 5.0 6.5 8.0	**HDD** Below 1500 1501 to 4500 4501 to 7500 Above 7500	**R-Value** 3.3 5.0 6.5 8.0
Inside a conditioned space	—	None	—	None
In an unconditioned space	**Duct wall TD** Less than 15 15 to 40 More than 40	None 3.3 5.0	**Duct wall TD** Less than 15 15 to 40 More than 40	None 3.3 5.0

1) This table applies to supply ducts and return ducts.
2) Duct wall TD = air temperature difference across the duct wall.
3) R-values apply to the insulation material only (air film resistance are not included).
4) The R-values specified above may have to be increased in order to prevent condensation.
5) A vapor retarder may be required.
6) Where exterior walls are used as plenum walls, wall insulation shall be required by the most restrictive condition of this section.
7) Unconditioned spaces include basements, attics and crawl spaces.
8) Published R-value data shall conform to ASTM C 518-85.

Figure 12-4

ASHRAE 90.2 — Table 6.2a Minimum Duct Insulation				1994
Duct location	Cooling		Heating	
	CDH	R-Value	HDD	R-Value
On roof or exterior of the building	Any	6	Any	6
Attic or garage	Below 15,000 15,001 to 30,000 Over 30,000	4 6 6	Below 3,000 3,001 to 6,000 Over 6,000	4 6 6
Basement or unvented crawl space under insulated floor	Below 15,000 15,001 to 30,000 Over 30,000	4 4 6	Below 3,000 3,001 to 6,000 Over 6,000	2 2 4
Under concrete slab (buried in the ground)	Refer to ACCA Manual 4 Installation Techniques for Perimeter Heating and Cooling Systems			
Inside a conditioned space (heating or cooling)	None			
Basement or unvented crawlspace with insulated walls (heating only)	None			

1) This table applies to supply ducts, return ducts, plenums and enclosures. This table does not apply to equipment cabinets.
2) CDH = Cooling degree hours; HDD = Heating degree days. (CDH and HDD values are listed in Section 9.)
3) If heating and cooling is provided, the insulation requirement is equal to the larger of the two R-values.
4) The minimum R-values are for the insulation material only. (They do not include air film resistances.)
5) If ducts are installed in wall, roof, ceiling or floor cavity that separates a conditioned space from the outdoor air or from an unconditioned space, insulation must be installed (as specifed in Section 5) between the duct wall and the exposed surface.
6) The R-values specified above may have to be increased in order to prevent condensation.
7) A vapor retarder must be installed on supply air ducts if cooling is provided and the mean dewpoint of the outdoor air is expected to exceed 60 °F during any month of the year. (Dewpoint temperature information is provided by Table 6.3.)

Figure 12-5

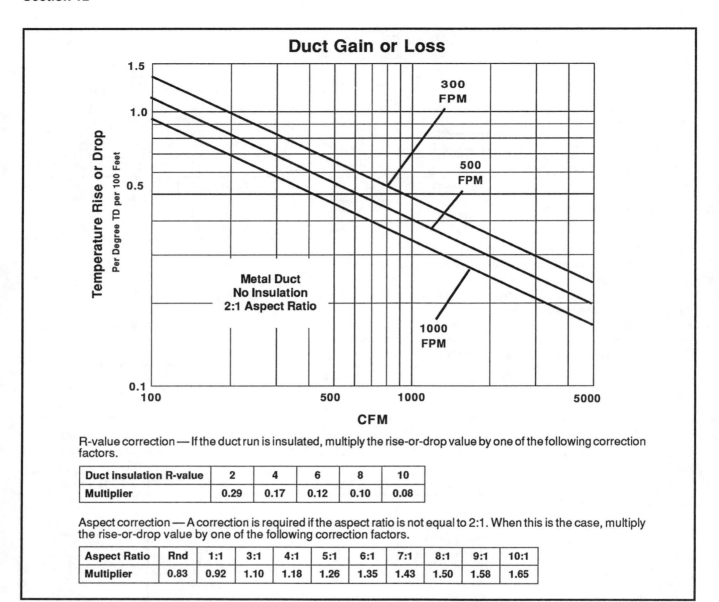

Duct Gain or Loss

R-value correction — If the duct run is insulated, multiply the rise-or-drop value by one of the following correction factors.

Duct insulation R-value	2	4	6	8	10
Multiplier	0.29	0.17	0.12	0.10	0.08

Aspect correction — A correction is required if the aspect ratio is not equal to 2:1. When this is the case, multiply the rise-or-drop value by one of the following correction factors.

Aspect Ratio	Rnd	1:1	3:1	4:1	5:1	6:1	7:1	8:1	9:1	10:1
Multiplier	0.83	0.92	1.10	1.18	1.26	1.35	1.43	1.50	1.58	1.65

Figure 12-6

Duct leakage that is associated with an *unconditioned space* is undesirable because leakage increases the loads on the HVAC equipment, increases operating costs and can have an adverse effect on comfort and air quality. This type of leakage translates into larger heating and cooling equipment, increased flow rates (CFM), larger ducts, larger fans, increased first cost and a larger demand (KW) on the power grid. (If leaky ducts are representative of local construction practices, designers tend to compensate for the problem by installing more heating and cooling capacity than would otherwise be required.)

Minimum Sealing Standards
Leakage is a function of the pressure in the duct, the size, shape and the length of the duct, construction details, sealant and workmanship. Some comments about sealing the joints and seams that are associated with residential duct systems are provided below. Refer to Appendix 4 for more information about the methods, materials and techniques that are associated with fabricating and sealing sheet metal, fibrous glass (board or liner) and flexible duct systems.

Duct Runs and Extended Plenums
The sealing requirements, that pertain to low pressure (positive or negative pressures less than 2 IWC) sheet metal duct runs and extended plenums apply to the transverse joints, which must be sealed. Longitudinal seams do not have to be sealed, but they must be tight. It also is necessary to make sure that metal gauges and the fabrication techniques comply with codes and industry standards.

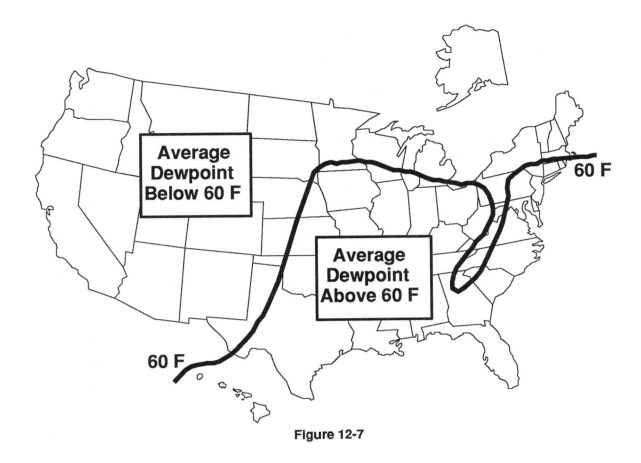

Figure 12-7

The fabrication and sealing requirements that pertain to fibrous board duct runs apply to the transverse joints and the longitudinal seams. The methods and materials that are associated with this work must comply with industry standards.

Round spiral duct, wire helix flexible duct and plastic pipe do not have to be sealed because they are airtight. Note that, as far as leakage is concerned, airtight ducts are the obvious choice if the duct run is located in an unconditioned space or if it is exposed to the outdoor air. Also note that plastic ducts are well suited for below-grade installations because they are watertight and because they do not rust or corrode. (Justified or not, local codes and utility regulations may restrict the use of certain types of duct materials.)

Stud Spaces and Panned Joist Spaces
It is possible to create an airway out of a stud space or panned joist space. Unfortunately, this approach to solving duct routing problems produces airways that are very leaky. (A leakage path can be established between the conditioned space and the attic, basement, crawl space or the outdoors.) Therefore, stud spaces and panned joist spaces should not be used as part of the air distribution system unless the airway can be completely sealed. This means sealing all of the cracks, joints and penetrations that are associated with the structural surfaces

and sealing the joints and seams that are associated with the panning material.

Fittings and Device Interface Connections
The joints and seams that are associated with branch takeoff fittings, elbows, tees, wyes and device interface connections should be sealed (regardless of the type of material that is used to fabricate the duct system). Airtight flexible connections are recommended when a duct interfaces with an air handler. Also seal the seams that are associated with flexible duct junction box connections.

Leakage at the Register and Grille Flanges
A substantial amount of leakage can occur at supply outlets and return grilles. (There are potential leakage paths to the attic, basement or other unconditioned spaces.) This leakage is produced when the material that is associated with a duct, boot or transition box is not sealed to the frame of the register or grille. Always provide a seal between the matting surface of the duct or duct fitting and the flange or frame that is associated with a diffuser, register or grille.

Return and Discharge Plenums
Return plenums and discharge plenums that are attached to the central air handling equipment tend to leak at the seams and joints. These seams and joints should be sealed.

In some cases, an air handler is mounted on top of a plenum that is fabricated out of wood framing and plasterboard. These plenums have been found to have serious leakage problems when the seams and the pipe penetrations are not sealed. And, they can be outrageously leaky if one or two of the plenum walls are coincident with a partition or an exterior wall. For example, if this type of plenum is fabricated before the plasterboard is applied to the wall studs (partition or exterior wall), the plasterboard will stop at the top of the plenum and the inside of the plenum will be open to the wall cavity. Since this cavity extends to the ceiling and to the floor, it can create a leakage path between the plenum and the attic, garage, basement or a crawl space. These leakage paths can be eliminated if the inside surfaces of this type of plenum are paneled and thoroughly sealed with a suitable mastic.

Any building cavity (chase, ceiling space, crawl space or stairwell) that is used as a plenum will cause serious leakage problems when these cavities are not completely isolated from the ancillary spaces (attic, basement, garage and crawl spaces) and the outdoors. The insides of these types of plenums must be paneled and thoroughly sealed with mastic.

Note that the leakage that is associated with plenums that are close to the air handler will be larger than the leakage that occurs at some remote point in a duct run. The larger leakage rate occurs because the pressure differences near the air handler are larger than the pressure differences at some remote point in the duct system.

Air Handler Cabinets
Air handler cabinet leaks are caused by bent or missing panels, poor or damaged panel seals, cracks at the duct-unit connection points, cabinet penetrations and knockout openings. Note that single package air handlers are completely exposed to the weather, which increases the potential for rust and corrosion damage that can create leakage paths. Any type of cabinet leak is very important because the maximum pressure differences occur at the air handler. All air handler cabinet leaks should be sealed.

Equipment in Closet with Louvered Door
Leakage from the attic, basement, crawl space or from other unconditioned spaces can be a problem when the air handler is located in a closet that has a louvered door that serves as a central return grille. If the free area of the louver is too small, the closet will be subject to a negative pressure and leakage paths to the ancillary spaces could be established.

Methods, Materials and Workmanship
All seams and joints must be fabricated in accordance with industry standards (refer to Appendix 4). Tapes and mastics must be applied in accordance with industry standards. Tapes and mastics must be suitable for the intended application (regarding deterioration caused by aging, moisture and sunlight). And, there must be no inexcusable oversights (missing duct runs or fittings, disconnections, or penetrations and openings that are not sealed).

Damage
Even if the duct system has been properly installed, serious leakage problems can be traced to system abuse. This damage could be caused by other trades, occupants, pets and rodents. If there is a high potential for damage to occur after the system has been installed, the system should be fabricated out of suitable materials and protected by guards and shields where necessary.

Duct Leakage Estimates
The information presented by Figure 12-8 and on the next page by Figure 12-9 can be used to estimate the leakage CFM that is associated with a duct system. (Figure 12-8 provides guidance regarding the leakage class that is associated with various types of residential duct systems and Figure 12-9 correlates the leakage CFM per 100 square feet of duct surface area with static pressure.) Note that the accuracy of the leakage estimate will depend on the designer's ability to assign a leakage class (CL value) to the duct system. In this regard, the leakage class that is associated with an unsealed duct system is speculative because the leakage is defined by a wide range of CL values, but a reasonable amount of accuracy can be expected if the duct system is built and sealed in accordance with industry standards.

Leakage Class (CL)		
Duct System	Sealed [1]	Unsealed [6]
Fabricated Sheet Metal [2]	48	48 to 192
Fibrous Glass [3]	24	24 to 192
Wire Helix (Flexible) [4]	12	12 to 192
Metal — Round Spiral [5]	6	6 to 96
Plastic (Glued Joints)	3	NA

1) Transverse joints, fitting joints and boot-grille flanges
2) Rectangular trunk and round runouts
3) Rigid glass trunks and flexible or sheet metal runouts
4) Flexible trunks, flexible runouts with junction boxes
5) Round spiral trunks and round spiral runouts
6) Based on measurements made during field tests. In extreme cases (excessive use of building cavities and panning, deterioration, physical damage or disconnections) the leakage CFM can be equal to 30 or 40 percent of the blower CFM.

Figure 12-8

The accuracy of the leakage estimate also is affected by the static pressure value that is used in the calculation. This can be problematic because the static pressure gradually changes in the direction of the flow and abruptly changes when the flow passes through a device. Therefore, the designer must select a pressure that is representative of the average operating condition. Also note that the static pressure is positive on the supply side of the system and negative on the return side of the system, and that the magnitude of these two pressures

Duct Leakage Chart

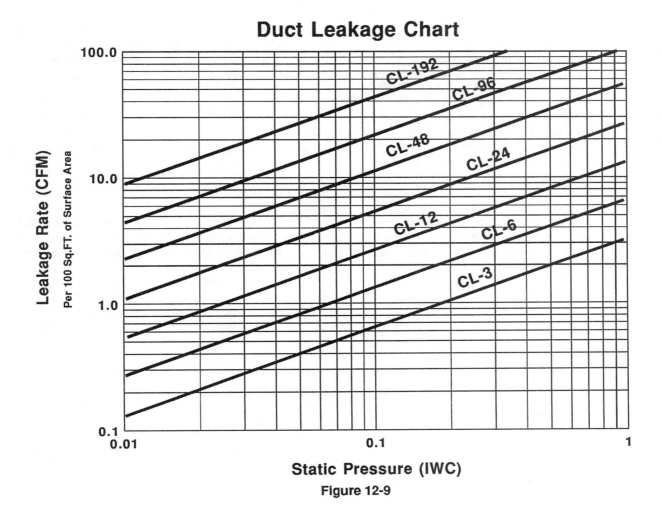

Static Pressure (IWC)

Figure 12-9

could be quite different. Therefore, separate leakage calculations should be made for each side of the system.

There is also a problem associated with predicting the leakage class of duct systems that feature more than one type of duct construction — a sheet-metal-duct-board system, for example. In these cases it would be logical to use a weighted average leakage class, based on the surface areas that are associated with each type of construction.

Example
Estimate the leakage CFM that is associated with a duct system that is located in an unconditioned space. The external static pressure that is produced by the blower (at 1,000 CFM) is equal to 0.55 IWC, but 0.12 IWC is dissipated by the devices that are associated with the air handler. The total equivalent length of the longest supply run is equal to 325 feet and the total equivalent length of the longest return run is equal to 120 feet. The surface area of the supply system is equal to 430 SQ.FT. (250 SQ.FT. of rectangular trunk duct and 180 SQ.FT. of round runout duct) and there is 120 SQ.FT. of surface area associated with the rectangular return ducts. All of the duct runs are sheet metal and all of the joints are sealed.

Leakage class = 48

External pressure = 0.55 - 0.12 = 0.43 IWC

$$\text{Starting pressure on supply side} = \frac{0.43 \times 325}{325 + 120} = 0.31 \text{ IWC}$$

Starting pressure on return side = 0.43 - 0.31 = 0.12 IWC

Average pressure on supply side = 0.31/2 = 0.155 IWC

Average pressure on return side = 0.12/2 = 0.06 IWC

Supply-side leakage rate = 15 CFM per 100 SQ.FT.

Return-side leakage rate = 8 CFM per 100 SQ.FT.

$$\text{Supply-side leakage} = \frac{15 \times 430}{100} = 64.5 \text{ CFM}$$

$$\text{Return-side leakage} = \frac{8 \times 120}{100} = 9.6 \text{ CFM}$$

Total leakage = 64.5 + 9.6 = 74.1 CFM (about 7 percent)

12-4 Leakage Loads

Field studies, which have been made in every part of the country, show that duct leakage has an adverse effect on the efficiency of a residential HVAC system and the associated building envelope. This loss of efficiency increases the amount of energy that is required to operate the HVAC system, increases the demand load on the utility service and increases the cost of heating and cooling the home.

Infiltration Loads Depend on Blower Operation
Duct leakage increases the equipment run time and the blower operating hours. This in turn exacerbates the infiltration problem because envelope leakage is much larger when the blower is operating. Figure 12-10, which is based on test data of a few homes, shows how fan operation can affect the infiltration rate when leaky ducts are located in an unconditioned space.

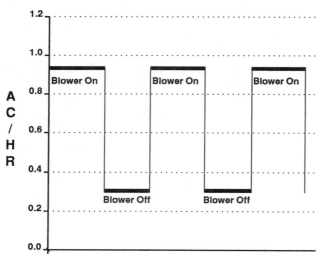

The AC/HR values on this chart are based on a case study of a few Florida homes.

Figure 12-10

Loads Induced by Duct Leakage
More energy is required to heat, cool and dehumidify a home when duct leakage increases the load that is associated with the structure or the duct system. In some cases, the ambient air that is associated with this load enters through the cracks in the building envelope and in other cases it enters through the return side of a duct system that is located in an unconditioned space or an ancillary space — an attic, an open crawl space, an enclosed crawl space or a basement, for example. (The interaction between duct leakage, the pressure in the occupied space and infiltration is discussed in Section 14.)

The size of the leakage-induced infiltration load (and the amount of energy that is wasted) also depends on the difference (temperature and the moisture) between the air that exfiltrates from the envelope or the supply duct, and the

replacement air, which may come from the outdoors or an ancillary space. (Note that in the summer, the temperature in an ancillary space such as an attic can be much warmer than the outdoor air.)

The following examples show the magnitude of the loads that can be produced by 100 CFM of duct leakage. (Field tests have found many homes that have more than 100 CFM of duct leakage. Some homes had leakage rates of 300 to 400 CFM — or more!)

Example 1
Calculate the cooling and heating loads that are associated with leaky supply ducts that are located in an open crawl space. Base the calculations on 100 CFM of supply-side leakage (which will create a negative pressure in the home that will induce 100 CFM of envelope infiltration). Make this calculation for a hot humid day when the condition of the supply air is 55 °F and 60 GR/LB, and the condition of the outdoor air is 90 °F and 90 GR/LB; and on a cold winter day when the temperature of the heated air is 105 °F and the temperature of the outdoor air is 20 °F.

Sensible load = 1.1 x 100 x (90-55) = 3,850 BTUH

Latent load = 0.68 x 100 x (90-60) = 2,040 BTUH

Total cooling load = 5,890 BTUH

Total heating load = 1.1 x 100 x (105-20) = 9,350 BTUH

Example 2
Calculate the cooling and heating loads that are associated with leaky return ducts that are located in an open crawl space. Base the calculations on 100 CFM of return-side leakage (which will create a positive pressure in the home that will produce 100 CFM of envelope exfiltration). Make this calculation on a hot humid day when the condition of the return air is 75 °F and 65 GR/LB, and the condition of the outdoor air is 90 °F and 90 GR/LB; and on a cold winter day when the temperature of the return air is 70 °F and the temperature of the outdoor air is 20 °F.

Sensible load = 1.1 x 100 x (90-75) = 1,650 BTUH

Latent load = 0.68 x 100 x (90-65) = 1,700 BTUH

Total cooling load = 3,350 BTUH

Heating load = 1.1 x 100 x (70-20) = 5,500 BTUH

Example 3
Calculate the cooling and heating loads that are associated with leaky return ducts that are located in an attic. Base the calculations on 100 CFM of return-side leakage (which will create a positive pressure in the home that will produce 100

CFM of envelope exfiltration). Make this calculation on a hot humid day when the condition of the return air is 75 °F and 65 GR/LB, and the condition of the attic air is 130 °F and 90 GR/LB; and on a cold winter day when the temperature of the return air is 70 °F and the temperature of the attic air is 20 °F.

Sensible load = 1.1 x 100 x (130-75) = 6,050 BTUH

Latent load = 0.68 x 100 x (90-65) = 1,700 BTUH

Total cooling load = 7,750 BTUH

Heating load = 1.1 x 100 x (70-20) = 5,500 BTUH

Example 4

Calculate the cooling and heating loads that are associated with a leaky duct system that is located in an attic. Base the calculations on 100 CFM of supply-side leakage and 100 CFM of return-side leakage (which will create a neutral pressure in the home). Make this calculation on a hot humid day when the condition of the supply air is 55 °F and 60 GR/LB, and the condition of the attic air is 130 °F and 90 GR/LB; and on a cold winter day when the temperature of the supply air is equal to 105 °F and the temperature of the attic air is equal to 20 °F.

Sensible load = 1.1 x 100 x (130-55) = 8,250 BTUH

Latent load = 0.68 x 100 x (90-60) = 2,040 BTUH

Total cooling load = 10,290 BTUH

Total heating load = 1.1 x 100 x (105-20) = 9,350 BTUH

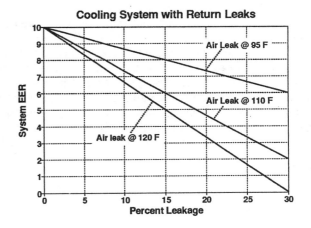

Figure 12-11

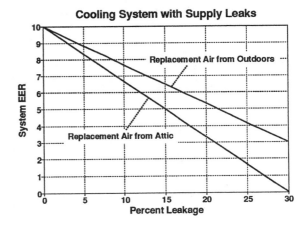

Figure 12-12

12-5 Efficiency, Operating Cost and Demand Load

Duct leakage can affect the efficiency of the heating and cooling machinery, the efficiency of the building envelope and the combined efficiency of all the systems that are associated with a home. Duct leakage also affects the operating cost and the demand load.

Cooling System Efficiency

The relationship between duct leakage and cooling efficiency is illustrated by Figure 12-11, which shows how the seasonal cooling efficiency is affected by return-side leaks, and by Figure 12-12, which shows how the seasonal cooling efficiency is affected by supply-side leaks. Note that in these diagrams, the seasonal EER values do not represent the mechanical efficiency of the cooling machinery. In this case the EER values are "overall" efficiencies, which represent the combined efficiency of the entire system (envelope, ducts and machinery). These "system" efficiencies are based on the output energy that would be required if there were no leaks and the input energy that is required when there are leaks.

Effect on Refrigeration Cycle Efficiency

The leakage that is associated with the return side of the duct system can have a significant effect on the condition of the air that enters a DX coil, and consequently on the efficiency of a condensing unit (see page 13-8). And, efficiency will be degraded when return-side leaks pull in air that contains dirt, dust and pollen that clogs filters, fouls coils and covers fan surfaces. (Note that a clogged return air filter-grille exacerbates return-side leakage problems because more air is pulled in from the unconditioned space and less air is returned through the filter.)

Effect on Heat Pump Efficiency (Heating)

Besides the increased infiltration load, the energy that is wasted depends on the operating mode and the efficiency of the device that provides the additional increment of capacity that is required to condition the replacement air. For example, the efficiency of a heat pump unit depends on how much second-stage heat is required, which depends, in part, on the size of the infiltration load that is caused by duct leakage (see page 13-9). Figure 12-13 shows how the COP (coefficient of performance) of a heat pump unit (refrigeration machinery and electric resistance heating coil) is affected by duct leakage. Note that the efficiency of the heat pump unit is reduced as the duct leakage increases. This loss in efficiency occurs because the additional load that is associated with the duct leakage produces a larger heating load on the heat pump and this translates into an upward shift in the balance point of the heat pump system. This shift means that more second-stage heat (COP = 1) is required to satisfy the seasonal heating load.

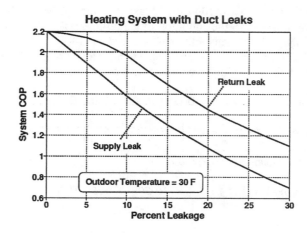

Figure 12-14

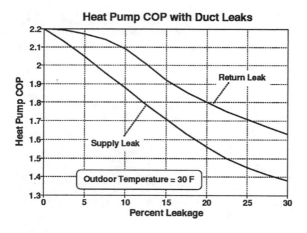

Figure 12-13

Figure 12-14 shows another way to think about the relationship between duct leakage and heating efficiency. In this figure, the COP values do not represent the mechanical efficiency of a heat pump unit that is subject to an increased load. In this case the COP values are "overall" efficiencies, which represent the combined efficiency of the entire system (envelope, ducts and machinery). These "system" efficiencies are based on the output energy that would be required if there was no duct leakage and the input energy that is required when there are duct leaks. (Compare Figure 12-13 with Figure 12-14.)

Operating Cost
Operating cost is directly related to energy use. When duct leakage causes an increase in the equipment load or a reduction in the equipment efficiency, there will be a corresponding increase in operating cost. This increase will depend on the size of the added load, the efficiency reduction that is associated with the device that is used to neutralize this load and the marginal cost of the fuel that is consumed by this device.

Demand Loads
The demand load on a utility increases in proportion to the collective inefficiencies of the homes (and their HVAC systems) that are connected to the system. When duct leaks are involved, these inefficiencies are larger when the blower is

operating (see Figure 12-10). During extreme weather conditions (the **Manual J** design conditions, for example) the unavoidable heating or cooling loads will be at or near their peak, the air handling equipment will be operating continuously (or nearly continuously) and the unnecessary losses that are caused by duct leakage will be maximized. These duct leakage losses represent a significant and avoidable demand on the utility service. Figure 12-15 shows how duct leaks affect the demand that is associated with a heat pump system during a cold winter day in northern Florida. In this example, the peak demand on the utility service can be reduced by 30 percent if the duct leakage is reduced by 70 percent. (Note that an even larger reduction in demand would be expected if this house was located in a colder climate.)

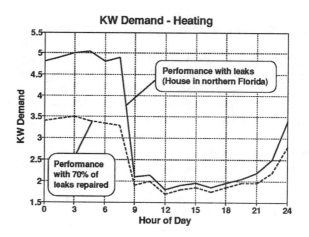

Figure 12-15

On the next page, Figure 12-16 shows how duct leaks affect the demand that is associated with a heat pump system during a hot summer day in northern Florida. In this example, the peak demand on the utility service can be reduced by 25 percent if the duct leakage is reduced by 70 percent.

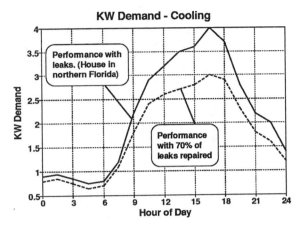

KW Demand - Cooling

Figure 12-16

12-6 Figure of Merit

Researchers are developing a method that can be used to rate the efficiency of an air distribution system. This rating, which is called a figure of merit (FOM) is expressed as a percentage. This percentage is calculated by dividing the energy that would be required without a duct system by the energy that would be required if a duct system was involved.

$$FOM = \frac{Conditioning\ energy\ without\ distribution\ system}{Conditioning\ energy\ with\ distribution\ system}$$

As indicated by the discussion and examples that have been provided by sections 12-1 through 12-5, there are a number of processes and interactions associated with the figure of merit concept. The factors that affect the FOM value include blower power, supply-side conduction losses, return-side conduction losses, supply-side leakage losses, return-side leakage losses, reductions in mechanical efficiency and changes (increase or decrease) in the infiltration load. The effect of these factors can be isolated if the figure of merit equation is rewritten in the following form:

$$FOM = \frac{(MEF)_{with}}{(MEF)_{no}} \times \frac{(Envelope)_{no}}{(Envelope)_{with} + DLL + DWCL}$$

- $(MEF)_{with}$ represents the mechanical efficiency of the fuel conversion equipment when it is used in conjunction with a distribution system. This factor includes the blower energy and the net effect that leakage and conduction losses have on the annual efficiency of the fuel conversion equipment. (Return-side leakage and conduction losses affect the equipment efficiency because they alter the condition of the air entering the equipment.)

- $(MEF)_{no}$ is the mechanical efficiency of the fuel conversion equipment when there is no air distribution system.

- $(Envelope)_{no}$ represents the annual energy required for the structure when there is no air distribution system.

- $(Envelope)_{with}$ represents the annual energy required for the structure when there is an air distribution system. This factor includes the infiltration load adjustments that are associated with supply-side and return-side leakage.

- DLL represents the energy that is required to offset the loads that are associated with supply-side and return-side leakage.

- DWCL represents the energy that is required to offset the supply-side and return-side duct wall conduction losses.

For example, calculate the FOM value if the annual COP (heating and cooling combined) of the equipment is equal to 2.1 without a duct system and 1.9 with a duct system; and the annual envelope energy requirement is equal to 300 million BTU/YR without a duct system and 315 million BTU/YR with a duct system; and the duct leakage losses add 20 percent to the annual energy load; and the duct wall conduction losses add 10 percent to the annual energy load.

$$FOM = \frac{1.9}{2.1} \times \frac{300}{(315 + 60 + 30)} = 0.67$$

Section 13
Duct Leakage and System Interactions

Duct leakage and return path restrictions affect the efficiency of the duct system, the performance of the building envelope, the efficiency and effectiveness of the HVAC equipment, the capacity of the exhaust equipment and the power of the vents that are associated with fuel burning devices. In most cases these effects are interactive. This section discusses these relationships.

13-1 Complex Systems

An air distribution system can be very simple — as far as cause-and-effect relationships are concerned — providing that the duct system is continuous, tight, well insulated and only has one inlet and one outlet. This type of system is depicted by Figure 13-1.

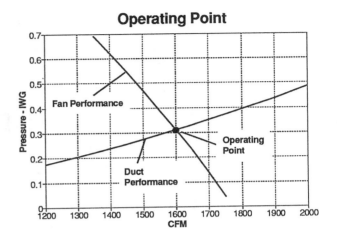

Figure 13-2

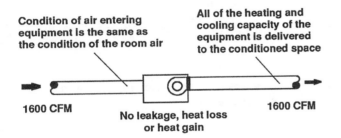

Figure 13-1

As far as the air flow is concerned, the operating point of this simplest of duct systems is completely defined by the blower performance (flow versus resistance curve) and the duct performance (resistance versus flow curve) — as indicated by Figure 13-2. This operating point is obvious because there is only one duct run and because there is no coupling between the duct system and the building envelope or any of the other systems that are associated with the structure.

On the next page, Figure 13-3 shows a more elaborate system that consists of the building envelope, the HVAC equipment, a manifold duct system, a discontinuous return path, exhaust equipment, appliances and a fireplace. This complex system is characterized by a set of relationships that describe the interaction, coupling and connections that are associated with the various subsystems. In this case, the performance of one subsystem is dependent on the performance of the other subsystems. The common thread that ties all of these systems together is pressure. For example, pressure differences affect the infiltration rate; the duct leakage; the supply CFM values; the return CFM values; the performance of the flues, vents and combustion appliances; the performance of the fireplace; and the performance of the exhaust equipment.

13-2 Pressure Differences

The pressure differences that are associated with a complex system consist of indoor-to-outdoor pressure differences, room-to-room pressure differences; the pressure difference between a conditioned space and an unconditioned or ancillary space; and the difference between the pressure in a conditioned space and in a duct run. These pressure differences are affected by the leakage areas that are associated with the exterior envelope, the wind, the height of the structure, the flues and vents, the exhaust equipment, some types of appliances, the operating mode of the blower (on-off), the leakage areas that are associated with the duct runs, the leakage areas that are associated with the interior partitions and doors, and the sophistication of the return air system. Note that these pressure differences are quite small, usually a few pascals (25 pascals is approximately equal to 0.10 IWC), and they are not constant. Therefore, as these pressures fluctuate, infiltration rates and air flow rates may increase, decrease or they may have a binary nature — appearing when certain conditions exist and disappearing when these conditions change. More information about the various factors that affect the pressure in a conditioned space is provided below.

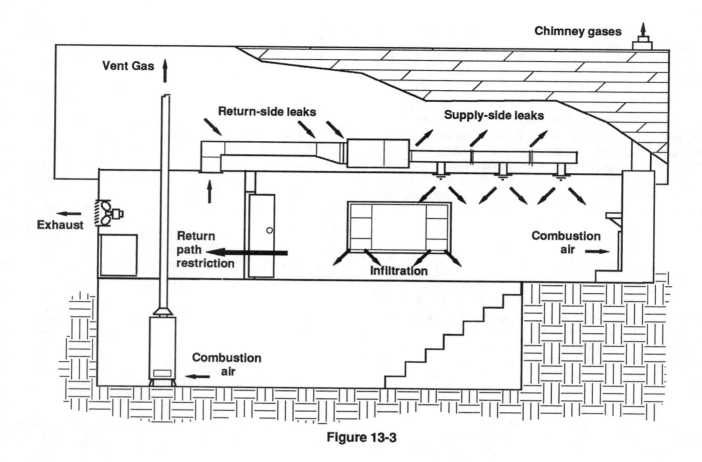

Figure 13-3

Envelope Leakage Areas

The envelope leakage areas (holes and cracks) determine the tightness of the house. The size and location of these openings affect infiltration, exfiltration and the ability of the envelope to hold pressure.

Wind

The wind is a driving force that causes infiltration. Wind blowing on an exterior surface produces a high pressure at that surface. At the same time, a low pressure is created on the leeward side of the house. This condition can cause a positive or negative pressure in the house, depending on the relationship between the wind direction and the leakage areas.

If the wind blows toward a large percentage of the crackage area and there is a negligible amount of leeward crackage, the space will be pressurized and indoor air will leak out through remaining cracks. If there is negligible windward crackage area and a large amount of leeward crackage, indoor air will be extracted through the leeward cracks, the space will be depressurized and outdoor air will enter through remaining cracks. If the crackage area that is associated with single-family detached housing is evenly distributed around the perimeter of the house, the pressure in the house will usually be slightly negative. (Tests on single-family Florida homes indicate that the indoor pressure typically ranges from 0 to -4 pascals, depending on the velocity of the wind.) Figure 13-4

shows the pressure conditions that are likely to be created when the wind acts alone.

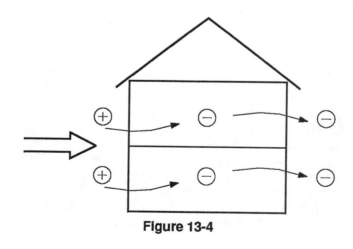

Figure 13-4

Buoyancy Effect

The height of the structure determines the power of the buoyancy effect; therefore, this effect is more conspicuous in a multistory home than it is in a single-story home. In any case, when the buoyancy effect acts alone, the buoyancy forces produce a pressure difference between the lower level and the upper level. Depending on the height of the house and the temperature of the outdoor air, this pressure difference can range from 0 pascals to more than 8 pascals. In the winter, the pressure will be positive at the upper level (0 to +4 pascals or more, with respect to the outdoors) and negative at the lower level (0 to -4 pascals or less, with respect to the outdoors). This pressure difference causes air to flow into the cracks that are distributed around the lower level and out of the cracks that are distributed around the upper level. This situation will be reversed in the summer if the home is air conditioned, but the pressures will be smaller because the indoor-outdoor temperature difference is smaller. Figure 13-5 shows the pressure conditions that are created when the buoyancy effect acts alone.

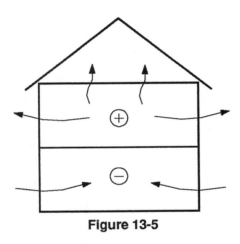

Figure 13-5

Flues and Vents

When the vent effect acts alone, the buoyancy forces produce a pressure difference between the top of the vent and the inside of the house. This causes a negative pressure inside of the house. This "draft pressure" depends on the height of the vent and the temperature difference between the flue gas and the outdoor air. Even on cold days, the draft pressure can be quite

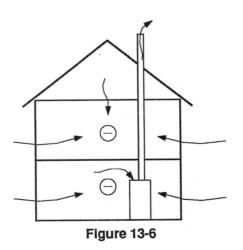

Figure 13-6

small, perhaps as small as -5 pascals. (When the equipment is not active the draft pressure will be even smaller.) This negative pressure causes air to flow into all of the cracks that are associated with the building envelope. Figure 13-6 shows the pressure conditions that are created when the vent effect acts alone.

Exhaust Equipment and Appliances

Exhaust fans and some appliances, such as clothes dryers, produce a negative pressure in the house. Small exhaust fans and clothes dryers produce negative pressures in the range of -1 to -6 pascals. Large exhaust fans can produce negative pressures that could exceed -30 pascals. This negative pressure causes air to flow into all of the cracks that are associated with the building envelope and it can cause venting problems if it overpowers the natural draft that is produced by a stack or chimney. Figure 13-7 shows the pressure conditions that are created when the exhaust effect acts alone.

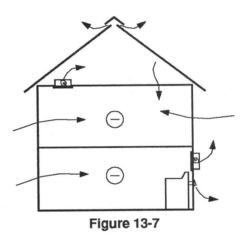

Figure 13-7

Blower Operation

Blower operation causes substantial pressure fluctuations at various points in a complex system. When the blower is on, it pressurizes the supply-side ducts and depressurizes the return-side ducts; and it may affect the pressure in a conditioned space (which will be pressurized if the space is decoupled from a return air path) or the pressure in an ancillary space (if leaky ducts are installed in an ancillary space). The positive pressure within the supply side of a duct system typically ranges from 0.10 to 0.30 IWC. (25 to 75 pascals). The negative pressure within the return side of a duct system typically ranges from -0.10 to -0.30 IWC. (-25 to -75 pascals). The pressures that are associated with a conditioned space or an ancillary space usually range from zero to 25 pascals, depending on the effectiveness of the return system, the tightness of the duct runs and the tightness of the space. The various pressures and pressure differences that are associated with blower operation affect duct leakage, envelope leakage and the performance of supply outlets, flues, vents and chimneys.

Duct Leakage

When the duct system is located in a space that has access to the outdoor air (attic, open crawl space or vented cavity), duct leakage can produce a positive pressure or a negative pressure in the dwelling. Return-side leaks can cause a positive pressure throughout the whole house. (The additional portion of the return air that comes from an attic or crawl space enters the house with the supply air and exfiltrates through the envelope crackage. As far as the house is concerned, the supply CFM exceeds the return CFM.) Figure 13-8 shows the pressure conditions that are created when leaking return air ducts (acting alone) are located in a vented, unconditioned space.

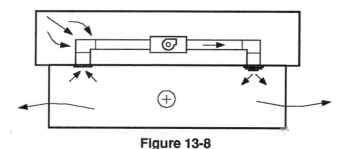

Figure 13-8

Supply-side leaks cause a negative pressure in the conditioned space. (The additional portion of the return air that replaces the air that is expelled to an attic or crawl space infiltrates through the building envelope. As far as the house is concerned, the return CFM exceeds the supply CFM.) Figure 13-9 shows the pressure conditions that are created when leaking supply ducts (acting alone) are located in a vented, unconditioned space.

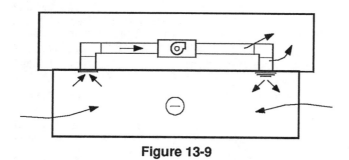

Figure 13-9

When the ducts are located in a vented, unconditioned space, the amount of positive pressure or negative pressure that is produced in the house depends on the amount of duct leakage (leakage CFM), on how the duct leaks are distributed between the supply side and the return side, and on the tightness of the

structure. If all of the leaks are on the supply side, the pressure in the house could range from -1 to -6 pascals (or lower). If all of the leaks are on the return side, the pressure in the house could range from +1 to +6 pascals (or higher). If the leaks are on both sides of the duct system, the pressure in the house will depend on how the leakage CFM of one side compares to the leakage CFM on the other side. If the leaks are equally distributed between the supply side and the return side, the pressure in the house will be neutral. Figure 13-10 summarizes this behavior.

Duct Leakage versus Pressure in Space				
Envelope Tightness	Return Leakage	Supply Leakage	Air Balance	Space Pressure
Tight	250	0	+250	+6
Loose	250	0	+250	+2
Tight	250	100	+150	+3
Loose	250	100	+150	+1
Tight	250	250	0	0
Loose	250	250	0	0
Tight	100	250	-150	-3
Loose	100	250	-150	-1
Tight	0	250	-250	-6
Loose	0	250	-250	-2

Figure 13-10

When the duct system is located in the conditioned space, duct leakage can produce a positive or negative pressure in the area where the duct is located. Return-side leaks produce a negative pressure and supply-side leaks produce a positive pressure. The pressure that is produced in a particular area will depend on the leakage CFM and the tightness of the area. In these cases the pressures could range from +8 to -8 pascals or more.

Discontinuous Return Path

If there are no other factors involved, the pressure inside any room and the pressure in the core of the house depend on return air path restrictions. If there is an adequate return path for every room or zone, the supply CFM and the return CFM that are associated with each room will be equal, so no pressure differentials will be created. An adequate return path can be established by providing a ducted return for every room or isolated zone or by using one or more central returns (in the core areas) and transfer grilles (which establish a path between the isolated rooms and the central returns).

If one or more rooms are isolated from a return air opening (by tight-fitting interior doors which are closed), the pressure in the isolated room will be positive and the pressure in the core of the house will be negative. The positive pressure that is produced in an isolated room will depend on the supply CFM, the tightness of the duct run and the tightness of the room. When there are no other factors involved, a positive pressure of a few pascals to more than 10 pascals is possible. (If a room is perfectly tight, the pressure in the room will equal the pressure in the branch duct and there will be no air flow into the room.)

The negative pressure that is produced in the core area will depend on the difference between the return CFM and the supply CFM; on the tightness of the surrounding walls, interior partitions and doors; and on the tightness of the return ducts. When there are no other factors involved, a negative pressure of a few pascals to more than -10 pascals is possible.

Sometimes a primary return air path is restricted by a filter-grille that has a dirty filter. In this case, the duct leakage that occurs on the return side of the system will be exacerbated and there will be a corresponding pressure increase in most rooms or in all of the house. In any case, the pressure changes that are associated with an inadequate return path affect duct leakage, envelope leakage and the performance of supply outlets, flues, vents and chimneys.

13-3 Synergistic Effects

The leakage and flow rates that are associated with the building envelope (which would include exhaust equipment and the fireplace), the duct system, the HVAC equipment (and vents) and some household appliances (and vents) are affected by pressure differences. As discussed above, these pressure differences are caused by various "drivers" such as the wind, the buoyancy forces that are caused by air temperature differences, the buoyancy forces that are associated with vents and chimneys, the exhaust equipment, the blower and duct leaks.

Figure 13-11 summarizes the effect that the various drivers have on the pressure in the conditioned space. Note that it would be unusual to find any one of these drivers acting alone. Normally, groups of these drivers act in concert, so a wide range of space pressure conditions are possible, depending on which drivers are active. For example, if there is no wind and no vent or exhaust equipment in operation, the pressure in the space will be close to zero if no heating or cooling is required

Pressure Drivers — Residential Structures			
Subsystem	**Pressure Produced (Pascals)** [1]		**Conditions**
	Lower Level	Upper Level	
Envelope Crackage	+4 to -4	+4 to -4	Depends on the wind velocity and crack locations
Buoyancy Effect	0 to -4	0 to +4	Depends on height and indoor/outdoor temperatures
Toilet Exhaust	-1 to -6	-1 to -6	When fan is operating
Dryer Vents	-1 to -6	-1 to -6	When dryer is operating
Kitchen Exhaust	-10 to -30	-10 to -30	When fan is operating
Fossil Fuel Vents [2]	-1 to -5	-1 to -5	When burner is firing, combustion air from indoors
Fire Place Flue [2]	-1 to -5	-1 to -5	When in use, combustion air from indoors
Supply Duct Leaks (U) [3]	-1 to -8	-1 to -8	When blower is operating
Return Duct Leaks (U) [3]	+1 to +6	+1 to +6	When blower is operating
Supply Duct Leaks (C) [3]	+1 to +8	+1 to +8	When blower is operating
Return Duct Leaks (C) [3]	-1 to -10	-1 to -10	When blower is operating
No Return in Room [4]	+2 to +10	+2 to +10	Blower operating, interior door closed
Return in Core Area [4]	-2 to -15	-2 to -15	Blower operating, one or more interior doors closed

Note 1) The pressure ranges in this table are common, but higher or lower pressures are possible.
Note 2) This is the pressure in the room that contains the combustion device, not the draft pressure.
Note 3) U designates ducts that are in an unconditioned space. C designates ducts that are in a conditioned space.
Note 4) Inadequate return path — interior doors isolate perimeter rooms from a central return in the core area.

Figure 13-11

(the duct leak and return path drivers will be equal to zero). On the other hand, the pressure in the space could be decidedly negative (say -10 to -20 Pascals) if one or more exhaust drivers are operative while the (air handler) blower activates a supply leak driver or a return path driver. Or, the pressure in the space could be positive if the appropriate leakage and return path drivers are active while the other drivers are dormant. Comments on how the space pressure affects the performance of the various subsystems that are associated with a home are provided by the following paragraphs.

Supply CFM

The supply CFM that is delivered to a room will be reduced when the room is pressurized and increased when the room is subject to a negative pressure. The CFM that is delivered by the blower also is affected by the pressures that are associated with the various rooms. For example, when the house has a single central return, the CFM that is delivered to the rooms that are isolated from the return (by closing the interior doors) will decrease, the CFM that is delivered to the core rooms (that are served by the central return) will increase, and the fan CFM will decrease. In this case, the fan CFM decreases because the interior doors act like dampers, which have the effect of increasing the resistance of all the duct runs. Figures 13-12 and 13-13 illustrate this behavior.

Figure 13-12 shows the flow rates that occur when all of the interior doors are open. In this case the fan delivers 1,000 CFM against 0.20 IN.WG. of resistance and the flow to rooms A, B, C and D is equal to 100 CFM, 150 CFM, 350 CFM and 400 CFM, respectively.

Figure 13-13 illustrates what could happen when the interior doors to rooms A and B are closed. In this case, the CFM that is delivered to rooms A and B drops to 52 CFM and 105 CFM,

respectively; the CFM that is delivered to rooms C and D increases to 370 CFM and 420 CFM; the blower CFM decreases to 947 CFM; and the system resistance increases to 0.22 IN.WG. (In this case, the doors throttle the flow to some rooms and cause a larger flow to the other rooms; but larger flow to these rooms causes more resistance in the ducts that run to these rooms. The resistance increases in every duct run and the blower CFM is reduced.)

Envelope Leakage Rate

The infiltration CFM that is associated with a room will be reduced when the room is pressurized and increased when the room is subject to a negative pressure. But, Figure 13-11 indicates that there are many pressure drivers that affect the pressure in a room. Therefore, the pressure in the space (and the infiltration rate) is determined by a complex interaction between the wind velocity, the envelope leakage, the duct leakage, blower operation (on versus off), the stack effect, exhaust fans, flues for combustion appliances, return air paths and the location of the filter.

Note that changes in the infiltration rate could reduce or increase the pollutants and the humidity in the conditioned space, depending on the situation. If pollutants or humidity are generated within the space, the adverse effects will be diluted by "clean, dry" infiltration. If pollutants or humidity are associated with the air that leaks in from outside of the conditioned space, they will be introduced into the space by infiltration.

Also note that the performance of flues and vents that are associated with combustion equipment and fireplaces is very sensitive to the pressure in the room that contains the combustion device. A negative pressure as small as -3 Pascals can cause vent backdrafting. Since the pressure in the space is

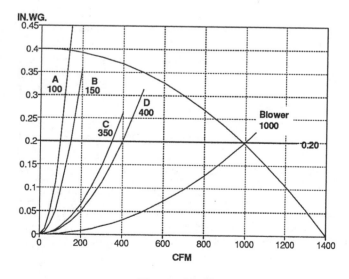

Figure 13-12

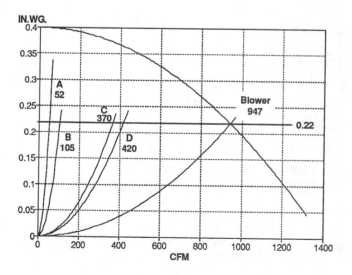

Figure 13-13

constantly changing, the danger of backdrafting depends on the combination of drivers that are active at any given time. Figure 13-11 demonstrates that there are many scenarios that can cause a problem. Simple acts like energizing an exhaust fan, operating a clothes dryer, or closing or opening a door can cause an unsafe condition. (Note that in some cases, an effort to repair duct leaks and structural leaks could produce a combination of pressure drivers that create a negative pressure situation that, in turn, causes a venting problem.)

Exhaust equipment
The performance of exhaust equipment and vented household appliances is affected by the pressure in the room where the equipment is located. The exhaust CFM will decrease as the pressure in the room becomes more negative and increase if the pressure in the room becomes more positive. (If the various pressure drivers combine to create a large negative pressure in the space, the effectiveness of the exhaust equipment might be completely neutralized.)

The flow rates that are associated with various types of residential exhaust equipment are listed below (assuming that the equipment has access to an unrestricted supply of air). Obviously, if two or more of these devices operate simultaneously, they will compete with each other for the available supply of air and the CFM that is associated with each device will be reduced. This situation will be exacerbated if other drivers, such as duct leaks or return path problems, contribute to the negative pressure situation.

- Kitchen = 100 to 200 CFM
- Bath = 50 CFM
- Clothes dryer = 100 to 150 CFM
- Central vacuum = 100 CFM
- Kitchen range = 250 to 500 CFM

Supply Duct Leaks (Unconditioned Space)
Leaks from a supply duct to an unconditioned space do not affect the performance (capacity and efficiency) of the mechanical equipment, but they do degrade the overall performance of the HVAC system because they increase the load on the equipment. Supply-side leaks also can create comfort and air quality problems.

- This type of leak depressurizes the conditioned space (because the CFM that is supplied to the space is less than the CFM that is returned from the space) and increases infiltration into the conditioned space. Note that additional infiltration from the outdoors or from an ancillary space will affect operating cost, comfort and air quality.

- This type of leak wastes air that has already been conditioned (heated, or cooled and dehumidified), which is ultimately replaced by air that is not conditioned at all. This exchange wastes energy and increases the operating cost. Note that the loss of conditioned supply air is more serious than the loss of neutral return air because the temperature

difference and the moisture difference between the wasted air and the replacement air is larger. (In some cases, during the cooling season, the replacement air may be hotter than the outdoor air — the air that infiltrates from an attic, for example.)

- This type of leak does not alter the temperature rise across the heating equipment, or the temperature-humidity drop that is associated with a cooling coil because it does not alter the condition of the air entering the equipment. (The condition of the air leaving the equipment depends on the condition of air entering the equipment, the blower CFM and the capacity of the equipment.)

- This type of leak does not affect the mechanical efficiency of refrigeration cycle equipment because it does not alter the condition of the air entering the indoor coil.

- This type of leak will put an unnecessary load on the auxiliary heating coil that is associated with a heat pump. This parasitic load raises the thermal balance point and reduces the seasonal efficiency of the heat pump system.

Supply Duct Leaks (Conditioned Space)
When air movement within the home is unrestricted, leaks from a supply duct to a conditioned space do not substantially affect the performance (capacity and efficiency) of the mechanical equipment and they do not increase the load on the equipment. However, this type of leak can affect the pressure in isolated rooms, and this could have an indirect effect on the equipment load.

- This type of leak does not increase the infiltration load or the load on the equipment, providing that the air is free to move around the various rooms in the home.

- This type of leak does not alter the temperature rise across heating equipment or the temperature-humidity drop that is associated with a cooling coil because it does not alter the condition of the air entering the equipment.

- This type of leak does not affect the equipment efficiency because it does not alter the condition of the air entering the equipment.

- This type of leak tends to increase the pressure in a space that is isolated from an adequate return air path.

- If this type of leak pressurizes a space, there will be a decrease in the infiltration to that space.

- If rooms that are isolated by closing an interior door are pressurized, the exfiltration that is associated with these rooms might cause other rooms to be depressurized and air will infiltrate into the depressurized rooms. This situation causes an increase in the infiltration load, the load on the equipment and the operating cost.

• If this type of leak pressurizes a space, there could be a decrease in the supply CFM that is delivered to the space. (The air balance in other rooms also could be affected by room-to-room pressure differences.)

• If this type of leak pressurizes a space, contaminants could be transferred to other rooms in the house.

Return Duct Leaks (Unconditioned Space)

Leaks from an unconditioned space to a return duct increase the load on the mechanical equipment, affect the performance (capacity and efficiency) of the equipment and degrade the overall performance of the HVAC system. Return-side leaks also can create comfort and air quality problems.

• Return-side leaks pressurize the conditioned space (because the CFM that is supplied to the space exceeds the CFM that is returned from the space) and decreases the infiltration that is associated with the conditioned space.

• Since this type of leak draws air from the outdoors or from an ancillary space, it will increase the operating cost.

• Since this type of leak draws air from the outdoors or from an ancillary space, it can have an adverse affect on the indoor humidity.

• Since this type of leak draws air from the outdoors or from an ancillary space, it can affect air quality in the conditioned space. (It might improve or degrade the quality of the indoor air, depending on the quality of the air that surrounds the return duct. If the replacement air is of good quality, it will dilute contaminants that are generated inside the space. If the replacement air is of poor quality, it will degrade the quality of the indoor air.)

• Return-side leaks waste neutral air (room air that exfiltrates from the rooms) and replaces it with air that has not been conditioned at all. This exchange wastes energy and increases the operating cost. Note that the loss of neutral air is not as serious as the loss of fully conditioned supply air because the temperature difference and the moisture difference between the wasted air and the replacement air is smaller. (In some cases, during the cooling season, the replacement air may be hotter than the outdoor air — the air in the attic, for example).

• Return-side leaks alter the temperature rise across the heating equipment, the temperature-humidity drop associated with cooling equipment and the sensible heat ratio of the cooling coil. In some case, the air leaving the equipment (supply air) may not be capable of neutralizing the load, which may be a heating, sensible cooling or latent load. (The condition of the air leaving the equipment depends on the condition of air entering it, the blower CFM and the capacity of the equipment.)

• This type of leak affects the mechanical efficiency of refrigeration-cycle equipment because it alters the condition of the air entering the indoor coil.

• This type of leak will put an unnecessary load on the auxiliary heating coil that is associated with a heat pump. This parasitic load lowers the thermal balance point and reduces the seasonal efficiency of the heat pump unit.

Figure 13-14 provides an example of how the return-side leaks associated with a duct that is installed an attic affect the performance of a cooling unit. In this example, the return duct has a 20 percent leakage rate and the attic is hot and humid. (This type of attic condition is typical in the Southeast and Midwest during a hot summer day.) Note that when compared to a "no leakage" situation, the sensible load increases by 13,200 BTUH and latent load increases by 4,900 BTUH. Also note that the sensible capacity increases by about 4,000 BTUH, the latent capacity decreases by about 1,800 BTUH and the leaving DB and WB temperatures also increase dramatically. It is obvious that this system will not be able to maintain an acceptable level of comfort during a hot summer day.

Return Leakage Effect — Design Day Cooling		
	No Leakage	20% Leakage
Coil CFM	1200	1200
Leakage CFM	0	240
Sensible load	28000	41200
Sensible capacity	28320	32250
Latent load	6500	10900
Latent capacity	7080	5250
Entering DB	75	85
Leaving DB	54	61
Entering WB	63	67
Leaving WB	52	57 ·

1200 CFM cooling unit, leaky return duct in attic
Outdoor air condition = 95 DB and 95 GR/LB
Attic DB = 125, Attic moisture = 95 GR/LB
Equipment size based on "tight" ducts
Cooling capacities extracted from manufacturers' data

Figure 13-14

On the next page Figure 13-15 shows how the return-side leaks associated with a duct that is installed in an attic affect the heating performance of an air-source heat pump. (As in the previous example, the return duct has a 20 percent leakage rate and the attic temperature is equal to the outdoor temperature.) Note that the return-side leakage (240

CFM) increases the design heating load by 18,480 BTUH. Also note that the balance point shifts up by about 7 degrees and the design load on the resistance heating coil increases by 5.4 KW. It follows that these effects will translate into a substantial increase in energy use and operating cost. This is demonstrated by the associated bin calculation, which shows that approximately 9,600 KWH of extra energy is required to heat the leakage load (in Akron, Ohio). At 0.065 cents per KWH, this 9,600 KWH of wasted energy adds about $624 to the annual heating bill.

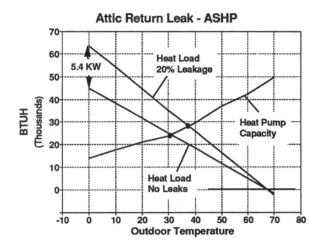

Attic Return Leak - ASHP

Approximate Energy Wasted by Leakage				
Bin	COP	Bin Hrs	Leakage Load	BTU x 10^6
0-10	1.0	75	17107	1.28
10-20	1.0	341	14360	4.90
20-30	1.0	1076	11613	12.50
30-40	1.5	1525	8867	9.01
40-50	2.5	1285	6120	3.15
50-60	2.9	1420	3373	1.65
60-70	3.4	1563	627	0.29
Akron, Ohio 240 CFM			Total BTU/YR KWH/YR	32,780,000 9604

Figure 13-15

Return Duct Leaks (Conditioned Space)

When air movement within the home is unrestricted, leaks from a conditioned space to a return duct do not substantially affect the performance (capacity and efficiency) of the mechanical equipment and they do not increase the load on the equipment. However, this type of leak can affect the pressure in isolated rooms and this could have an indirect effect on the equipment load.

- This type of leak does not increase the infiltration load or the load on the equipment, providing that the air is free to move around the various rooms in the home.

- This type of leak does not alter the temperature rise that is associated with heating equipment, or the temperature-humidity drop associated with a cooling coil because it does not alter the condition of the air entering the equipment.

- This type of leak does not affect the equipment efficiency because it does not alter the condition of the air entering the equipment.

- This type of leak tends to reduce the pressure in a space that is isolated from other rooms.

- If this type of leak depressurizes a space, there will be an increase in the infiltration in that space.

- If isolated rooms are depressurized, the increased infiltration to these rooms might cause other rooms to be pressurized and air will exfiltrate from the pressurized rooms. This situation causes an increase in the infiltration load, the load on the equipment and the operating cost.

- If this type of leak depressurizes a space, there could be an increase in the supply CFM that is delivered to the space. (The air balance in other rooms also could be affected.)

- If this type of leak depressurizes a space, contaminants could be transferred to other rooms in the house.

13-4 Building Damage

Since duct leakage can affect the pressure in the conditioned space, it can affect the infiltration or exfiltration rates and, consequently, it can affect the indoor humidity, the direction of moisture migration and the rate of moisture migration. Therefore, building damage such as mold, mildew and rot may occur when duct leakage produces a condition that causes high indoor humidity or uncontrolled moisture migration. This damage can be caused by moisture that condenses on exposed surfaces (windows and window frames are usually the first surfaces to show condensation) or within the layers of a structural component (an outside wall, for example). In the winter, condensation will occur if the dewpoint of the indoor air or the exfiltrating air is higher than the temperature of an exposed surface or a concealed structural surface. The potential for serious damage is increased if this condensation freezes. In the summer, condensation can occur if the dewpoint of the outdoor air is above 75 °F, providing that the temperature of a structural surface is below 75 °F. Although this is not a problem for most of the country, it can occur in locations that are subject to very high humidity during the summer.

Section 14
Air Quality Issues

Duct leakage and inadequate return air paths can have a significant effect on the quality of the indoor air. In some cases the air quality problems that are created by the air distribution system can be very serious.

14-1 Problems Caused by the Duct System

The air quality problems that can be created by a defective air distribution system fall into three general categories, which are related to comfort, health and safety. Any one of these air quality problems, or any combination of these problems, is likely to occur if the air distribution system is handicapped by excessive leakage and/or return path restrictions.

Comfort
Comfort is compromised when infiltration (of outdoor air) creates drafts. Infiltration also can cause the indoor humidity to be too high or too low. And, comfort is degraded when the supply air outlets and the return air inlets are not able to deliver and extract the required air flow. (If the air circulation rate is not correct, the heating or cooling capacity of the supply air will not be balanced with the load. If the flow of supply air is incompatible with the size of the supply outlet, drafts and pockets of stagnant air can be created within the occupied space.)

Infiltration and air circulation problems are caused by pressure differences. The indoor-outdoor pressure difference controls the infiltration rate. As far as air circulation is concerned, the supply and return flow rates are affected by the room-to-duct pressure differences. In either case, the controlling pressures can be adversely affected by duct leakage and return path restrictions.

Also note that when leakage is associated with the return side of the duct system, it can have a significant effect on the operating characteristics of the HVAC equipment — particularly the ability of the equipment to control the temperature and humidity of the supply air. This, in turn, will affect comfort. When cooling is required, for example, the condition of the air leaving the indoor coil depends on the temperature and humidity of the air that enters the coil, which is affected by return-side duct leakage. Or, when heating is required, the temperature of the air leaving the heating device depends on the temperature of the air entering the device, which is affected by return-side duct leakage.

Health
Health can be adversely affected when duct leakage produces a condition (infiltration or negative pressure) that draws pollutants (dust, dirt, spores, fumes, odors, vapors, sewer gas, soil gas, radon gas, etc.) into the occupied space. This may occur directly through the leakage area that is associated with the building envelope or indirectly through the leakage area that is associated with the return air ducts. (Note that the leakage rate will be larger when return-side leakage occurs between a dirty filter grille and the air handling equipment.) In either case, the leakage path could involve the outdoor air — which may be polluted — or polluted air that is associated with an unconditioned space such as a garage, a basement or an enclosed crawl space.

Duct leakage also can produce conditions that lead to an accumulation of mold and mildew, which have the potential to cause health and odor problems. For example, a drip pan or a cooling coil are vulnerable to biological growth if dirt and dust are pulled in through return-side duct leaks. Or, in humid climates, duct leakage can cause high indoor humidity during the cooling season, which could lead to mold and mildew problems in the conditioned space. Another variation of the biological growth problem occurs when cold air leaks out of a supply duct, impinges on a nearby surface and causes the temperature of the surface to fall below the dewpoint of the ambient air. In this case, the resulting condensation produces an environment that encourages biological growth.

Every home needs a minimum amount of fresh air because health and comfort can be adversely affected when the infiltration rate is too low. Therefore, it is possible for duct leakage to have a positive effect on health and comfort. If duct leakage increases the infiltration rate, a tight structure benefits from the leakage, provided that the infiltrating air is of good quality. In this case a duct sealing project might degrade the indoor air quality (unless mechanical ventilation is used to maintain an adequate fresh air exchange rate).

Safety
Duct leakage can have a direct effect on the pressure within the house, within the various rooms of the house and within the buffer zones that are associated with the house. In some cases, this leakage can cause negative pressures, which have an adverse effect on combustion appliances, fireplaces, flues and vents. Dangerous and even deadly situations occur when duct leaks induce negative pressures that cause backdrafting, spilling and flame rollout.

Duct leakage can also cause furnace heat exchanger damage. This situation occurs when the furnace is located in a small enclosed equipment room or closet that is not well ventilated. During summer cooling, air leaks that are associated with the supply plenum, the return plenum or the furnace cabinet can "condition" the air side of the heat exchanger and cause condensation to form on the combustion side of the heat exchanger (which is exposed to outdoor air).

14-2 Collective Effect of Pressure Drivers

As described above, duct leakage and return path restrictions can create pressure conditions that adversely affect the quality of the indoor air. These pressure drivers act in concert with other pressure divers that are not directly associated with the air distribution system. Therefore, the effect that the air distribution system has on the quality of the indoor air must be analyzed from a "systems" point of view. This approach— which focuses on cause-and-effect relationships as they apply to the tightness of the duct system, the geometry of the return air paths, the leakage area of the building envelope, the performance characteristics of the primary HVAC equipment, the effectiveness of the flues and vents, the influence of household fuel burning appliances, the effect of household exhaust equipment and the impact on the occupants — is discussed in Section 13 of this manual.

14-3 Duct Board and Duct Liner

According to the North American Insulation Manufacturers Association (NAIMA) there is no research (as of 1994) that indicates that duct board or duct liner creates a hazard that will have a chronic effect on the health of the homeowner or the installer-fabricator. However, airborne glass fibers can cause temporary skin and respiratory irritations. These irritations are a mechanical reaction to glass fibers that rub against or become embedded in tissue surfaces. But, if the duct system is properly designed, installed and "blown down," the concentration of airborne fibers in the conditioned space will be too small to create a health or comfort problem for the occupants of the home. (When properly installed, duct board and duct liner does not erode over time.) As far as fabrication and testing is concerned, workers can shield themselves from loose fibers by wearing protective clothing and filter devices, and by observing the appropriate work practices.

14-4 Duct Cleaning

If dust, dirt, mildew and mold accumulate in the air distribution system, these contaminants can cause allergic reactions and create health hazards. If an inspection indicates that an accumulation of foreign material has been deposited or is growing on the surfaces that are associated with the air paths, the problem may be corrected by a duct cleaning effort. However, there is a possibility that this endeavor will exacerbate the problem if this strategy is not appropriate for the situation at hand or if the cleaning work is not performed in accordance with industry standards. (In some cases encapsulation is the preferred remediation strategy.)

14-5 "Dirty Socks" Syndrome

People that have studied the problem believe that the so-called dirty socks syndrome (a foul odor produced by a heat pump) is caused by an accumulation of biological contaminants on the indoor heat pump coil. These researchers speculate that microorganisms — which are commonly found in the soil, water and air — are deposited on the indoor coil during the summer, when the coil is cold and wet, and that these colonies thrive and grow during the heating season, when the indoor coil is dry and warm. However, this coating, by itself, does not produce the odor problem, even when spores are entrained in the supply air. Evidently, the odor is produced when the airborne contaminants are burned. This condition can only occur during the heat pump defrost cycle when the electric resistance heater is energized, but even then, it might not occur unless the indoor coil is wet. In other words, there may be three conditions associated with an odor problem:

- Biological contaminants must be deposited on the coil

- The indoor coil might have to be wet

- The electric resistance heat must be on

Note that two of these three conditions cause the occurrence of the odor problem to be decidedly arbitrary. Evidently there are many homes that do not have a contaminated coil. And, even if the coil is coated, the indoor humidity (during the heating season) may be too low to cause wetting of the indoor coil during the defrost cycle. In any case, if the first condition is eliminated (no contamination), the problem cannot occur. Therefore, duct leakage could be a contributing factor if the leakage introduces contaminants into the return air or causes contaminated air to infiltrate into the conditioned space. (The dynamics of the dirty socks problem are still not fully understood. Contact the Air Conditioning and Refrigeration Institute (ARI) for information that postdates the publication of this manual.)

Section 15
Noise

Noise is always produced by the blower and also can be generated by air-side devices, dampers, fittings, supply outlets and return inlets. Noise also is created when air flow velocities are too high. And, noise is normally associated with the vibrations that are produced by the mechanical equipment. When noise is generated it can propagate through the duct system, it can be transmitted through or radiated from the duct walls and it can be transmitted through the structural components of a building.

The noise that is produced by the HVAC system must not create an unacceptable condition in the occupied space. Noise can be controlled by keeping air flow velocities low, by using aerodynamic fittings, by using duct liner or duct board, by avoiding "line of sight" connections between a noise source and an outlet or an inlet and by using properly located balancing dampers. Ducts should be fabricated with adequate reinforcement and breaks. Equipment and ducts should be mounted or supported with devices that isolate or absorb vibration.

15-1 Blower Noise

The noise that is generated by the blower will propagate downstream though the supply duct and upstream, against the flow, in a return duct. If it is not attenuated, this noise will enter a room via the supply outlets and the return openings. Blower noise also can be transmitted through the equipment cabinet or the duct walls to the surrounding space.

15-2 Noise Generated in the Flow Path

Noise is created when turbulence is generated in a duct run. This turbulence is usually associated with inefficient fittings (elbows, tees, transitions and takeoffs) and sternly throttled dampers. Turbulence also can be created by the accessories and heat transfer devices that are installed in the airways. Regardless of the source, generated noise will propagate downstream though the supply duct and upstream in a return duct. If it is not attenuated, this noise will enter a room via the supply outlets and the return openings. Generated noise also can be transmitted through the duct walls to the surrounding space.

15-3 Noise Generated by Air Distribution Devices

Noise is generated when air flows through a grille, register or diffuser. The intensity of this noise depends on the velocity of the flow, which is commonly referred to as the face velocity or neck velocity. If either of these velocities is too high, or if the air distribution device is equipped with a damper that is severely throttled, an unacceptable level of noise will be generated and this noise will propagate directly into the room.

15-4 Transmitted Noise

Equipment room noise (or any type of noise) can be transmitted through the walls, partitions, ceilings and floors of the structure. The amount of transmitted noise that enters a room depends on the tightness of the structural assembly and the type of construction material. Tight, massive construction provides the most attenuation. Very light construction provides a small amount of attenuation. Small cracks and openings completely destroy the ability of a structural component to attenuate noise.

15-5 Crosstalk

Crosstalk refers to a situation where noise that is created in one room is transmitted into another room via a duct system or transfer grille. Crosstalk is likely to create a problem if the duct system or return path has a "line of sight" connection.

15-6 Vibration

Mechanical vibrations are produced by all types of rotating and reciprocating equipment. These vibrations always have the potential to create noise problems and in some cases they can cause structural damage.

Aerodynamic vibrations are produced when an unstable flow pattern is created by a fan or duct component. Unstable flows can cause the air flow to pulsate and surge and in some cases the ducts may vibrate. These types of vibrations are not normally a problem if the air side of the system is designed properly.

15-7 Attenuation

"Attenuation" refers to the reduction in the intensity of a noise that is propagating through a duct system. For example, the power level of the noise that is generated by a blower will continuously decrease as it moves through the various components of the duct system. This type of attenuation is always desirable because it dissipates the fan noise before it enters the room.

15-8 Room Absorption Effect

The construction and size of the room has a large effect on the loudness of the sound that enters the room. Noise generated by the HVAC system would be louder in a small "hard" room than it would be in a large "soft" room.

15-9 Designing for Noise Control

Noise control is a design requirement. Most of the problems that are associated with generated noise can be avoided by sizing ducts and selecting fittings, fans and devices in accordance with the recommendations made in this manual. In some cases, the designer must provide some type of attenuation or isolation to avoid a noise problem that is caused by the blower. The following paragraphs make recommendations and discuss procedures that can be used to control noise.

Supply Outlets and Return Inlets

The performance of supply air outlets and return hardware is documented in manufacturers' publications, but as far as residential equipment is concerned, this data may not include noise rating information. If a noise rating is not available, the face velocity or neck velocity (which is normally published) can be used as a guideline. Normally, a supply outlet will not generate objectionable noise if the face velocity or neck velocity is less than 700 FPM. This means that supply outlets should be selected to satisfy three criteria: the required supply CFM, the required throw and the maximum allowable face or neck velocity. As far as returns are concerned, objectionable noise will not be a problem if the face velocity is less than 500 FPM.

Note that even if the face or neck velocity is within an acceptable range, problems can be created by poor installation practices. For example, Figure 15-1 shows an installation that is characterized by a nonuniform flow through a close-coupled supply air outlet. This type of installation is not desirable because it produces turbulence, generates noise and distorts the air pattern. (In these situations, necks, collars, turning devices and equalizing grids must be used to control the flow into the outlet.) A second example of a noisy installation also is provided by Figure 15-1, which shows an abrupt offset between the outlet and the duct connecting point.

Noise Generated by Flow Control Devices

A register damper should not be used as a balancing damper because it will generate noise when it is adjusted to a hard throttle position. (Registers are only suitable for making minor adjustments to the supply air flow rate.) When an appreciable flow reduction is required, the adjustment should be made with a hand damper that is located as far from the supply air outlet as possible.

Velocity

The velocity of the air flow is very important, as far as generated noise is concerned. Excessive noise will not be

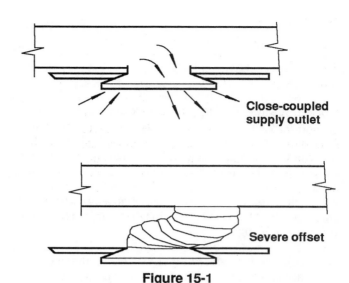

Close-coupled supply outlet

Severe offset

Figure 15-1

produced by fittings and devices if the velocities that are associated with the duct runs are within the limits that are recommended by this manual.

Fan Speed

Fan speed reductions translate into lower wheel velocities, slower flow rates and less noise, but a fan speed change may not be acceptable, as far as comfort is concerned. For example, a system that is providing satisfactory comfort (heating, cooling and dehumidification) before a fan speed change may not perform satisfactorily after a fan speed change. (It is important to remember that fan speed is directly related to equipment capacity and air delivery rates.)

Efficient Fittings

When velocity limits are observed, the flow through an aerodynamically efficient fitting will not be a source of noise. However, the potential for generated noise increases as the sophistication of the fitting geometry decreases. As far as noise (and pressure loss) is concerned, fittings that have radius turns, turning vanes and gradual transitions are preferable to square, unvaned fittings and abrupt transitions.

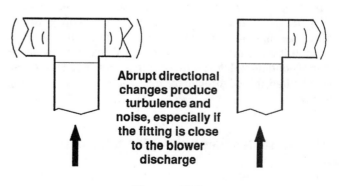

Abrupt directional changes produce turbulence and noise, especially if the fitting is close to the blower discharge

Figure 15-2

Duct Geometry

Always strive to acoustically decouple the blower or any other source of noise (a balancing damper, for example) from the occupied space. Design the duct system so that there are no short, straight connections between a blower (outlet and inlet) or a device and a room. Even long straight connections should be avoided. When duct flow velocities are low, elbows, tees, take-off fittings and transitions attenuate noise. Ideally, the air flow should turn at least twice as it moves along the path between the source of the noise and the room. Figure 15-3 shows supply and return openings that are too close to the blower, as far as attenuation is concerned, and alternative designs that decouple the occupied space from the blower noise.

Upstream Turbulence

Fittings and dampers should be installed only in the sections of the duct system that are characterized by a smooth well ordered flow pattern. Avoid installing any type of fitting or damper in the turbulent wake of an upstream disturbance. Also note that cushion heads (trunk extension past last take-off) are required at the end of every duct run.

Provide Attenuation

Propagating noise will be attenuated by turns and sound-absorbing materials. In this regard, lined elbows are very desirable because they are effective attenuating devices — especially if the liner is placed directly in the elbow as well as a short distance upstream and downstream from the elbow. A properly designed, acoustically lined plenum also can be used to attenuate noise. As far as straight runs are concerned, duct liner and duct board provide a noticeable amount of attenuation. In some designs, the components of the duct system may not provide enough attenuation, even if they are lined. When this is the case, sound traps can be used to provide the required attenuation.

- Line the first 5 feet of a supply trunk
- Line the first 10 feet of a return run
- Design the run so that it has two 90-degree turns

Duct Shape

Turbulence in the air stream may cause a duct wall to vibrate. Round ducts radiate less noise than square or rectangular

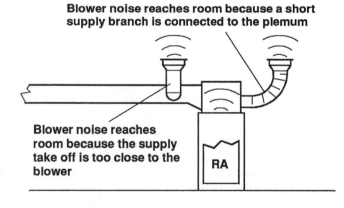

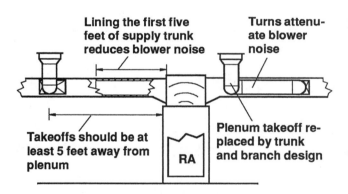

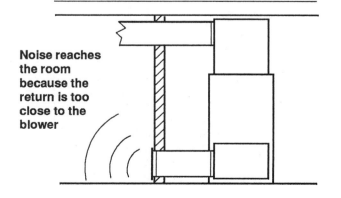

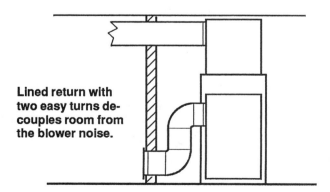

Figure 15-3

ducts because the curvature of a round duct wall tends to make it stiffer than a flat wall. Crossbreaks, beading and reinforcement reduce the noise that is radiated from rectangular shapes.

Prevent Crosstalk
Crosstalk refers to occupant-generated noise that is transmitted from one room to another. Crosstalk can be reduced or prevented by creating a duct geometry that has no line-of-sight connection between any of the supply or return openings (see Figure 15-4). Also avoid using door and wall grilles to transfer return air from a room to a central return. If a return air transfer is required, two grilles should be installed in the ceiling (on each side of the partition) and they should be connected by a lined duct or a fiberious board duct that has

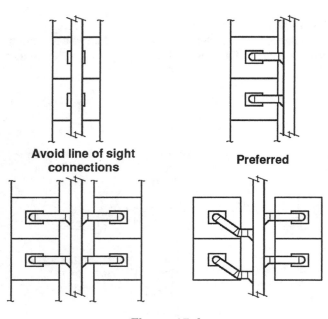

Avoid line of sight connections

Preferred

Figure 15-4

two 90-degree elbows. Of course a system that features duct liner, duct board and flex duct materials will be superior to a sheet metal system — as far as attenuation is concerned.

Duct Leakage
Seal the cracks, seams and joints in duct runs and equipment panels that are located in or acoustically coupled with the occupied space. (When airways are tightly sealed, the noise that is propagating through the duct — blower noise, for example — is isolated from the room because the air in the room is not affected by the pressure pulse in the duct.)

Low-frequency Noise
Duct board and duct liner provide some attenuation of high-frequency noise, but most duct materials and duct liners are transparent to low-frequency sound. Rooms under lay-in ceilings are especially susceptible to low-frequency noise. Mass provides the best defense against a breakout of low-frequency noise. However, the cost advantages of using lightweight materials usually preclude the use of mass as a solution.

Block Transmission
Sound can enter the occupied space by transmission through walls, ceilings and floors. Make sure that the wall, ceiling or floor between the equipment room and the occupied space is completely sealed (no crackage or penetrations). Sound absorbing material, or, in extreme cases, additional wall mass, may be required if noise transmission continues to be a problem after the wall is sealed.

Provide Vibration Isolation
Fans should be balanced. Fans and fan cabinets should be installed in accordance with the manufacturer's recommendations. Vibration pads should be installed under equipment. Flexible connections should be installed between the fan cabinet and the ductwork. Also use flexible connectors for rigid conduit and piping connections. Ducts should be supported and isolated in accordance with SMACNA standards. Whenever possible locate the HVAC equipment away from the rooms that should be quiet.

Section 16
Testing and Balancing

As far as comfort and efficiency are concerned, testing and balancing are just as important as the design calculations and the installation protocol (methods and materials). This section provides an overview of the testing, adjusting, balancing and inspection work that is associated with, or related to, the air-side of a residential HVAC system.

16-1 Scope of Work

A home is composed of many subsystems. Some of these subsystems have nothing to do with the comfort conditioning system, but others cannot be ignored by the HVAC contractor because they are part of the HVAC system or because they interact with the HVAC system. A comprehensive list of subsystems that may have to be tested includes the structural envelope, the air distribution system, the ventilation system, refrigerant-based heat transfer systems, fossil fuel heating systems, venting systems, water-based heat transfer systems, electrical systems and control systems. As far as the air-side performance is concerned, the testing involves the structural envelope, the air distribution system, the ventilation system and the venting systems.

16-2 Blower Door Testing

The HVAC contractor must evaluate the performance of the structural envelope because it determines the load on the heating and cooling equipment and because it affects the comfort of the occupants, the indoor air quality and the cost of operation. If an existing structure is involved, a "construction features" survey and a blower door test provide the information that is required for troubleshooting and retrofit work. When new construction is involved, the performance that has been promised by the drawings and specifications can be validated by inspections and tests.

As far as the air distribution system is concerned, blower door tests are useful because they can be used to test the tightness of the duct system. The two methods that pertain to this work are referred to as the subtraction method and the flow hood method.

Subtraction Method
Two leakage measurements are required for the subtraction method test: one with the supply registers and return grilles open and the other with the supply registers and return grilles sealed. After the tests are completed, an estimate of the duct leakage rate is obtained by subtracting the second value from the first. Note that this method only measures the leakage that is associated with the ducts that are located outside of the

conditioned space and that it does not duplicate the pressure gradients, pressure differences and the flow conditions that exist when the air distribution system is in operation. (The entire duct system is placed under a negative pressure, which is equal to 50 Pascals or less, depending on the leakage rate at the various leakage sites and on the resistance that is associated with the various duct runs.) There also are other problems with this test:

- Poor accuracy if the envelope is very leaky
- Accuracy sensitive to small errors in the test data
- Accuracy is affected by the wind conditions
- Not accurate when the duct leakage rate is low
- Overemphasizes leakage near grilles and registers
- Does not measure leaks to the conditioned space

Flow Hood Method
The flow hood test involves sealing all of the supply resisters and returns, except for one return grill. When the blower door is used to depressurize the house, the duct leakage can be measured by measuring the flow at the open return. This test produces an accurate leakage measurement because the measurement is based on a single test that is applied directly to the duct system and because the flow hood is a fairly accurate instrument. However, this test only measures the leakage that is associated with the ducts located outside of the conditioned space; this test does not duplicate the pressure gradients, pressure differences and the flow conditions that exist when the air distribution system is in operation. (Near the open grille, the negative pressure in the duct is approximately 50 Pascals, but the pressure at other points in the duct will be less negative, depending on the distance from the open grille and on the resistance of the flow path.) There also are other problems with this test:

- Pressures vary with the position of the leakage site
- Overemphasizes leakage near grilles and registers
- Does not measure leaks to the conditioned space
- Requires two pieces of equipment

When the blower door equipment is used to test the tightness of the building envelope, the leakage rate is measured after the house has been depressurized to -50 Pascals. This leakage rate is not equal to the infiltration CFM; it is only an indication of the tightness of the building. (There are some equations that can be used to make this conversion, but the accuracy of these equations varies, depending on the construction features of the home.)

16-3 Duct Blaster

A "duct blaster" can be used to measure duct leakage directly. (The duct blaster is similar to a small blower door.) When this test is performed, all the supply registers and return openings are sealed, except one return, which is fitted with the duct blaster apparatus. This test produces a credible leakage CFM estimate because the measurement is based on a single test that is applied directly to the duct system, and because the duct blaster is a fairly accurate instrument. However, this test cannot discriminate between leakage to a conditioned space and leakage to an unconditioned space and does not duplicate the pressure gradients, pressure differences and the flow conditions that exist when the air distribution system is in operation. (Both sides of the duct system are pressurized during the test.) There also are other problems with this test:

- Pressures vary with position of the leakage site
- Overemphasizes leakage near grilles and registers
- Does not measure leaks to unconditioned spaces
- Must use blower door test to measure leaks to outdoors

16-4 Pressure Measurements

As explained in Section 13, the pressures in the various rooms and enclosed spaces will fluctuate, depending on which pressure drivers are active. These pressures and pressure differences should be measured because this information can be used to evaluate the tightness of the duct system, the continuity of the return air paths, the effectiveness of the exhaust and venting systems, and the envelope infiltration.

16-5 Vents, Chimneys and Exhaust Systems

The capacity of vents, chimneys and exhaust systems can be certified by measuring the flow rates that are associated with the most adverse operating condition. This condition is created when the applicable pressure drivers combine to produce a "worst case" negative pressure in the room or space.

16-6 Safety

It is important to understand that leakage tests and duct sealing efforts can create unsafe conditions. These conditions can occur when testing or duct sealing produces a negative pressure in a room that contains combustion equipment. (Refer to Section 13 for more information about the relationship between duct leakage and the pressure in a room or space.) When this occurs, the combustion equipment could be subject to flue gas backdraft, flame rollout and combustion efficiency problems. (Properly vented combustion equipment can backdraft when the space pressure is as small as -1 to -5 Pascals; gas water-heater flame rollout can be caused by depressurization, and the combustion efficiency of a burner is a function of the pressure in the room.)

Because of the potential danger, leakage testing and duct sealing work must be done in accordance with documented procedures. If there is any question regarding safety, a series of carbon monoxide tests should be made before and after a duct sealing project. Do not proceed with a testing and sealing project if a CO test indicates unacceptably high levels in the room or in the flue gas (also issue warnings to the occupants and the proper authority, so that the problem can be immediately corrected).

16-7 Air-side Balancing

The primary objective of the balancing work is to ensure that each room receives the desired amount of supply air. (The design CFM values are tabulated on the duct sizing worksheet.) This is accomplished by making air-flow rate measurements and damper adjustments. The flow measurements that are involved with this work can be made at the supply air outlets; but other types of flow, pressure and temperature measurements may be required to evaluate other aspects of duct system performance, blower performance, or to estimate the duct leakage. The following paragraphs provide a brief summary of the types of tests that are associated with the air-side balancing work.

Supply CFM and Return CFM
The air flow that is associated with supply outlets and returns can be measured by using a flow hood, a velometer (with probe), a vane anemometer or a thermal anemometer. The flow hood is the easiest to use (provided that the size and shape of the hood is compatible with the size and shape of the air-side hardware) because it provides a direct readout of the flow rate. The other flow measuring devices are less convenient to use because multiple measurements may have to be averaged, A_k values may be required in order to convert the readout data into a CFM value, or an area measurement may be required to convert the velocity readout data into a CFM value.

Duct Flow
The air flow that is associated with a duct run can be directly measured by using a velometer or a manometer and a pitot tube. Both instruments use the same measurement technique, which is know as a "duct traverse." This traverse produces a series of data points. If a velometer is used, the readout data represents velocities, which must be averaged and multiplied by the cross-sectional area to obtain a CFM value. If the pitot tube is used, the readout data represents velocity pressures, which must be converted into velocities (FPM); then these velocities must be averaged and multiplied by the cross-sectional area (SQ.FT.) to obtain a CFM value.

The air flow that is associated with a duct run also can be measured indirectly, providing that the flow passes through an air-side device (a fin-tube coil, for example). When this method is used, the pressure drop that is associated with the device is measured with a pitot tube or static pressure gauge and then this pressure drop is converted into a flow rate. However, this conversion cannot be made unless the manufacturer has published a graph or table that summarizes the air-side performance of the device. (This graph or table would have to correlate air flow with pressure drop.)

Blower CFM

The blower CFM can be evaluated by measuring the flow that is associated with a trunk duct located immediately upstream or downstream from the blower. Or, if a blower table is available, the blower CFM can be estimated by correlating the pressure change across the blower and the blower speed with the blower CFM. (Do not assume that the blower CFM is represented by the sum of the supply outlet CFM values or the sum of the return air CFM values. This assumption is valid only if there is no duct leakage between the blower and the points of measurement.)

Duct Leakage

The leakage that is associated with a duct system can be estimated by comparing the upstream flow with the downstream flow. On the supply side of the system, the upstream flow is equal to the flow in the supply trunk (near the blower) and the downstream flow is equal to the total flow through the supply outlets. On the return side of the system, the upstream flow is equal to the total flow through the return grilles and the downstream flow is equal to the flow in the return trunk (near the blower).

Appendix 1
Equations and Tables

This appendix is a collection of equations and tables that might be used to design a residential duct system. In some cases, a brief description or discussion may be provided with an equation or table. Refer to the appropriate section in the main body of this manual for more information about a particular subject.

A1-1 Sensible Heat Equation

The sensible heat equation establishes the relationship between the supply air flow rate, the load that is associated with the conditioned space and the temperature difference between the supply air and the room air. Separate calculations are required for cooling and for heating because the design load, thermostat setpoint and supply air temperature depend on the mode of operation.

For Cooling:

$$CFM = \frac{Sensible\ Cooling\ Load\ BTUH}{1.1 \times (Room\ DB - Supply\ DB)}$$

For Heating:

$$CFM = \frac{Heating\ Load\ BTUH}{1.1 \times (Supply\ DB - Room\ DB)}$$

A1-2 Room Air Flow Equations

The air flow (CFM) that must be delivered to a room is based on the ratio of the room load and the equipment sizing load. This ratio is applied to the blower CFM (as determined during the equipment section process). For convenience, this calculation is made in two steps: first, a proportioning factor is created, and then the room CFM is evaluated. Separate calculations are required for heating and cooling.

$$Heating\ Factor\ (HF) = \frac{Blower\ CFM}{Design\ Heating\ Load}$$

$$Cooling\ Factor\ (CF) = \frac{Blower\ CFM}{Design\ Sensible\ Cooling\ Load}$$

$$Room\ CFM\ (Heat) = HF \times Room\ Heating\ Load$$

$$Room\ CFM\ (Cool) = CF \times Sensible\ Room\ Cooling\ Load$$

A1- 3 Friction Rate Equation

The friction rate equation defines the relationship between the available pressure (IWC), the total effective length (TEL) and a friction rate value (IWC/100). This equation is important because all the duct sizing slide rules and friction charts are based on the IWC/100 friction rate parameter.

$$Friction\ Rate = \frac{Available\ Pressure \times 100}{Total\ Effective\ Length}$$

A1-4 Duct Resistance Equation

The duct system resistance curve is a graph of duct pressure loss (PD) as a function of the flow rate (CFM). The effect of fan speed changes can be estimated by drawing the duct system performance curve and the fan performance curve on the same graph. (PD_x represents the pressure drop at CFM_x and PD_1 represents the pressure drop at CFM_1.)

$$PD_x = PD_1 \times \left[\frac{CFM_x}{CFM_1} \right]^2$$

A1- 5 Duct Flow Equation

The CFM that flows through a duct is equal to the cross-sectional area (SQ.FT.) multiplied by the average velocity of the flow (FPM). In design work, the flow rate and the design velocity are known and the cross-sectional area is calculated. In balancing work, the cross-sectional area and average velocity are measured and the CFM is calculated.

$$CFM = Velocity \times Area$$

A1-6 Equivalent Duct Size Based on Friction Rate

The following equations can be used to size rectangular ducts (W x H) and oval ducts (area A and perimeter P) so that they have the same friction rate (IWC/100 value) as a round duct.

For a rectangular ducts (W and H in inches):

$$Diameter = 1.30 \times \frac{(W \times H)^{0.625}}{(W + H)^{0.250}}$$

For oval ducts (A in square inches and P in inches):

$$Diameter = 1.55 \times \frac{A^{0.625}}{P^{0.250}}$$

A1-7 Hydraulic Diameter

Duct shapes that have the same hydraulic diameter will have the same friction rates (IWC/100 value). The following equation can be used to calculate the hydraulic diameter of any duct shape. (All dimensions should be in inches.)

$$Hydraulic\ Diameter = \frac{4 \times Cross\text{-}sectional\ Area}{Perimeter}$$

A1-8 Areas and Perimeters

The following equations can be used to calculate the cross-sectional areas (A) and perimeter dimensions (P) for round, rectangular and oval shapes. (All dimensions are in inches.)

Round (radius R and diameter D)

$$A = \pi R^2$$
$$P = \pi D$$

Rectangle (width W and height H)

$$A = W \times H$$
$$P = 2W + 2H$$

Oval (minor diameter B and major diameter A)

$$A = \pi B^2 / 4 + B \times (A\text{-}B)$$
$$P = \pi B + 2 \times (A\text{-}B)$$

Triangular (base B, height H and side S)

$$A = 0.50\ B \times H$$
$$P = B + 2S$$

A1-9 Recommended Velocities

Table 3-1, which is reproduced below, summarizes the design guidelines that pertain to duct flow velocity. This table also provides information about the maximum face velocity that is associated with supply outlets and return grilles.

A1-10 Duct System Efficiency

Refer to Section 12 for information about duct efficiency. Insulation standards (CABO-MEC and ASHRAE) can be found on page 12-3. A chart that can be used to estimate conduction losses is on page 12-4 and information that can be used to quantify duct leakage losses appears on pages 12-6 and 12-7.

Recommended Velocity (FPM)								
	Supply Side				Return Side			
	Recommended		Maximum		Recommended		Maximum	
	Rigid	Flex	Rigid	Flex	Rigid	Flex	Rigid	Flex
Trunk Ducts	700	600	900	700	600	600	700	700
Branch Ducts	600	600	900	700	400	400	700	700
Supply Outlet Face Velocity	Size for Throw		700		—		—	
Return Grille Face Velocity	—		—		—		500	
Filter Grille Face Velocity	—		—		—		300	

Table 3-1

Appendix 2
Friction Charts, Duct Slide Rules and Equivalency Tables

Friction charts and duct slide rules document the relationship between the performance parameters that are associated with ducted air flow. These parameters include the flow rate (CFM), the friction loss per 100 feet of straight duct (F/100 value), the round duct diameter (inches) and the average velocity of air moving through the duct (FPM). Duct slide rules and equivalency tables either duplicate the friction chart information or provide supplementary information, such as the equivalence between round and rectangular shapes.

A2-1 Friction Charts

Friction charts provide a graphical presentation of the physical relationships that are associated with ducted air flow. An example of a friction chart is provided on the next page by Figure A2-1. On this chart, the air flow rate is represented by the CFM values (on the Y-axis), the friction rate is represented by the F/100 values (on the X-axis), the round duct size is represented by the lines that slope from the lower left to the upper right and the velocity of the flow is represented by the lines that slope from the upper left to the lower right.

If any two of these four parameters are known, the lines that represent these parameters will intersect at some point on the chart and the other two parameters can be read from the chart at this point of this intersection. For example, if 100 CFM is flowing through a 7-inch galvanized metal duct, the friction rate will be equal to 0.04 IWC/100 and the velocity will be equal to 360 FPM (approximately). Figure A2-1 summarizes this mapping exercise.

Other inputs are processed in a similar manner. For example, Figure A2-2 also shows that if the flow rate is equal to 500 CFM and the maximum allowable velocity is equal to 900 FPM, the smallest possible duct diameter is equal to 10 inches (approximately) and the corresponding friction rate is equal to 0.13 IWC/100 (approximately).

Friction Rate versus Pressure Drop
Sometimes the designer must determine the pressure drop (IWC) that is associated with a duct run. This pressure drop is related to, but is normally not equal to, the friction rate. The exception occurs when the duct is exactly 100 feet long. In this case the pressure drop can be read directly from the duct slide rule because there is no difference between the friction rate (IWC/100 value) and the pressure drop value (IWC). For example, if the friction rate is equal to 0.08 IWC/100 and the duct is 100 feet long, the pressure drop must be equal to 0.08 IWC.

When a duct run is not exactly 100 feet long, the friction rate (IWC/100) and the pressure drop (IWC) will not be equal. In these cases the following equation defines the relationship between the friction rate and the pressure drop.

$$Pressure\ drop = \frac{Friction\ rate \times Duct\ length}{100}$$

For example, the galvanized metal friction chart shows that if 500 CFM flows through a 10-inch duct, the friction rate is equal to 0.13 IWC/100. In this case the pressure drop equation would be used to estimate the pressure drop that is associated with a particular duct run. The following calculations show that if the duct run is 70 feet long, the pressure drop must be equal to 0.056 IWC; and if the duct run is 170 feet long, the pressure drop must be equal to 0.136 IWC.

$$Pressure\ drop = \frac{0.08 \times 70}{100} = 0.056\ IWC$$

$$Pressure\ drop = \frac{0.08 \times 170}{100} = 0.136\ IWC$$

In the previous example, the friction chart was used to determine the friction rate that is associated with a known flow rate and duct size, and the pressure drop equation was used to convert this information into a pressure drop. In this case, the calculation procedure began with a reading of the friction chart and ended with a pressure drop calculation. In other cases, the calculation procedure flows in the opposite direction, beginning with an application of the pressure drop equation and terminating with a reading of the friction chart. This sequence of operation is typical of the **Manual D** duct sizing calculations, which convert pressure drop and flow rate information into a compatible duct size. For example, if 0.16 IWC of pressure is available to move 300 CFM through a duct run that is 177 feet long, the following calculation shows that the corresponding friction rate value must be equal to 0.080 IWC/100. The galvanized metal duct friction chart on page A2-4 shows that this friction rate value translates into a 9-inch duct size.

$$F/100\ value = \frac{Pressure\ drop \times 100}{Duct\ length}$$

$$F/100\ value = \frac{0.16 \times 100}{177} = 0.090$$

Figure A2-1
Round Galvanized Metal Duct
10 CFM to 2,000 CFM

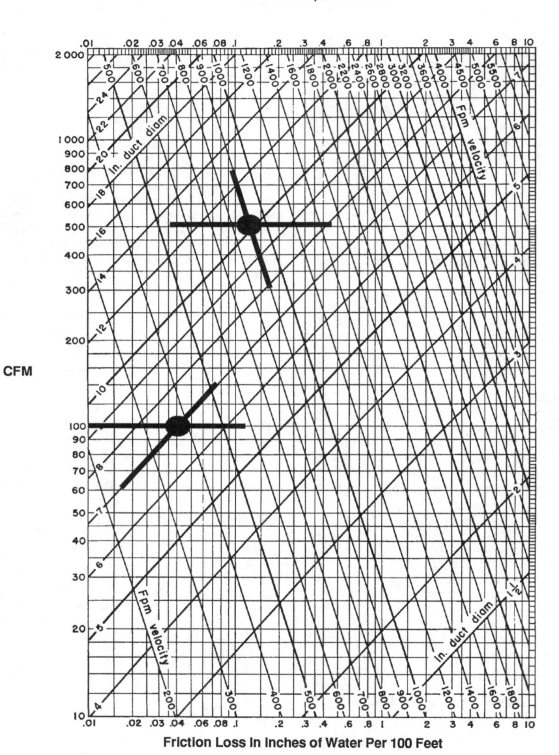

Friction Loss In Inches of Water Per 100 Feet

Notes:
1) Correction required for nonstandard air
2) 40 joints per 100 feet.
3) Roughness = 0.0005 feet

Duct Material

The information that is presented by a particular friction chart applies only to the duct material that is associated with the chart. In other words, a separate friction chart is required for each type of duct material. Refer to Charts 1 through 8 on the following pages for examples of friction charts that describe the performance of rigid metal ducts, rigid fiberious board ducts, rigid metal ducts lined with a fiberglass material, wire helix ducts and flexible metal ducts.

Sometimes a duct is fabricated from a material that is not documented, as far as a friction chart is concerned. In these cases the designer can use a friction chart that documents the performance of a similar but rougher material. For example, the galvanized metal chart can be used to evaluate the performance of ducts that are made with stainless steel, aluminum, carbon steel, spiral galvanized metal, smooth plastic and PVC materials.

Velocity Data

The velocity information that is associated with the friction chart applies only to a round shape. The velocity that is associated with an equivalent rectangular duct will always be lower than the velocity in the round duct. The following equation can be used to calculate the average velocity in any duct regardless of the shape.

$$Velocity\ (FPM) = \frac{Flow\ Rate\ (CFM)}{Cross\text{-}sectional\ Area\ (SQ.FT.)}$$

Rectangular Sizes

The dimensional size information that is provided by a friction chart is limited to round shapes. If another shape is desired, conversion tables (see Charts 12 and 13) can be used to find the dimensions of the equivalent rectangular or oval duct (or vice versa). Note that when a conversion table is used, "equivalent" means that the round and rectangular ducts will have the same friction rate. This equivalency does not extend to the velocity of the flow, which will be different for each equivalent size (refer to Section 12-1).

A2-2 Duct Slide Rules

Duct slide rules provide the same information as the friction chart and they are easier to read. (Duct slide rules are typically limited to a single material, but the ACCA duct slide rule documents the performance of four common materials.) Duct slide rules have another advantage over friction charts because they provide equivalent rectangular sizes, and some slide rules may provide even more information. For example, the ACCA duct slide rule has scales that can be used to calculate the following parameters:

- Velocity in a rectangular duct
- Cross-sectional area of a round shape
- Cross-sectional area of a rectangular shape
- Friction rate, pressure drop conversions
- Velocity pressure conversions
- Altitude corrections
- Temperature corrections

Chart 1
Round Galvanized Metal Duct
10 CFM to 2,000 CFM

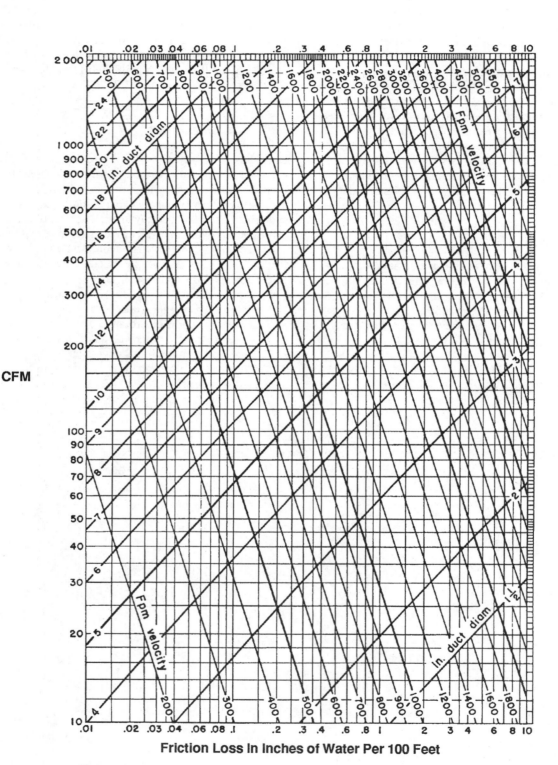

Friction Loss In Inches of Water Per 100 Feet

Notes:
1) Correction required for nonstandard air
2) 40 joints per 100 feet
3) Roughness = 0.0005 feet

Chart 2
Round Galvanized Metal Duct
1,000 CFM to 100,000 CFM

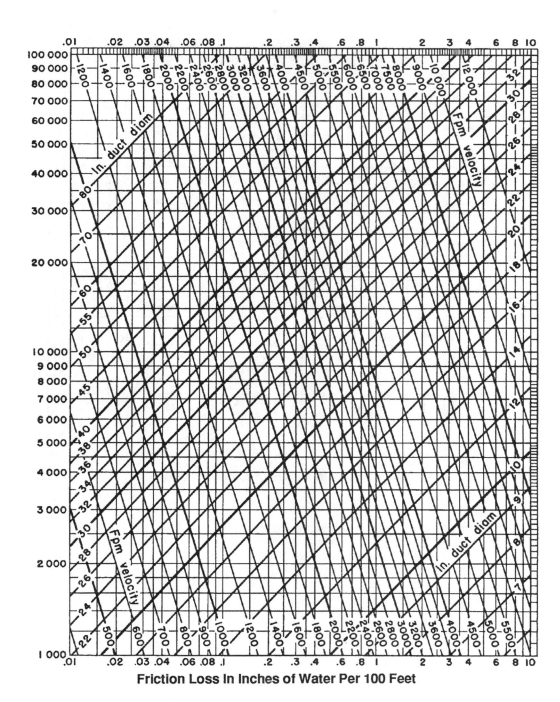

Friction Loss In Inches of Water Per 100 Feet

Notes:
1) Correction required for nonstandard air
2) 40 joints per 100 feet
3) Roughness = 0.0005 feet

Chart 3
Fiberglass Duct Board
10 CFM to 2,000 CFM

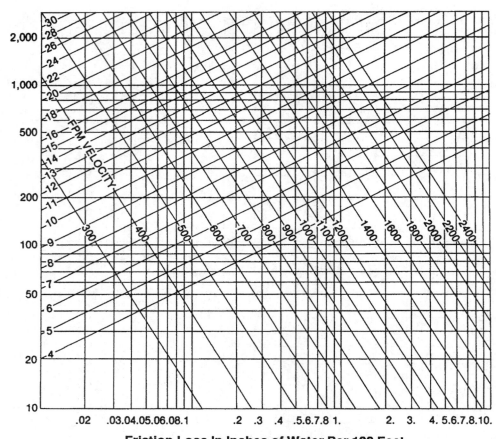

CFM

Friction Loss In Inches of Water Per 100 Feet

Notes:
1) Correction required for nonstandard air
2) Maximum allowable velocity 2,400 FPM
3) Maximum allowable temperature 250°F
4) Maximum allowable pressure 2 IWC

Chart 4
Fiberglass Duct Board
100 CFM to 100,000 CFM

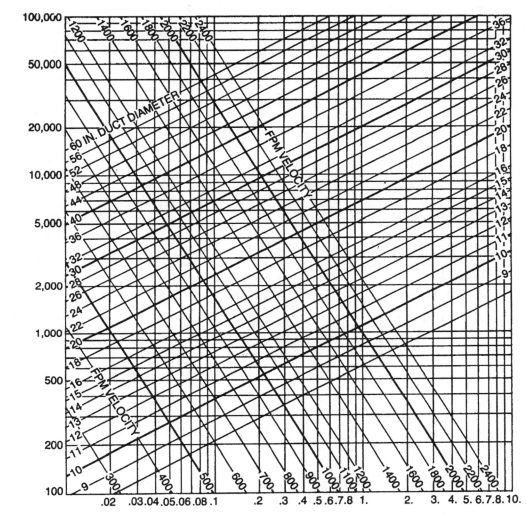

CFM

Friction Loss In Inches of Water Per 100 Feet

Notes:
1) Correction required for nonstandard air
2) Maximum allowable velocity 2,400 FPM
3) Maximum allowable temperature 250°F
4) Maximum allowable pressure 2 IWC

Chart 5
Rigid Round Fiberglass Duct

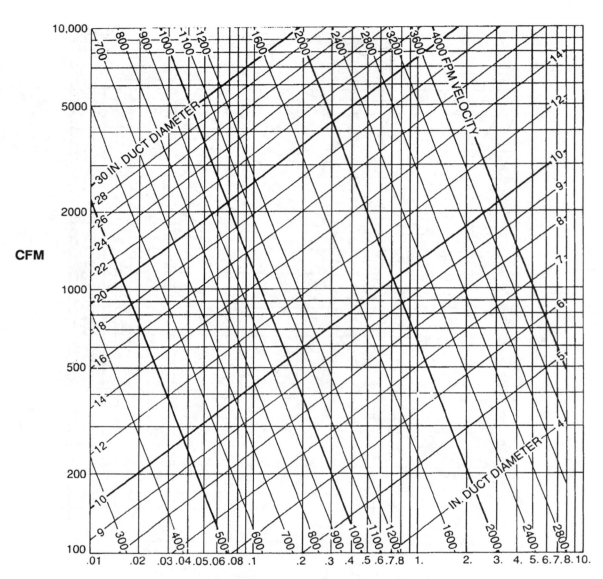

Friction Loss In Inches of Water Per 100 Feet

Chart 6
Fiberglass Duct Liner with Facing

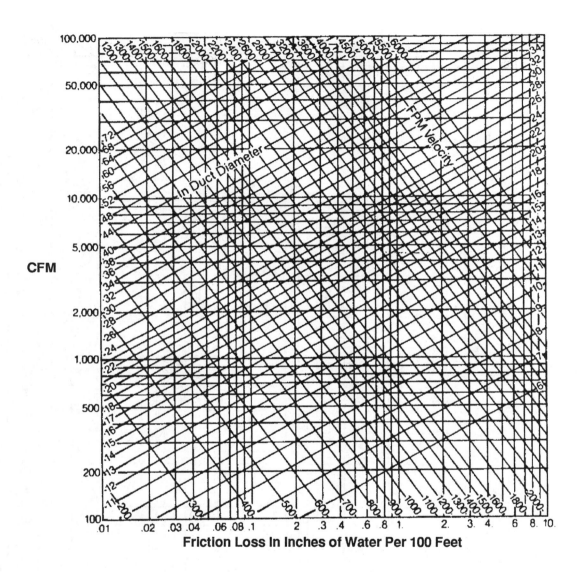

CFM (vertical axis)

Friction Loss In Inches of Water Per 100 Feet (horizontal axis)

Notes:
1) Correction required for nonstandard air
2) Maximum recommended velocity 5,000 FPM
3) Maximum allowable temperature 250°F

Chart 7
Flexible, Spiral Wire Helix Core Ducts

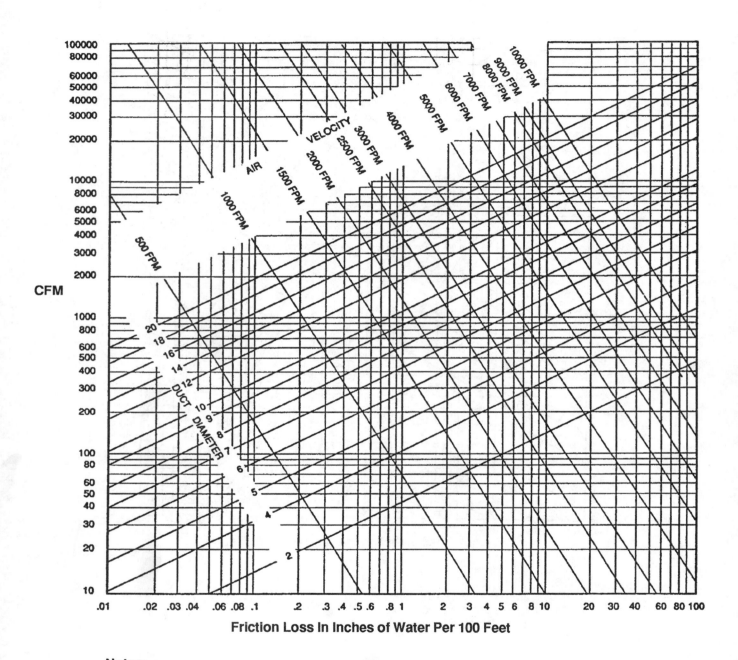

Friction Loss In Inches of Water Per 100 Feet

Notes:
1) Correction required for nonstandard air
2) Maximum velocity 2,400 FPM
3) Maximum temperature 250°F
4) Maximum positive pressure
   up to 12" I.D. - 2 IWC
   over 12" I.D. - 1 IWC
5) Maximum negative pressure 1 IWC

Chart 8
Flexible Metal Ducts

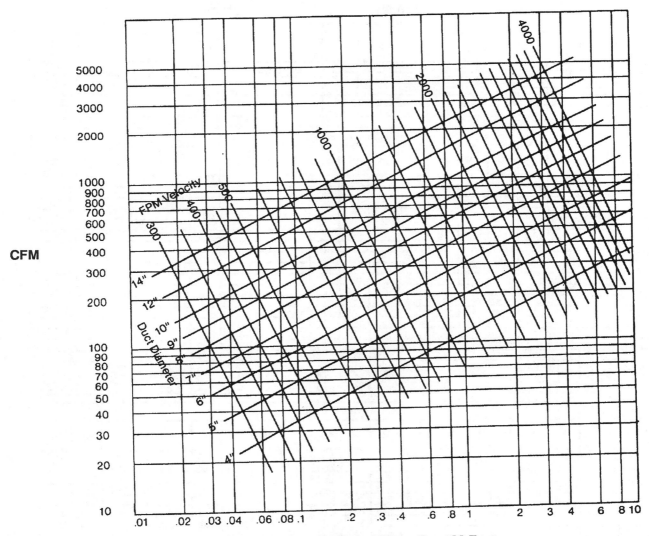

CFM (vertical axis)

Friction Loss In Inches of Water Per 100 Feet (horizontal axis)

Notes:
1) Correction required for nonstandard air
2) Maximum velocity 8,000 FPM
3) Maximum temperature 250°F (insulated), 400°F (noninsulated)
4) Maximum positive pressure (IWC)

	Up to 12"	12" to 16"	over 16"
Plain nonperforated	8"	8"	8"
Perforated acoustical	2"	2"	1"
High-pressure acoustical	8"	4"	4"

5) Maximum negative pressure (IWC)

	Up to 12"	Over 12"
Plain nonperforated	8"	8"
Perforated acoustical	2"	2"
High-pressure acoustical	8"	4"

Chart 9
Circular Equivalents of Rectangular Ducts

Based on Equal Friction

Side Rec. Duct	4.0	4.5	5.0	5.5	6.0	6.5	7.0	7.5	8.0	9.0	10.0	11.0	12.0	13.0	14.0	15.0	16.0
3.0	3.8	4.0	4.2	4.4	4.6	4.7	4.9	5.1	5.2	5.5	5.7	6.0	6.2	6.4	6.6	6.8	7.0
3.5	4.1	4.3	4.6	4.8	5.0	5.2	5.3	5.5	5.7	6.0	6.3	6.5	6.8	7.0	7.2	7.5	7.7
4.0	4.4	4.6	4.9	5.1	5.3	5.5	5.7	5.9	6.1	6.4	6.7	7.0	7.3	7.6	7.8	8.1	8.3
4.5	4.6	4.9	5.2	5.4	5.7	5.9	6.1	6.3	6.5	6.9	7.2	7.5	7.8	8.1	8.4	8.6	8.8
5.0	4.9	5.2	5.5	5.7	6.0	6.2	6.4	6.7	6.9	7.3	7.6	8.0	8.3	8.6	8.9	9.1	9.4
5.5	5.1	5.4	5.7	6.0	6.3	6.5	6.8	7.0	7.2	7.6	8.0	8.4	8.7	9.0	9.3	9.6	9.9

Side Rec. Duct	6	7	8	9	10	11	12	13	14	15	16	17	18	19	20	22	24	26	28	30
6	6.6																			
7	7.1	7.7																		
8	7.6	8.2	8.7																	
9	8.0	8.7	9.3	9.8																
10	8.4	9.1	9.8	10.4	10.9															
11	8.8	9.5	10.2	10.9	11.5	12.0														
12	9.1	9.9	10.7	11.3	12.0	12.6	13.1													
13	9.5	10.3	11.1	11.8	12.4	13.1	13.7	14.2												
14	9.8	10.7	11.5	12.2	12.9	13.5	14.2	14.7	15.3											
15	10.1	11.0	11.8	12.6	13.3	14.0	14.6	15.3	15.8	16.4										
16	10.4	11.3	12.2	13.0	13.7	14.4	15.1	15.7	16.4	16.9	17.5									
17	10.7	11.6	12.5	13.4	14.1	14.9	15.6	16.2	16.8	17.4	18.0	18.6								
18	11.0	11.9	12.9	13.7	14.5	15.3	16.0	16.7	17.3	17.9	18.5	19.1	19.7							
19	11.2	12.2	13.2	14.1	14.9	15.7	16.4	17.1	17.8	18.4	19.0	19.6	20.2	20.8						
20	11.5	12.5	13.5	14.4	15.2	16.0	16.8	17.5	18.2	18.9	19.5	20.1	20.7	21.3	21.9					
22	12.0	13.0	14.1	15.0	15.9	16.8	17.6	18.3	19.1	19.8	20.4	21.1	21.7	22.3	22.9	24.0				
24	12.4	13.5	14.6	15.6	16.5	17.4	18.3	19.1	19.9	20.6	21.3	22.0	22.7	23.3	23.9	25.1	26.2			
26	12.8	14.0	15.1	16.2	17.1	18.1	19.0	19.8	20.6	21.4	22.1	22.9	23.5	24.2	24.9	26.1	27.3	28.4		
28	13.2	14.5	15.6	16.7	17.7	18.7	19.6	20.5	21.3	22.1	22.9	23.7	24.4	25.1	25.8	27.1	28.3	29.5	30.6	
30	13.6	14.9	16.1	17.2	18.3	19.3	20.2	21.1	22.0	22.9	23.7	24.4	25.2	25.9	26.6	28.0	29.3	30.5	31.7	32.8

Side Rec. Duct	6	7	8	9	10	11	12	13	14	15	16	17	18	19	20	22	24	26	28	30
32	14.0	15.3	16.5	17.7	18.6	19.8	20.8	21.8	22.7	23.5	24.4	25.2	26.0	26.7	27.5	28.9	30.2	31.5	32.7	33.9
34	14.4	15.7	17.0	18.2	19.3	20.4	21.4	22.4	23.3	24.2	25.1	25.9	26.7	27.5	28.3	29.7	31.0	32.4	33.7	34.9
36	14.7	16.1	17.4	18.6	19.8	20.9	21.9	22.9	23.9	24.8	25.7	26.6	27.4	28.2	29.0	30.5	32.0	33.3	34.6	35.9
38	15.0	16.5	17.8	19.0	20.2	21.4	22.4	23.5	24.5	25.4	26.4	27.2	28.1	28.9	29.8	31.3	32.8	34.2	35.6	36.8
40	15.3	16.8	18.2	19.5	20.7	21.8	22.9	24.0	25.0	26.0	27.0	27.9	28.8	29.6	30.5	32.1	33.6	35.1	36.4	37.8
42	15.6	17.1	18.5	19.9	21.1	22.3	23.4	24.5	25.6	26.6	27.6	28.5	29.4	30.3	31.2	32.8	34.4	35.9	37.3	38.7
44	15.9	17.5	18.9	20.3	21.5	22.7	23.9	25.0	26.1	27.1	28.1	29.1	30.0	30.9	31.8	33.5	35.1	36.7	38.1	39.5
46	16.2	17.8	19.3	20.6	21.9	23.2	24.4	25.5	26.6	27.7	28.7	29.7	30.6	31.6	32.5	34.2	35.9	37.4	38.9	40.5
48	16.5	18.1	19.6	21.0	22.3	23.6	24.8	26.0	27.1	28.2	29.2	30.2	31.2	32.2	33.1	34.9	36.6	38.2	39.7	41.2
50	16.8	18.4	19.9	21.4	22.7	24.0	25.2	26.4	27.6	28.7	29.8	30.8	31.8	32.8	33.7	35.5	37.2	38.9	40.5	42.0
52	17.1	18.7	20.2	21.7	23.1	24.4	25.7	26.9	28.0	29.2	30.3	31.3	32.3	33.3	34.3	36.2	37.9	39.6	41.2	42.8
54	17.3	19.0	20.6	22.0	23.5	24.8	26.1	27.3	28.5	29.7	30.8	31.8	32.9	33.9	34.9	36.8	38.6	40.3	41.9	43.5
56	17.6	19.3	20.9	22.4	23.8	25.2	26.5	27.7	28.9	30.1	31.2	32.3	33.4	34.4	35.4	37.4	39.2	41.0	42.7	44.3
58	17.8	19.5	21.2	22.7	24.2	25.5	26.9	28.2	29.4	30.6	31.7	32.8	33.9	35.0	36.0	38.0	39.8	41.6	43.3	45.0
60	18.1	19.8	21.5	23.0	24.5	25.9	27.3	28.6	29.8	31.0	32.2	33.3	34.4	35.5	36.5	38.5	40.4	42.3	44.0	45.7
62		20.1	21.7	23.3	24.8	26.3	27.6	28.9	30.2	31.5	32.6	33.8	34.9	36.0	37.1	39.1	41.0	42.9	44.7	46.4
64		20.3	22.0	23.6	25.1	26.6	28.0	29.3	30.6	31.9	33.1	34.3	35.4	36.5	37.6	39.6	41.6	43.5	45.3	47.1
66		20.6	22.3	23.9	25.5	26.9	28.4	29.7	31.0	32.3	33.5	34.7	35.9	37.0	38.1	40.2	42.2	44.1	46.0	47.7
68		20.8	22.6	24.2	25.8	27.3	28.7	30.1	31.4	32.7	33.9	35.2	36.3	37.5	38.6	40.7	42.8	44.7	46.6	48.4
70		21.1	23.1	24.5	26.1	27.6	29.1	30.4	31.8	33.1	34.4	35.6	36.8	37.9	39.1	41.2	43.3	45.3	47.2	49.0
72			23.3	24.8	26.4	27.9	29.4	30.8	32.2	33.5	34.8	36.0	37.2	38.4	39.5	41.7	43.8	45.8	47.8	49.6
74			23.6	25.1	26.7	28.2	29.7	31.2	32.5	33.9	35.2	36.4	37.7	38.8	40.0	42.2	44.4	46.4	48.4	50.3
76			23.8	25.3	27.0	28.5	30.0	31.5	32.9	34.3	35.6	36.8	38.1	39.3	40.5	42.7	44.9	47.0	48.9	50.9
78			24.1	25.6	27.3	28.8	30.4	31.8	33.3	34.6	36.0	37.2	38.5	39.7	40.9	43.2	45.4	47.5	49.5	51.4
80				25.8	27.5	29.1	30.7	32.2	33.6	35.0	36.3	37.6	38.9	40.2	41.4	43.7	45.9	48.0	50.1	52.0
82				26.1	27.8	29.4	31.0	32.5	34.0	35.4	36.7	38.0	39.3	40.6	41.8	44.1	46.4	48.5	50.6	52.6
84				26.4	28.1	29.7	31.3	32.8	34.3	35.7	37.1	38.4	39.7	41.0	42.2	44.6	46.9	49.0	51.1	53.2
86				26.6	28.3	30.0	31.6	33.1	34.6	36.1	37.4	38.8	40.1	41.4	42.6	45.0	47.3	49.6	51.7	53.7
88				26.9	28.6	30.3	31.9	33.4	34.9	36.4	37.8	39.2	40.5	41.8	43.1	45.5	47.8	50.0	52.2	54.3
90				27.1	28.9	30.6	32.2	33.8	35.3	36.7	38.2	39.5	40.9	42.2	43.5	45.9	48.3	50.5	52.7	54.8
92					29.1	30.8	32.5	34.1	35.6	37.1	38.5	39.9	41.3	42.6	43.9	46.4	48.7	51.0	53.2	55.3
96					29.6	31.4	33.0	34.7	36.2	37.7	39.2	40.6	42.0	43.3	44.7	47.2	49.6	52.0	54.2	56.4

Chart 9 (Continued)
Circular Equivalents of Rectangular Ducts

Based on Equal Friction

Side Rec. Duct	Dimensions in Inches																			
	32	34	36	38	40	42	44	46	48	50	52	56	60	64	68	72	76	80	84	88
32	35.0																			
34	36.1	37.2																		
36	37.1	38.2	39.4																	
38	38.1	39.3	40.4	41.5																
40	39.0	40.3	41.5	42.6	43.7															
42	40.0	41.3	42.5	43.7	44.8	45.9														
44	40.9	42.2	43.5	44.7	45.8	47.0	48.1													
46	41.8	43.1	44.4	45.7	46.9	48.0	49.2	50.3												
48	42.6	44.0	45.3	46.6	47.9	49.1	50.2	51.4	52.5											
50	43.6	44.9	46.2	47.5	48.8	50.0	51.2	52.4	53.6	54.7										
52	44.3	45.7	47.1	48.4	49.7	51.0	52.2	53.4	54.6	55.7	56.8									
54	45.1	46.5	48.0	49.3	50.7	52.0	53.2	54.4	55.6	56.8	57.9									
56	45.8	47.3	48.8	50.2	51.6	52.9	54.2	55.4	56.6	57.8	59.0	61.2								
58	46.6	48.1	49.6	51.0	52.4	53.8	55.1	56.4	57.6	58.8	60.0	62.3								
60	47.3	48.9	50.4	51.9	53.3	54.7	60.0	57.3	58.6	59.8	61.0	63.4	65.6							
62	48.0	49.6	51.2	52.7	54.1	55.5	56.9	58.2	59.5	60.8	62.0	64.4	66.7							
64	48.7	50.4	51.9	53.5	54.9	56.4	57.8	59.1	60.4	61.7	63.0	65.4	67.7	70.0						
66	49.4	51.1	52.7	54.2	55.7	57.2	58.6	60.0	61.3	62.6	63.9	66.4	68.8	71.0						
68	50.1	51.8	53.4	55.0	56.5	58.0	59.4	60.8	62.2	63.6	64.9	67.4	69.8	72.1	74.3					
70	50.8	52.5	54.1	55.7	57.3	58.8	60.3	61.7	63.1	64.4	65.8	68.3	70.8	73.2	75.4					
72	51.4	53.2	54.8	56.5	58.0	59.6	61.1	62.5	63.9	65.3	66.7	69.3	71.8	74.2	76.5	78.7				
74	52.1	53.8	55.5	57.2	58.8	60.3	61.9	63.3	64.8	66.2	67.5	70.2	72.7	75.2	77.5	79.8				
76	52.7	54.5	56.2	57.9	59.5	61.1	62.6	64.1	65.6	67.0	68.4	71.1	73.7	76.2	78.6	80.9	83.1			
78	53.3	55.1	56.9	58.6	60.2	61.8	63.4	64.9	66.4	67.9	69.3	72.0	74.6	77.1	79.6	81.9	84.2			
80	53.9	55.8	57.5	59.3	60.9	62.6	64.1	65.7	67.2	68.7	70.1	72.9	75.4	78.1	80.6	82.9	85.2	87.5		
82	54.5	56.4	58.2	59.9	61.6	63.3	64.9	66.5	68.0	69.5	70.9	73.7	76.4	79.0	81.5	84.0	86.3	88.5		
84	55.1	57.0	58.8	60.6	62.3	64.0	65.6	67.2	68.7	70.3	71.7	74.6	77.3	80.0	82.5	85.0	87.3	89.6	91.8	
86	55.7	57.6	59.4	61.2	63.0	64.7	66.3	67.9	69.5	71.0	72.5	75.4	78.2	80.9	83.5	85.9	88.3	90.7	92.9	
88	56.3	58.2	60.1	61.9	63.6	65.4	67.0	68.7	70.2	71.8	73.3	76.3	79.1	81.8	84.4	86.9	89.3	91.7	94.0	96.2
90	56.8	58.8	60.7	62.5	64.3	66.0	67.7	69.4	71.0	72.6	74.1	77.1	79.9	82.7	85.3	87.9	90.3	92.7	95.0	97.3
92	57.4	59.3	61.3	63.1	64.9	66.7	68.4	70.1	71.7	73.3	74.9	77.9	80.8	83.5	86.2	88.8	91.3	93.7	96.1	98.4
94	57.9	59.9	61.9	63.7	65.6	67.3	69.1	70.8	72.4	74.0	75.6	78.7	81.6	84.4	87.1	89.7	92.3	94.7	97.1	99.4
96	58.4	60.5	62.4	64.3	66.2	68.0	69.7	71.5	73.1	74.8	76.3	79.4	82.4	85.3	88.0	90.7	93.2	95.7	98.1	100.5

Note:
Equation for circular equivalent of a rectangular duct:

$$D_e = 1.30\,[(ab)^{0.625}/(a + b)^{0.250}]$$

Where:
a = length of one side of rectangular duct, inches.
b = length of adjacent side of rectangular duct, inches.
D_e = circular equivalent of rectangular duct for equal friction and capacity, inches.

Chart 10
Circular Equivalents of Oval Duct
Based on Equal Friction

Dimensions in Inches

	3	4	5	6	7	8	9	10	11	12	14	16	18	20	22	24	26	28	30	32	34	36	38	40
7		5.7																						
8	5.1		6.6	6.9																				
9	5.6	6.2		7.7																				
10		6.7	7.3		8.7	9.0																		
11	6.0		7.9	8.4		9.8																		
12	6.4	7.2		8.9	9.4		10.8	11.0																
13		7.6	8.4		10.1	10.6		11.9																
14	6.7		8.8	9.6		11.2	11.5																	
15	7.0	8.0		10.1	10.7					13.8														
16			9.3					13.4	13.6															
17	7.3	8.4					12.9																	
18					11.7	12.4				15.3														
19			10.0	11.0					15.0															
20							14.0	14.7			17.5													
21					12.6	13.5				16.7			19.9											
22				11.8					16.3			19.5												
23							15.1	15.7			18.9													
24						14.4							21.6											
25				12.5						18.0		20.9			23.9									
26								16.7						23.6										
27						15.2					20.2		23.1			25.9								
28				13.2						19.1					25.6									
29								17.7				22.3		25.2			27.9							
30						15.9					21.3					28.1								
31				13.8						20.1			24.5		27.2			29.9						
32								18.5				23.5					29.7							
33						16.6					22.4			26.6		29.3			32.0					
34				14.3						20.9			25.7					31.7						
35								19.3				24.7			28.7		31.3			34.0				
36						17.3					23.4			27.9					33.7					

Dimensions in Inches

	3	4	5	6	7	8	9	10	11	12	14	16	18	20	22	24	26	28	30	32	34	36	38	40
37				14.9						21.9			27.0			30.8		33.4			36.0			
38								20.1				25.7			30.0					35.8				
39						17.9					24.4			29.2			32.8		35.4			38.0		
40										22.7			28.1			32.2					37.8			
41				15.4				20.8				26.8			31.3			34.9		37.4			40.0	
42											25.3			30.3			34.3					39.8		
43						18.6				23.5			29.1			33.5			37.0		39.5			42.0
44				15.9								27.7			32.5			36.4					41.8	
45								21.5			26.1			31.4			35.6			39.0		41.5		
46						19.1							30.2			34.7			38.5					43.8
47										24.3		28.6			33.7			37.8			41.1		43.5	
48								22.1						32.5			36.9			40.5				
49						19.6					26.9		31.1			35.9			39.9			43.1		45.6
50										25.0					34.8			39.1			42.6			
51								22.8				29.4		33.4			38.1			42.0			45.2	
52						20.2					27.7					37.0			41.2			44.7		
53										25.7			32.0		35.8			40.3			44.1			47.2
54								23.3				30.2					39.3			43.3			46.7	
55											28.4			34.4		38.1			42.5			46.2		
56										26.3			32.9					41.5			45.5			48.8
57								23.8				31.0			36.7		40.4			44.6			48.2	
58											29.1			35.3					43.7			47.6		
59										26.9			33.7			39.2		42.6			46.8			50.4
60								24.4			29.6	31.8		36.1	37.8		41.3		44.5	45.9		48.5	49.7	
62										27.5			34.5			40.1		43.5			48.1			51.8
64								25.1			30.5	32.7		37.1	38.9		42.5		46.0			50.2		
66								25.4		28.3		33.3	35.4		39.6			44.8		48.0	49.7		52.4	
68										28.6	31.2			38.0		42.0			47.1			51.9		54.5
70								26.0			31.5	34.1	36.2		40.6		44.4	46.0		49.4	50.9		54.1	
72								26.3		29.2									48.6		51.6	53.1		56.2

Appendix 3
Fitting Equivalent Lengths

This appendix provides information about the air flow resistance that is associated with various types of supply and return fittings. For residential duct systems, this resistance is quantified by assigning an equivalent length value to each type of fitting.

Equivalent Length

Many designers assume that the equivalent length of a fitting is an invariable and unconditional description of the aerodynamic efficiency of the fitting. This is not true! The equivalent length of a fitting is in fact a conditional pressure loss value that has been converted to a "length" by using an equation that contains an arbitrary friction rate value.

Some of the conditions that affect the aerodynamic performance of the fitting could include the geometry, the entering and leaving flow rate(s) or the entering and leaving velocities. For example, Figure 1 shows that the fitting loss coefficient that is associated with a simple elbow depends on the geometry of the fitting and the CFM that flows through the fitting. In this case, the loss coefficient could vary from less than 0.13 to more than 1.5. This loss coefficient can be converted to a pressure loss by multiplying it by the velocity pressure that is associated with the flow. With a residential system, this velocity pressure could vary from less than 0.01 IWC (at 400 FPM) to more than 0.05 IWC (at 900 FPM). This means that the pressure loss across the fitting could vary from 0.0013 IWC to 0.075 IWC, as shown below:

0.13 x 0.01 = 0.0013
1.5 x 0.01 = 0.015
0.13 x 0.05 = 0.0065
1.5 x 0.05 = 0.075

Note that the fitting loss estimate is in pressure units (IWC), which is exactly the type of information that will ultimately be required. (The pressure that is generated by the fan must be equal to or greater than the pressure loss that is associated with the duct run.) Equivalent length units (FT) are contrived as a matter of convenience. This way, the resistance of a duct run can be represented by the effective length (equivalent length of the fittings plus the straight run length) of the duct run. Once the effective length value is known, a friction rate value can be used to convert the effective length into a pressure loss value or vice versa. The following equation can be used for this work. (If just one fitting is involved, this equation can be used to calculate its equivalent length.)

Length = 100 x pressure drop / friction rate

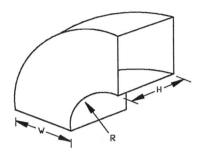

R/W	H/W										
	0.25	0.50	0.75	1.00	1.50	2.00	3.00	4.00	5.00	6.00	8.00
0.5	1.5	1.4	1.3	1.2	1.1	1.0	1.0	1.1	1.1	1.2	1.2
0.75	0.57	0.52	0.48	0.44	0.40	0.39	0.39	0.40	0.42	0.43	0.44
1.0	0.27	0.25	0.23	0.21	0.19	0.18	0.18	0.19	0.20	0.27	0.21
1.5	0.22	0.20	0.19	0.17	0.15	0.14	0.14	0.15	0.16	0.17	0.17
2.0	0.20	0.18	0.16	0.15	0.14	0.13	0.13	0.14	0.14	0.15	0.15

Reynolds Number Correction (N)		
CFM	R/W <0.75	R/W > 0.75
50 to 200	1.15	1.60
200 to 400	1.10	1.50
400 to 800	1.05	1.35
800 to 1000	1.03	1.30
1000 to 1500	1.00	1.15
1500 to 2000	1.00	1.05
Above 2000	1.00	1.00
Adjusted loss coefficient = C x N		

Figure 1

For example, the equivalent length of the fitting that is described above could vary from less than 1 foot to more than 94 feet, depending on the value for the loss coefficient, the reference velocity and the friction rate reference value. The details of the calculations that are associated with estimating the equivalent length of this fitting are summarized below:

100 x 0.075 / 0.08 = 94
100 x .075 / 0.15 = 50
100 x 0.0013 / 0.08 = 1.625
100 x 0.0013 / 0.15 = 0.867

The conclusion that can be drawn from this discussion is that equivalent length data (EL) should be accompanied by a statement that documents the reference velocity (V_r) and the reference friction rate value (F_r) that were used to generate the equivalent length information. In this manual, the equivalent length values that are associated with the various types of fittings are so annotated. If required, the equivalent length (EL_x) that is associated with another velocity (V_x) or another friction rate (F_x) can be calculated by using the following equation:

$$EL_x = EL \times (V_x / V_r)^2 \times (F_r / F_x)$$

For example, some of the equivalent length values that are presented on the following pages are based on a 900 FPM reference value and a 0.08 friction rate. If one of these equivalent length values is equal to 65 feet, use the previous equation to find the equivalent length that is associated with a 700 FPM velocity and a 0.12 friction rate value.

$$EL_x = 65 \times (700 / 900)^2 \times (0.08 / 0.12) = 26 \text{ feet}$$

Group 1
Supply Air Fittings at the Air Handling Equipment
Reference Velocity = 900 FPM
Reference Friction Rate = 0.08 In.Wg. per 100 Feet

1-A
EL = 35

1-B
EL = 10

Plenum size is large when compared to duct size

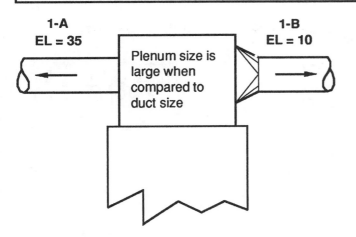

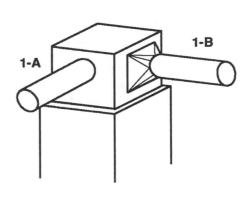

1-C
EL = 35

1-D
EL = 10

H/2

H

Plenum size is large when compared to duct size

45 Deg.

10" Minimum

10" Minimum

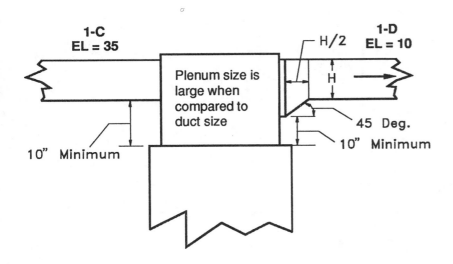

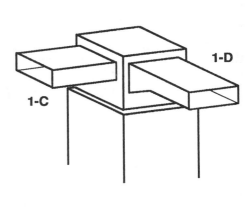

1-E
EL = 10

30 Deg.

Plenum size is large when compared to duct size

45 Deg.

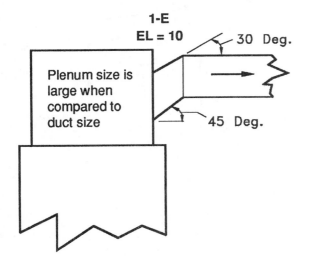

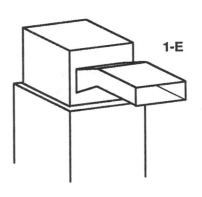

Group 1 — Continued
Supply Air Fittings at the Air Handling Equipment
Reference Velocity = 900 FPM
Reference Friction Rate = 0.08 In.Wg. per 100 Feet

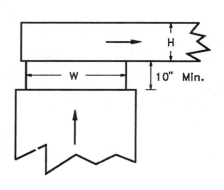

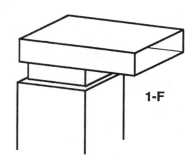

Bull Head 1-F	H / W	EL
	0.50	120
	1.0	85

Tapered Head 1-G	H / W	EL
	0.50	35
	1.0	25

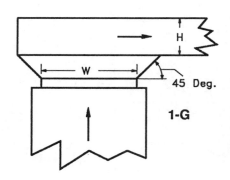

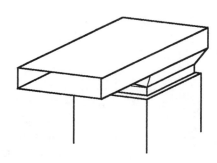

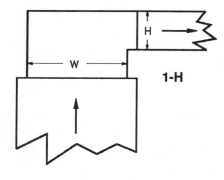

No Vanes 1-H	H / W	EL
	0.5	120
	1.0	85

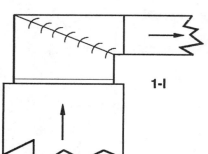

With Vanes 1-I	EL = 20

Group 1 — Continued
Supply Air Fittings at the Air Handling Equipment
Reference Velocity = 900 FPM
Reference Friction Rate = 0.08 In.Wg. per 100 Feet

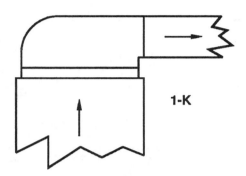

1-K

Mitered Inside Corner 1-K	EL = 85

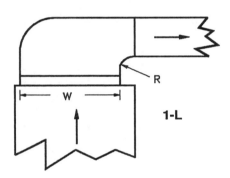

1-L

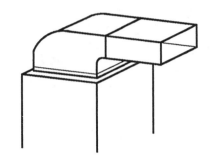

Radius Ell No Vanes 1-L	R / W	EL
	0.25	40
	0.50	20
	1.0	10

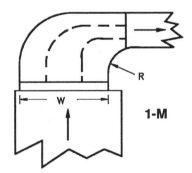

1-M

		1-Vane	2-Vane
Radius Ell With Vanes 1-M	R / W	EL	EL
	0.05	30	20
	0.25	20	10
	0.50	10	10

Add the EL for the transition to the EL that is associated with the elbow (or tee) that is upstream from the transition

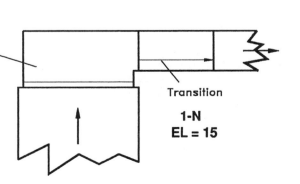

Transition

1-N
EL = 15

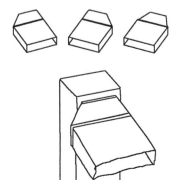

Group 1 — Continued
Supply Air Fittings at the Air Handling Equipment
Reference Velocity = 900 FPM
Reference Friction Rate = 0.08 In.Wg. per 100 Feet

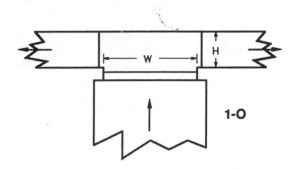

1-O

Bull Head No Vanes 1-O	H / W	EL
	0.50	120
	1.0	85

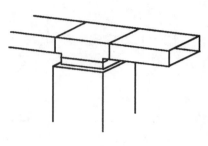

1-P

Vaned Tee 1-P	EL = 20

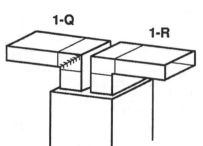

1-Q

1-R

Radius Elbow 1-S	Vanes	EL
	0	60
	1	40
	2	30

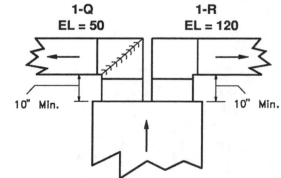

1-Q
EL = 50

1-R
EL = 120

10" Min.

10" Min.

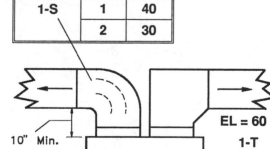

10" Min.

EL = 60
1-T

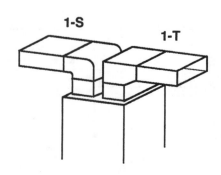

1-S

1-T

Group 2
Branch Takeoff Fittings at the Supply Trunk
Reference Velocity = 900 FPM
Reference Friction Rate = 0.08 In.Wg. per 100 Feet

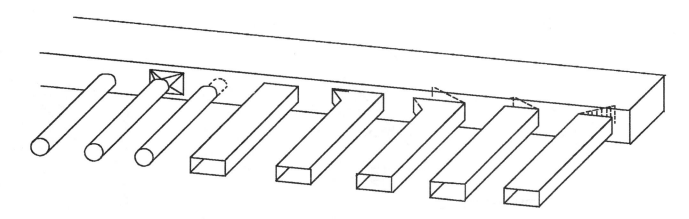

EL Values		Number of Downstream Branches to End of Trunk Duct or Number of Downstream Branches to a Trunk Reducer					
Fitting		**0**	**1**	**2**	**3**	**4**	**5 or More**
	2-A	35	45	55	65	70	80
	2-B	20	30	35	40	45	50
	2-C	65	65	65	65	70	80
	2-D	40	50	60	65	75	85
	2-E	25	30	35	40	45	50
	2-F	20	20	20	20	25	25
	2-G	65	65	65	70	80	90
	2-H	70	70	70	75	85	95

Note: If the trunk has a reducer, count down to the reducer; then begin counting (again) after the reducer

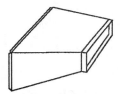

Refer to Fitting 2-D

Refer to Fitting 2-A or 2-C

Refer to Fitting 2-E

Group 2 — Continued
Branch Takeoff Fittings at the Supply Trunk
Reference Velocity = 900 FPM
Reference Friction Rate = 0.08 In.Wg. per 100 Feet

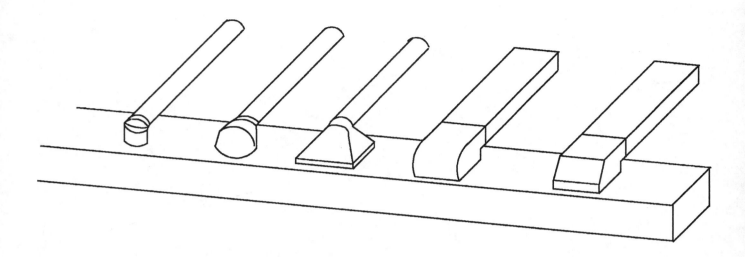

EL Values		Number of Downstream Branches to End of Trunk Duct or Number of Downstream Branches to a Trunk Reducer					
Fitting		0	1	2	3	4	5 or More
	2-I	65	75	85	95	100	110
	2-J	50	60	65	70	75	80
	2-K	50	60	65	70	75	80
	2-L	70	80	90	95	105	115
	2-M	70	80	90	95	105	115

Note: If the trunk has a reducer, count down to the reducer; then begin counting (again) after the reducer

Refer to Fitting 2-J

Refer to Fitting 2-J

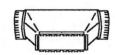

Refer to Fitting 2-I

Group 2 — Continued
Branch Takeoff Fittings at the Supply Trunk
Reference Velocity = 900 FPM
Reference Friction Rate = 0.08 In.Wg. per 100 Feet

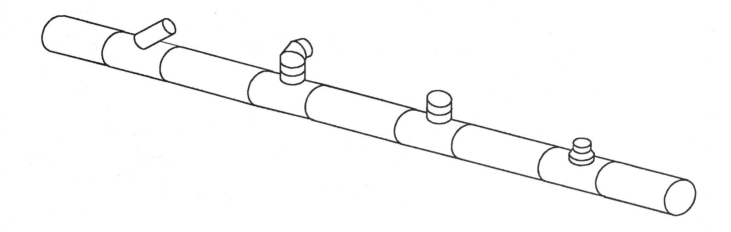

EL Values		Number of Downstream Branches to End of Trunk Duct or Number of Downstream Branches to a Trunk Reducer					
Fitting		0	1	2	3	4	5 or More
	2-N	35	35	40	40	40	40
	2-O	55	65	75	85	90	100
	2-P	50	55	60	65	70	75
	2-Q	10	10	15	20	20	25
Note: If the trunk has a reducer, count down to the reducer; then begin counting (again) after the reducer							

Group 3
Reducing Trunk Takeoff Fittings
Reference Velocity = 900 FPM
Reference Friction Rate = 0.08 In.Wg. per 100 Feet

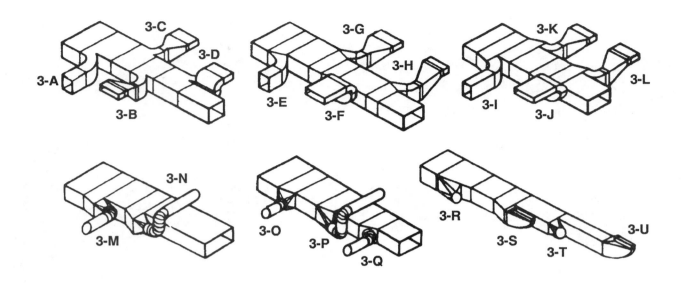

Fitting ID	EL	Description of Assembly
3-A and 3-I	15	Full radius takeoff
3-B and 3-L	30	Full radius takeoff plus offset transition
3-C and 3-K	20	Full radius takeoff plus straight transition
3-D and 3-J	35	Radius takeoff elbow (see S) plus easy-bend elbow
	55	Tight radius takeoff elbow (see S) plus easy-bend elbow
	110	Mitered inside corner takeoff elbow (see S) plus easy-bend elbow
3-E	30	Transition wall takeoff
3-F	3D + 15	Transition wall takeoff elbow (radius, tight radius or mitered corner) plus easy-bend elbow
3-G	35	Transition wall takeoff plus straight-aspect transition
3-H	35	Transition wall takeoff plus offset-aspect transition
3-M	25	In line eased takeoff fitting (see T) plus one elbow
3-N	40	In line eased takeoff fitting (see T) plus two elbows
3-O and 3-R	20	Transition wall eased takeoff fitting (see note)
3-P	50	Transition wall eased takeoff fitting plus two elbows (see note)
3-Q	35	Transition wall eased takeoff fitting plus one elbow (see note)
3-S and 3-U	15	Full radius takeoff elbow
	35	Tight inside radius takeoff elbow
	90	Mitered inside corner takeoff elbow
3-T	10	In line eased takeoff fitting
Note:		Add 15 feet to the equivalent length if a round sleeve is simply butted into the transition wall.

Group 3 — Continued
Reducing Trunk Takeoff Fittings
Reference Velocity = 900 FPM
Reference Friction Rate = 0.08 In.Wg. per 100 Feet

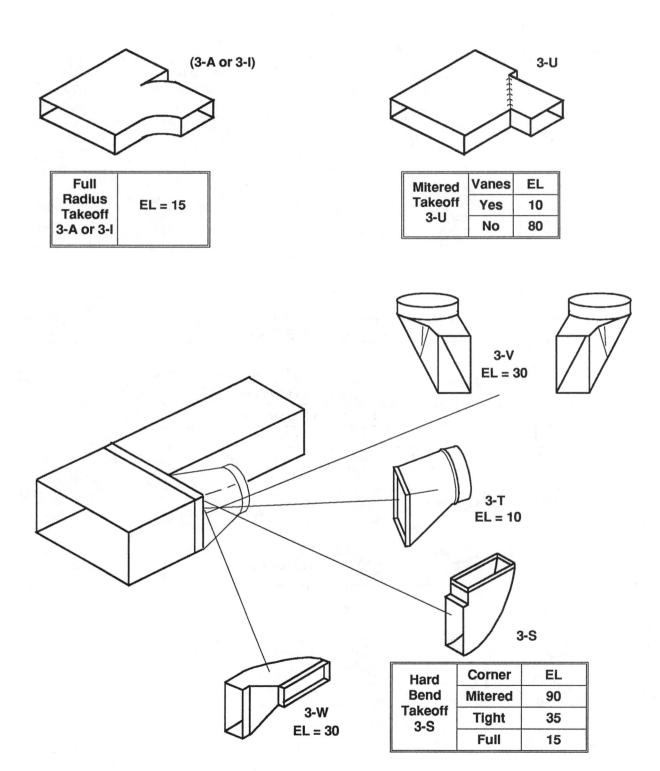

(3-A or 3-I)

Full Radius Takeoff 3-A or 3-I	EL = 15

3-U

Mitered Takeoff 3-U	Vanes	EL
	Yes	10
	No	80

3-V
EL = 30

3-T
EL = 10

3-S

3-W
EL = 30

Hard Bend Takeoff 3-S	Corner	EL
	Mitered	90
	Tight	35
	Full	15

Group 4
Supply Air Boot and Stack Head Fittings
Reference Velocity = 900 FPM
Reference Friction Rate = 0.08 In.Wg. per 100 Feet

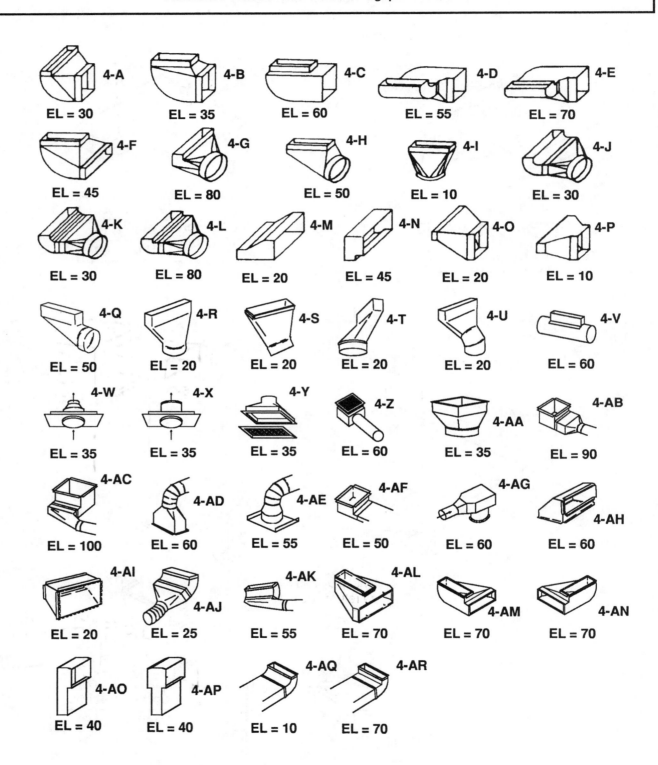

4-A   EL = 30
4-B   EL = 35
4-C   EL = 60
4-D   EL = 55
4-E   EL = 70

4-F   EL = 45
4-G   EL = 80
4-H   EL = 50
4-I   EL = 10
4-J   EL = 30

4-K   EL = 30
4-L   EL = 80
4-M   EL = 20
4-N   EL = 45
4-O   EL = 20
4-P   EL = 10

4-Q   EL = 50
4-R   EL = 20
4-S   EL = 20
4-T   EL = 20
4-U   EL = 20
4-V   EL = 60

4-W   EL = 35
4-X   EL = 35
4-Y   EL = 35
4-Z   EL = 60
4-AA   EL = 35
4-AB   EL = 90

4-AC   EL = 100
4-AD   EL = 60
4-AE   EL = 55
4-AF   EL = 50
4-AG   EL = 60
4-AH   EL = 60

4-AI   EL = 20
4-AJ   EL = 25
4-AK   EL = 55
4-AL   EL = 70
4-AM   EL = 70
4-AN   EL = 70

4-AO   EL = 40
4-AP   EL = 40
4-AQ   EL = 10
4-AR   EL = 70

Group 5
Return Air Fittings at the Air Handling Equipment
Reference Velocity = 700 FPM
Reference Friction Rate = 0.08 In.Wg. per 100 Feet

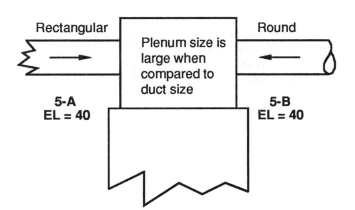

Rectangular

Plenum size is large when compared to duct size

Round

5-A
EL = 40

5-B
EL = 40

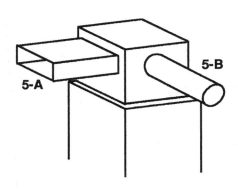

Rectangular

Plenum size is large when compared to duct size

Round

EL = 40
5-C

EL = 40
5-D

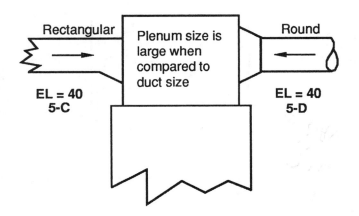

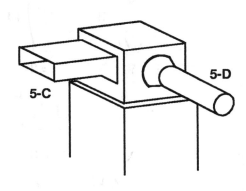

Plenum size is comparable to duct size

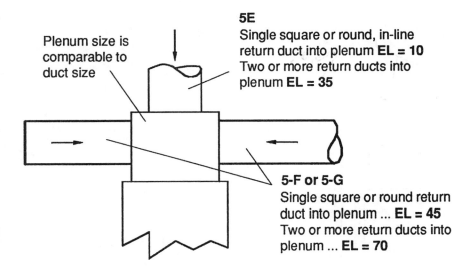

5E
Single square or round, in-line return duct into plenum **EL = 10**
Two or more return ducts into plenum **EL = 35**

5-F or 5-G
Single square or round return duct into plenum ... **EL = 45**
Two or more return ducts into plenum ... **EL = 70**

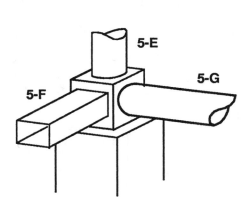

Group 5 — Continued
Return Air Fittings at the Air Handling Equipment
Reference Velocity = 700 FPM
Reference Friction Rate = 0.08 In.Wg. per 100 Feet

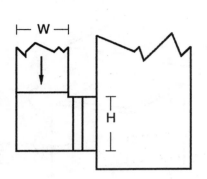

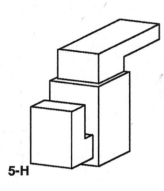

5-H

Square Elbow 5-H	H / W	EL
	1	45
	2	30

Mitered Inside Corner 5-I	H / W	EL
	1	45
	2	30

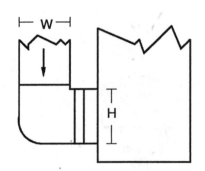

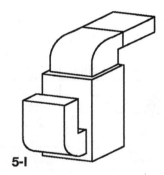

5-I

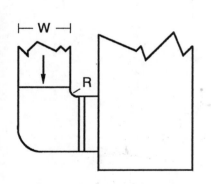

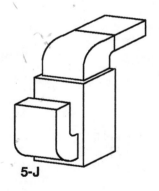

5-J

Radius Elbow 5-J	R / W	EL
	0.25	20
	0.50	15
	1.00	10

Square Elbow with Vanes 5-K	EL
	10

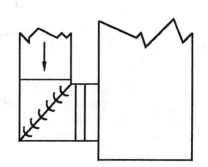

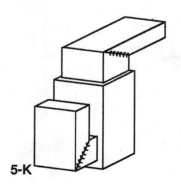

5-K

Group 5 — Continued
Return Air Fittings at the Air Handling Equipment
Reference Velocity = 700 FPM
Reference Friction Rate = 0.08 In.Wg. per 100 Feet

5-L
EL = 75

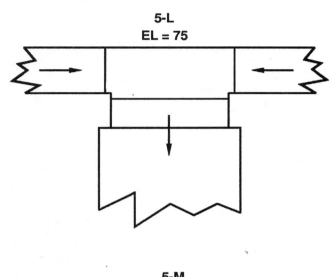

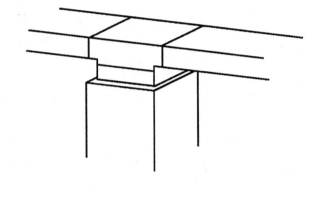

5-M
EL = 10

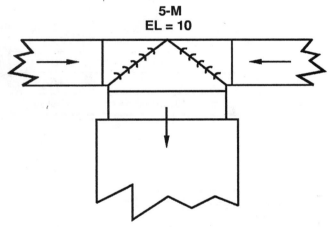

5-N
EL = 55

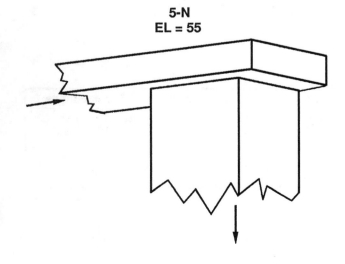

5-O
EL = 35

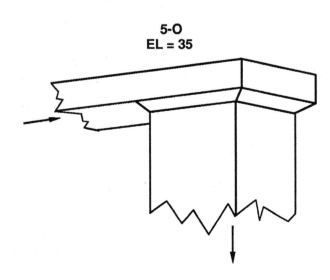

Group 6
Branch Return Air Fittings at the Return Trunk
Reference Velocity = 700 FPM
Reference Friction Rate = 0.08 In.Wg. per 100 Feet

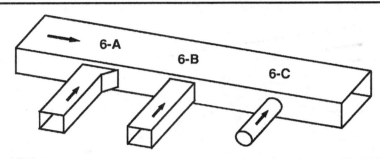

CFM1/CFM2	6-A Branch EL	6-A Trunk EL	6-B Branch EL	6-B Trunk EL	6-C Branch EL	6-C Trunk EL
0.40 or less	10	10	10	10	10	10
0.50	25	25	40	25	30	25
0.60	40	25	40	25	50	25
0.70	60	25	75	25	75	25
0.80	75	25	110	25	115	25
1.00	75	NA	110	NA	115	NA

The branch EL value applies to the turn and the trunk EL value applies to the upstream fittings (see example below).

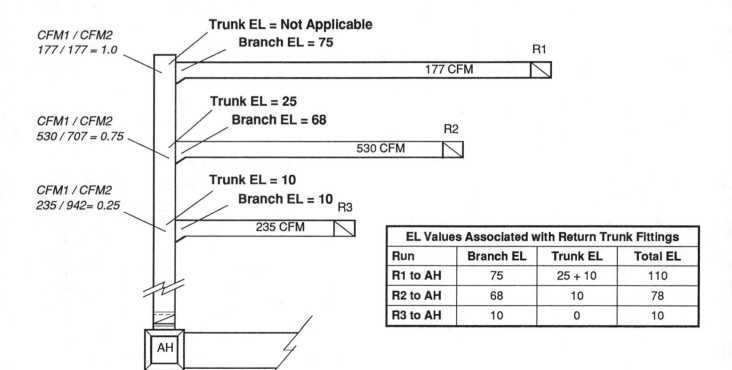

CFM1 / CFM2
177 / 177 = 1.0

Trunk EL = Not Applicable
Branch EL = 75

R1
177 CFM

CFM1 / CFM2
530 / 707 = 0.75

Trunk EL = 25
Branch EL = 68

R2
530 CFM

CFM1 / CFM2
235 / 942 = 0.25

Trunk EL = 10
Branch EL = 10 R3
235 CFM

AH

EL Values Associated with Return Trunk Fittings			
Run	Branch EL	Trunk EL	Total EL
R1 to AH	75	25 + 10	110
R2 to AH	68	10	78
R3 to AH	10	0	10

Group 6 — Continued
Branch Return Air Fittings at the Return Trunk
Reference Velocity = 700 FPM
Reference Friction Rate = 0.08 In.Wg. per 100 Feet

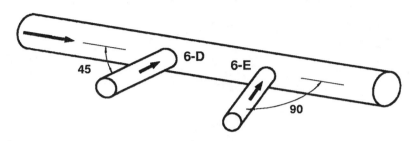

CFM1/CFM2	Branch EL	Trunk EL
0.10	10	5
0.20	15	5
0.30	20	5
0.40	30	5
0.60	30	5
0.80	30	5
1.00	30	NA
Refer to example below		

6-D

CFM1/CFM2	Branch EL	Trunk EL
0.10	15	10
0.20	30	10
0.30	40	10
0.40	40	10
0.50	40	25
0.80	40	25
1.00	40	NA
Refer to example below		

6-E

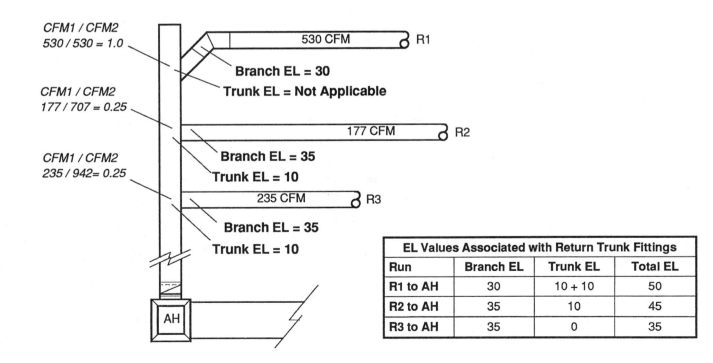

CFM1 / CFM2
530 / 530 = 1.0

530 CFM — R1

Branch EL = 30
Trunk EL = Not Applicable

CFM1 / CFM2
177 / 707 = 0.25

177 CFM — R2

Branch EL = 35
Trunk EL = 10

CFM1 / CFM2
235 / 942 = 0.25

235 CFM — R3

Branch EL = 35
Trunk EL = 10

AH

EL Values Associated with Return Trunk Fittings			
Run	Branch EL	Trunk EL	Total EL
R1 to AH	30	10 + 10	50
R2 to AH	35	10	45
R3 to AH	35	0	35

Group 6 — Continued
Return Air Boot Fittings
Reference Velocity = 700 FPM
Reference Friction Rate = 0.08 In.Wg. per 100 Feet

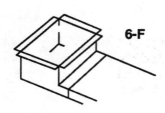

6-F

EL = 25

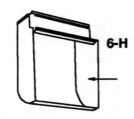

6-H

EL = 15

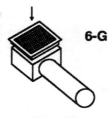

6-G

EL = 30

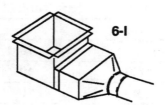

6-I

EL = 30

6-J

EL = 55

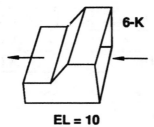

6-K

EL = 10

6-L

EL = 20

6-M

EL = 20

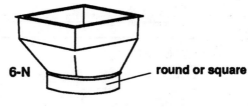

6-N   round or square

EL = 10

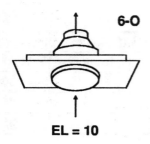

6-O

EL = 10

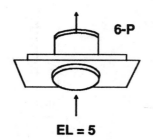

6-P

EL = 5

Group 7
Panned Joists and Panned Stud Return Air Fittings
Reference Velocity = 700 FPM
Reference Friction Rate = 0.08 In.Wg. per 100 Feet

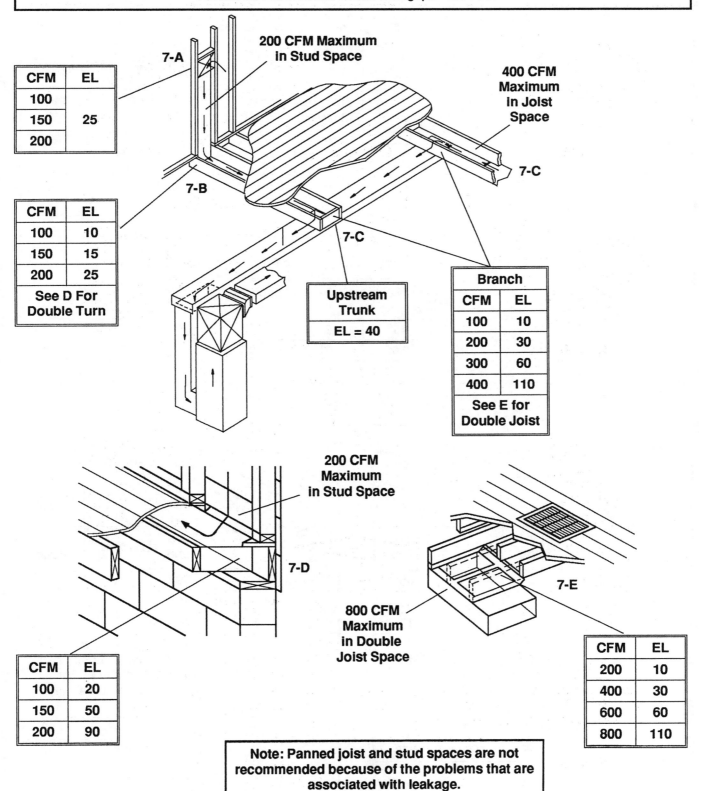

200 CFM Maximum in Stud Space

7-A

CFM	EL
100	
150	25
200	

400 CFM Maximum in Joist Space

7-C

7-B

CFM	EL
100	10
150	15
200	25
See D For Double Turn	

7-C

Upstream Trunk

EL = 40

Branch	
CFM	EL
100	10
200	30
300	60
400	110
See E for Double Joist	

200 CFM Maximum in Stud Space

7-D

800 CFM Maximum in Double Joist Space

7-E

CFM	EL
100	20
150	50
200	90

CFM	EL
200	10
400	30
600	60
800	110

Note: Panned joist and stud spaces are not recommended because of the problems that are associated with leakage.

Group 8
Elbows and Offsets
Reference Velocity = 900 FPM
Reference Friction Rate = 0.08 In.Wg. per 100 Feet

Round and Oval Elbow EL Values

R/D	Smooth	4 or 5 Piece	3 Piece	Smooth Mitered	Easy Bend	Hard Bend	3-Piece 45°	2-Piece 45°
Mitered (R = 0)	—	—	—	75	4 Piece 25	4 Piece 30	10	15
0.75	20	30	35	—				
1.0	15	20	25	—	3 Piece 30	3 Piece 35		
1.5 or Larger	10	15	20	—				

For Smooth-radius Round Elbows
— Angles (θ) Less Than 90° —
Multiply EL by the Following Factor

20°	30°	45°	60°	75°	110°	130°	150°
0.31	0.45	0.60	0.78	0.90	1.13	1.20	1.28

8-A — Continued

Radius Elbow EL Values (8-B)

R/W	Hard Bend	H / W = 1	Easy Bend
Mitered (R = 0)	90	75	65
0.25	35	30	25
0.5 or Larger	20	15	10

For Angles (θ) Less Than 90° Multiply EL by the Following Factor

30°	45°	60°
0.45	0.60	0.78

Radius Elbow EL Values (8-C)

R/W	Hard Bend	H / W = 1	Easy Bend
Mitered (R = 0)	30	25	40
0.25	10	10	10
0.5 or Larger	5	5	5

For Angles (θ) Less Than 90° Multiply EL by the Following Factor

30°	45°	60°
0.45	0.60	0.78

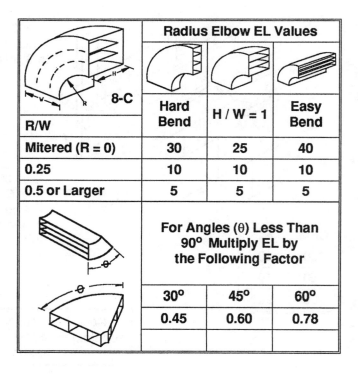

Group 8 — Continued
Elbows and Offsets
Reference Velocity = 900 FPM
Reference Friction Rate = 0.08 In.Wg. per 100 Feet

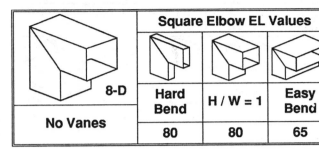

	Square Elbow EL Values		
8-D	Hard Bend	H / W = 1	Easy Bend
No Vanes	80	80	65

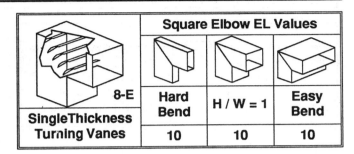

	Square Elbow EL Values		
8-E SingleThickness Turning Vanes	Hard Bend	H / W = 1	Easy Bend
	10	10	10

L/H	EL
1	160
2	260
4	190

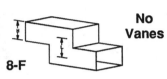

No Vanes

8-F

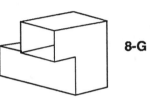

8-G

EL = 200
No Vanes

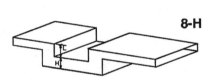

8-H

EL's H/L	No Vanes	With Vanes
0.5	55	—
1.0	330	55
1.5	430	55
2.0	470	55

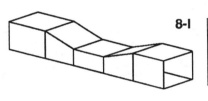

8-I

EL = 20

4 — 45° Ells

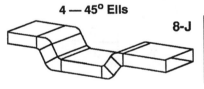

8-J

EL = 20

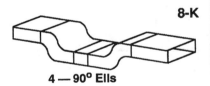

8-K

4 — 90° Ells

R/H	EL
Mitered (R=0)	250
0.25	100
0.50	20
1	20

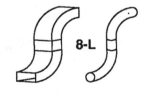

8-L

Double Ell — 1 Plane

1.7 x EL value
for single elbow

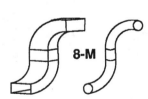

8-M

Double Ell — 2 Plane

2 x EL value
for single elbow

EL = 10

8-N

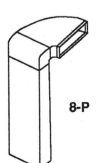

8-P

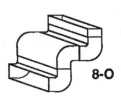

8-O

Inside Corner	EL
Miter (R=0)	235
R = 0.25	90
R > 0.50	45

EL Values	Inside Corners	
Riser	Miter	Radius
3-1/4 x 10	75	60
3-1/4 x 12	90	75
3-1/4 x 14	90	75

Group 9
Supply Trunk Junction Fittings
Reference Velocity = 900 FPM
Reference Friction Rate = 0.08 In.Wg. per 100 Feet

The equivalent lengths in this group apply when the flow in a secondary trunk duct is a substantial percentage of the flow in the upstream (primary) duct. Refer to Group 2, Branch Takeoff Fittings, for information about the equivalent lengths that are associated with branch runouts.

	EL
Branch	35
Main	5

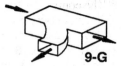

9-G

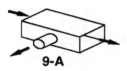

9-A

	EL
Branch	80
Main	5

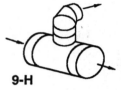

9-H

	EL
Branch	100
Main	5

	EL
Branch	80
Main	5

9-B

	EL
Branch	85
Main	5

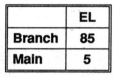

9-I

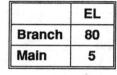

9-C

	EL
Branch	80
Main	5

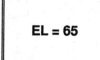

9-J

	EL
Branch	25
Main	5

	EL
Branch	75
Main	5

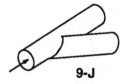

9-D

EL = 65

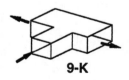

9-K

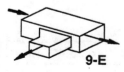

9-E

	EL
Branch	50
Main	5

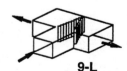

9-L

EL = 20

	EL
Branch	45
Main	5

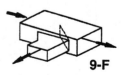

9-F

EL = 20

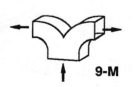

9-M

Group 9 — Continued
Supply Trunk Junction Fittings
Reference Velocity = 900 FPM
Reference Friction Rate = 0.08 In.Wg. per 100 Feet

The equivalent lengths in this group apply when the flow in a secondary trunk duct is a substantial percentage of the flow in the upstream (primary) duct. Refer to Group 2, Branch Takeoff Fittings, for information about the equivalent lengths that are associated with branch runouts.

EL = 70

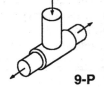

9-P

9-N

EL = 15

EL = 55

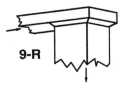

9-Q

EL = 15

9-O

EL = 35

9-R

Group 10
Return Trunk Junction Fittings
Reference Velocity = 700 FPM
Reference Friction Rate = 0.08 In.Wg. per 100 Feet

The equivalent lengths in this group apply when the flow in two return trunks merge. Refer to Group 6, Branch Return Fittings, for information about the equivalent lengths that are associated with branch return ducts.

EL = 25

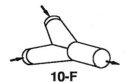

10-E

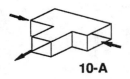

10-A

EL = 75

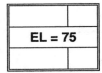

10-F

EL = 35

EL = 10

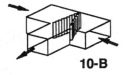

10-B

EL = 75

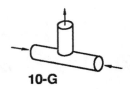

10-G

10-C

EL = 10

EL = 25

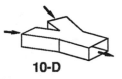

10-D

Group 11
Flexible Duct Junction Boxes and Radius Bends
Reference Velocity = As Indicated
Reference Friction Rate = 0.08 In.Wg. per 100 Feet

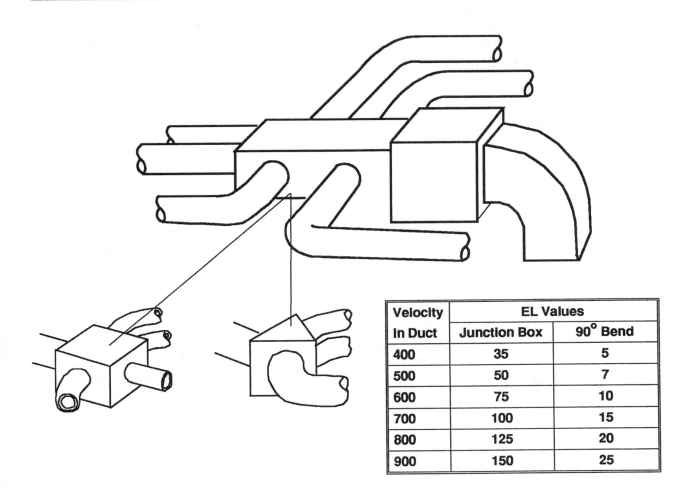

| Velocity | EL Values | |
in Duct	Junction Box	90° Bend
400	35	5
500	50	7
600	75	10
700	100	15
800	125	20
900	150	25

For bends that are not equal to 90°, multiply the 90° equivalent length by the ratio of the desired angle to the 90° angle.

Example: Find EL for a 45° bend if the velocity equals 700 FPM

15 x 45 / 90 = 7.5 FT

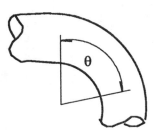

Group 12
Transitions (Diverging)
Reference Velocity = 900 FPM
Reference Friction Rate = 0.08 In.Wg. per 100 Feet

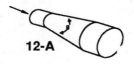

12-A

EL Values	A1/A2	A1/A2
Slope	2	4
1:1	20	40
2:1	20	40
4:1	20	30

12-F

EL Values	A1/A2	A1/A2
Slope	2	4
1:1	20	40
2:1	20	40
4:1	15	30

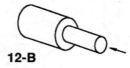

12-B

EL Values	A1/A2	A1/A2
Slope	2	4
Abrupt	20	40

12-G

EL Values	A1/A2	A1/A2
Slope	2	4
Abrupt	20	40

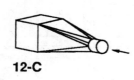

12-C

EL Values	A1/A2	A1/A2
Slope	2	4
1:1	20	40
2:1	20	40
4:1	20	30

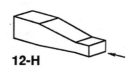

12-H

EL Values	A1/A2	A1/A2
Slope	2	4
1:1	20	40
2:1	20	40
4:1	15	25

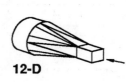

12-D

EL Values	A1/A2	A1/A2
Slope	2	4
1:1	20	40
2:1	20	40
4:1	20	30

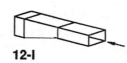

12-I

EL Values	A1/A2	A1/A2
Slope	2	4
1:1	20	35
2:1	15	25
4:1	10	10

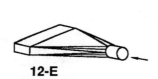

12-E

EL = 25

Group 12
Transitions (Converging)
Reference Velocity = 900 FPM
Reference Friction Rate = 0.08 In.Wg. per 100 Feet

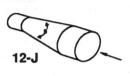

12-J

EL Values	A1/A2	A1/A2
Slope	2	4
1:1	10	10
2:1	5	5
4:1	5	5

12-O

EL Values	A1/A2	A1/A2
Slope	2	4
1:1	10	10
2:1	5	5
4:1	5	5

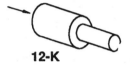

12-K

EL Values	A1/A2	A1/A2
Slope	2	4
Abrupt	25	25

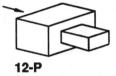

12-P

EL Values	A1/A2	A1/A2
Slope	2	4
Abrupt	30	30

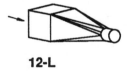

12-L

EL Values	A1/A2	A1/A2
Slope	2	4
1:1	10	10
2:1	5	5
4:1	5	5

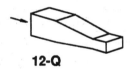

12-Q

EL Values	A1/A2	A1/A2
Slope	2	4
1:1	10	10
2:1	5	5
4:1	5	5

12-M

EL Values	A1/A2	A1/A2
Slope	2	4
1:1	10	10
2:1	5	5
4:1	5	5

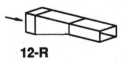

12-R

EL Values	A1/A2	A1/A2
Slope	2	4
1:1	5	5
2:1	5	5
4:1	5	5

12-N

EL = 10

Group 12
Oval Transition Plenums and Abrupt Squeezes
Reference Velocity = 900 FPM or as Indicated
Reference Friction Rate = 0.08 In.Wg. per 100 Feet

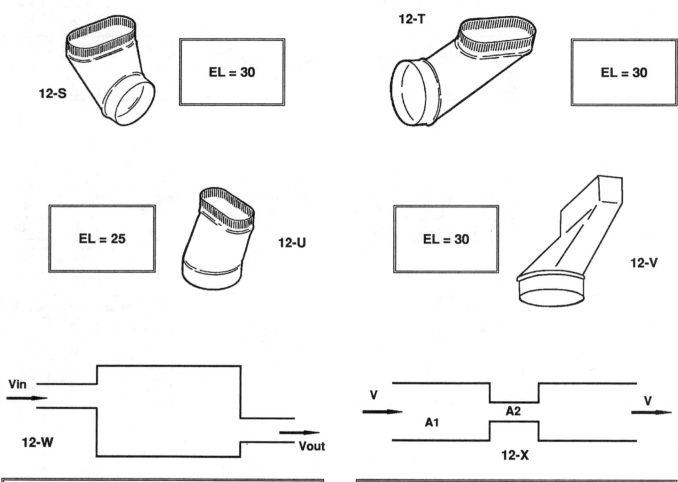

Flow Through Large Plenum				
EL Values	**V_{in}**			
V_{out}	600	700	800	900
600	70	85	105	125
700	80	95	115	135
800	99	105	125	145
900	105	120	140	160

Abrupt Squeeze		
EL Values	**A1/A2**	
V	2	4
600	90	510
700	120	690
800	160	900
900	200	1140

Group 13
Manual Balancing Dampers
Reference Velocity = 900 FPM
(Damper Blade in Wide Open Position)

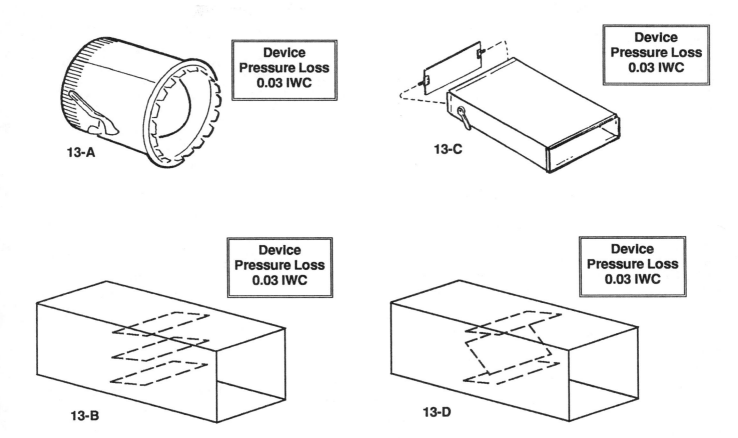

**Device
Pressure Loss
0.03 IWC**

13-A

**Device
Pressure Loss
0.03 IWC**

13-C

**Device
Pressure Loss
0.03 IWC**

13-B

**Device
Pressure Loss
0.03 IWC**

13-D

Appendix 4
Duct Construction Standards

This appendix provides some information about duct system fabrication and installation requirements. These requirements pertain to material performance criteria, fabrication procedures, installation techniques and sealing methods. A comprehensive discussion of any of these subjects can be found in the standards and codes that are noted below.

4-1 Pertinent Standards and Codes

Duct construction standards deal with material performance requirements, assembly and fabrication techniques, installation procedures, closure and sealing, insulation requirements and repair issues. Some of this guidance directly applies to fabricator-installers and the remainder of the information concerns the companies that manufacturer basic materials.

Fibrous Board Duct Standards
The North American Insulation Manufacturers Association (NAIMA) standards apply to fibrous glass duct systems. Refer to the **Fibrous Glass Residential Duct Construction Standards** publication for information about systems that will be subjected to pressures (positive or negative) that are less than 0.50 IWC. Note that this standard does not apply to every residential system because some residential equipment features a blower that can produce pressures that exceed 0.50 IWC. In these cases refer to the NAIMA **Fibrous Glass Residential Duct Construction Standards, Low Velocity Systems, 2 IWC Maximum Static Pressure** publication. Both of these standards are subject to the following limitations:

- Duct board 1 inch thick or 1-1/2 inch thick
- Round rigid fibrous glass duct
- Flexible duct
- Operating temperatures below 250 °F
- Risers less than two stories high

Also refer to Underwriters Laboratory (UL) publication **UL 181 1990 Edition**. This publication is concerned with fibrous board and flexible duct materials requirements and fabrication techniques. Some of the subjects that are discussed in this standard are:

- Strength test (tension and torsion)
- Load versus deflection tests
- Structural integrity tests (containment and collapse)
- Duct friction tests
- Duct leakage tests
- Duct wall conduction losses

- Noise attenuation and noise transmission tests
- Flame spread and smoke development
- Burning and flame penetration
- Corrosion and erosion tests
- Resistance against mold and mildew
- Puncture resistance and impact tests

For information on sealing, refer to **UL 181A**. This standard includes information that was extracted from **UL 181**, SMACNA **AFTS 100** and other material that was submitted by duct tape manufacturers. Some of the requirements that are associated with this standard are:

- Continuous seal on all joints and seams
- Pressure-sensitive tape must conform to **UL 181A/P**
- Heat-activated tape must conform to **UL 181A/H**
- Proper application of staples and tape
- Apply glass fabric and mastic as per manufacturer's instructions (mastic and tape are usually associated with fire-rated assemblies)

The Sheet Metal and Air Conditioning Contractors National Association (SMACNA) also publishes standards that apply to fibrous board duct systems. Refer to the **Fibrous Glass Duct Construction Standard, 6th Edition.**

The integrity of a duct system, as far as closure is concerned, also depends on supports and hangers (to prevent stress on seams and joints), reinforcement (to prevent panel sag due to gravity and budge due to pressure differences), external loads (to avoid loads that might damage ducts and fittings) and interface connections (use screws and washers to attach fiber board duct to sheet metal flanges and tabs).

Flexible Duct Standards
For information about flexible duct systems, refer to the **Flexible Duct Performance and Installation Standard, 2nd edition, 1991**, as published by the Air Diffusion Council (ADC). This standard covers materials performance requirements, fabrication techniques, installation procedures and performance testing. Also refer to the **UL 181** standard and to the **HVAC Duct Construction standards, 1st edition, 1985**, as published by SMACNA. Some of the guidance that is provided by these standards is associated with making connections and splices (fittings and closure), excessive length (cut to length, no coils, detours or compression), short lengths (do not stretch duct), supports and hangers, change of directions (avoid tight bends that restrict airway) and exposure (avoid sunlight, heat or physical damage).

Metal Duct Standards

Metal duct construction standards are published by the Sheet Metal and Air Conditioning Contractors National Association; refer to **HVAC Duct Construction standards, 1st edition, 1985**. This document provides guidance regarding installation and fabrication of metal ducts and metal ducts that are fitted with duct liner. Information on external duct insulation (duct wrap) is provided by the **Commercial and Industrial Insulation Standards, 3rd Edition, 1988** publication, as published by Midwest Insulation Contractors Association (MICA). Some of the subjects that are covered in these two standards pertain to fabrication (seams, joints, fittings and connections), metal gauge requirements, reinforcement, bracing, closure, insulation attachment, fasteners, adhesives, hangers and supports.

Thermoplastic (PVC) Duct Standards

Information about PVC duct system is provided by the SMACNA. Refer to the **Thermoplastic Duct (PVC) Construction Manual**.

Duct Insulation Standards

Information about duct insulation materials requirements, thermal performance, installation techniques and sealing requirements is provided by the SMACNA **HVAC Duct Construction Standards, 1st edition, 1985**, and the MICA **Commercial and Industrial Insulation Standards, 3rd Edition, 1988**. Also refer to the NAIMA publication that is titled **A Guide to Insulated Air Duct Systems**. Some of the recommendations provided by these documents are presented below:

Duct Liner
- Apply adhesives liner to metal (90% coverage)
- Adhesive material performance (ASTM C916)
- Mechanical fasteners required
- End Caps and facing prevent erosion

Duct Wrap
- Install with facing exposed
- Cut to recommended "strechout" dimension
- Compressed thickness not less than 75 percent
- Do not compress at corner bends
- Apply staples and tape as per MICA standard

Rigid Board Insulation
- Use pins and clips as per applicable standards
- Seal joints with tape
- Use fabric and mastic to build weatherproof jacket

Other Standards

The documents that are listed above are not the only standards that apply to duct systems. A list of other pertinent documents is provided below. These documents cover materials, construction, installation, testing, safety and efficiency issues.

- **HVAC Air Duct Leakage Testing Manual**, published by SMACNA

- International Conference of Building Officials (ICBO) **Uniform Building Code** (UBC) and **Uniform Mechanical Code** (UMC)

- Southern Building Code Congress International (SBCCI) **Standard Building Code** (SBC) and **Standard Mechanical Code** (SMC)

- Building Officials and Code Administrators International (BOCA) **Basic Building Code** (BBC) and **Basic Mechanical Code** (BMC)

- Building Officials and Code Administrators International (BOCA) **Model Energy Code** (MEC)

- American Society of Air Conditioning and Refrigeration Engineers (ASHRAE) **Standard 90.2**

- **HVAC Air Duct Leakage Testing Manual** as published by SMANCA

- NFPA **Standard 90A and 90B** fire and smoke standards

- Various ASTM and UL standards that deal with materials performance requirements and performance testing; also refer to local codes and regulations

4-2 Performance Checklists

The North American Insulation Manufacturers Association document titled **A Guide to Insulated Air Duct Systems** includes field inspection checklists that can be used to evaluate the materials and workmanship that are associated with a duct system installation. These checklists are reproduced below. More detail about any items in these checklists can be found in the documents and standards that are published by SMACNA, NAIMA and the ADC.

Fibrous Glass Duct Construction
- Is duct system static pressure within specified limits?
- Does insulation R-value meet code requirements?
- Is the EL rating (475 or 800) printed on the board?
- Are all sheet metal accessories of galvanized steel?
- Is foil closure tape marked UL 181A/P or UL 181A/H?
- Are all seams and joints properly stapled?
- Do closures otherwise meet NAIMA requirements?
- Does equipment installation meet NAIMA requirements?
- Do reinforcement elements meet NAIMA requirements?
- Do hangers and supports meet NAIMA requirements?
- Are ducts free from unrepaired tears or punctures?

Flexible Duct Systems
- Is duct system static pressure within product limits?
- Does insulation R-value meet code requirements?

- Are all sheet metal accessories of galvanized steel?
- Is the UL label attached to the flexible duct jacket?
- Are connections to trunk ducts airtight and insulated?
- Do closures otherwise meet ADC requirements?
- Does flexible duct support meet ADC requirements?
- Is the duct system free from sharp bends or kinks?
- Are the duct runs free from loops and coils?
- Are the duct runs cut to length (no stretching)?
- Does fitting fabrication meet ADC requirements?
- Do hangers and supports meet ADC requirements?
- Are vertical flexible duct runs correctly supported?
- Are ducts free from unrepaired tears or punctures?

Metal Ducts with Duct Liner
- Is duct system air velocity within product limits?
- Are all sheet metal joints tightly sealed to prevent air leakage?
- Do fittings and connections meet SMACNA requirements?
- Do reinforcement elements meet SMACNA requirements?
- Do hangers and supports meet SMACNA requirements?
- Is the coated or mat-faced airstream surface of the liner visible?
- Is adhesive coverage adequate to ensure adhesion of liner to metal?
- Are mechanical fasteners also used to secure the liner, and at the proper spacing?
- Are transverse joints tightly butted, with no gaps between pieces?

- Are all corner joints tight and overlapped?
- Are leading edges and transverse joints of the liner coated?
- Are leading edges of the liner nosed with sheet metal when required (depending on the velocity of the air flow)?
- Are top panels of duct liner board supported by side panels?

Metal Ducts with External Wrap
- Were all joints in sheet metal ductwork tightly sealed before applying duct wrap insulation?
- Do fittings and connections meet SMACNA requirements?
- Do reinforcement elements meet SMACNA requirements?
- Do hangers and supports meet SMACNA requirements?
- Is the duct wrap insulation's installed R-value clearly printed on the facing?
- Are all the insulation seams properly stapled with outward-clinching staples every 6 feet?
- Are the insulation seams tightly taped with pressure-sensitive tape matching the facing?
- Was manufacturer's stretch-out dimension used so that duct wrap is not excessively compressed at corners?
- If rectangular ducts are 24-inches wide or greater, is duct wrap insulation secured to bottom with mechanical fasteners to prevent sagging of insulation?

Metal Ducts with Rigid External Insulation
- Were all joints in sheet metal ductwork tightly sealed before installing insulation?

Recommended Applications for Duct materials							
	Duct Material and Type of Insulation						
Duct Location	Duct Board	Rigid Round Fiber Glass	Sheet Metal with Liner (1)	Sheet Metal with Wrap	Sheet Metal Bare	Sheet Metal Rigid Exterior	Flexible Insulated
Attic	X	X	X	X			X
Basement — Unconditioned	X	X	X	X			X (2)
Basement — Conditioned	X	X			X		X (2)
Enclosed Crawl Space	X	X	X	X			X
Open Crawl Space			X			X	
Exterior Wall Cavity or Chase	X	X	X				X
Interior Wall Cavity or Chase	X	X			X		X
Soffit or Ceiling Plenum	X	X	X	X			X
In Conditioned Space	X	X			X		X
Roof or Outdoor Location						X	

Notes:
1) The R-value must be suitable for the application
2) There must be no possibility of physical damage

Figure A4-1

- Do fittings and connections meet SMACNA requirements?
- Do reinforcement elements meet SMACNA requirements?
- Do hangers and supports meet SMACNA requirements?
- Are mechanical fasteners the right length for the insulation thickness, so that there is no "oil-canning" effect?
- Are mechanical fasteners (weld pins with speed clip washers) spaced at the correct intervals?
- Are seams of insulation boards tightly taped with pressure-sensitive tape matching the facing?
- Is pressure-sensitive tape at least 3-inches wide (5-inches wide if used in place of shiplapped joints in rigid board)?
- Is field jacketing canvas, mastic or cement evenly and uniformly applied, with no gaps or seams?

- Are all fasteners tightly sealed with pressure-sensitive tape matching the insulation facing?

4-3 Recommended Materials Based on Location

Duct fabrication materials and duct insulating materials must be selected for the intended use. This decision must be based on the location of the duct system because of the potential for damage caused by physical abuse by humans or animals, wetting or condensation. Figure A4-1 on the previous page provides guidance on this matter.

Index

V (Continued)

W

Z

Notes

Notes

Notes

Notes

Notes

Claude Sessoms

28 x 18

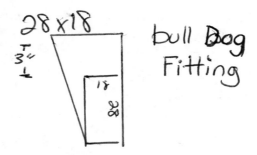

bull Dog
Fitting